Renaissance Banff

Mathematics, Music, Art, Culture

Conference Proceedings
2005

Reza Sarhangi and Robert V. Moody, Editors

Renaissance Banff
Mathematics, Music, Art, Culture

Scientific Organizers

Ivar Ekeland
Director, Pacific Institute
for the Mathematical Sciences
Department of Mathematics
University of British Columbia, Canada

Nassif Ghoussoub
Scientific Director, Banff International
Research Station
Department of Mathematics
University of British Columbia, Canada

Robert V. Moody
Department of Mathematics
and Statistics
University of Victoria, Victoria
British Columbia, Canada

Christiane Rousseau
Department of Mathematics
and Statistics
University of Montréal, Québec, Canada

Reza Sarhangi
Department of Mathematics
Towson University
Towson, Maryland, USA

Coxeter Day

Donald W. Crowe
Department of Mathematics
University of Wisconsin-Madison
Madison, Wisconsin, USA

Chandler Davis
Departemnt of Mathematics
University of Toronto
Toronto, Ontario, Canada

Doris Schattschneider
Mathematics and Computer Science
Moravian College
Bethlehem, Pennsylvania, USA

Marjorie Senechal
Mathematics Department
Smith College
Northampton, Massachusetts, USA

Bridges for Teachers, Teachers for Bridges

Mara Alagic
Department of Curriculum and Instruction
Wichita State University
Wichita, Kansas, USA

Bridges Visual Art Exhibit

Robert W. Fathauer
Tessellations Company
Phoenix, Arizona, USA

Renaissance Banff, Mathematics, Music, Art, Culture
Conference Proceedings, 2005

Editors:

Reza Sarhangi
Department of Mathematics
Towson University
Towson, Maryland, USA

Robert V. Moody
Department of Mathematics and Statistics
University of Victoria, Victoria
British Columbia, Canada

ISBN: 0-9665201-6-5
ISSN: 1099-6702
Price: US $45.00, CAN $55.00

Prepared with the help of Southwestern College, Winfield, Kansas, USA. Printed by Central Plain Book Manufacturing, Winfield, Kansas, USA.

Distributed by MATHARTFUN.COM (http://mathartfun.com).

Cover design: *Van Gogh meets Riemann* by Bart de Smit
Renaissance Banff logo: Robert J. Krawczyk
Cover layout: Chris K. Palmer

Contents

Bridges for Teachers, Teachers for Bridges

Preface

Mathematics has periodically been employed not only to interpret and analyze art and architecture, but also to directly integrate with artistic products. During the European Renaissance, art, mathematics, architecture, science, and music flourished side by side. This is no longer the case, and although many artists and scientists are calling for ways to regain the lost mutual understanding, appreciation, and exchange, it has been hard to know how to create environments in which this can happen in a meaningful way.

No less a divide exists between mathematics and the general public. All human beings are fluent in recognizing and appreciating patterns, and are able to deal effortlessly with the abstractions of language, music, visual art, and theatre. Yet most people think that they have a latent aversion to mathematics and are largely unaware of how deeply embedded it is in the world around them. Still, we have seen over and over again how fascinated and excited people become when mathematical connections are presented in ways which relate to their experiences and trigger their natural curiosities and aesthetic sensibilities.

The Bridges Conferences, created in 1998 and running annually since, have provided a remarkable model of how these divides can be crossed. Here practicing mathematicians, scientists, artists, educators, musicians, writers, computer scientists, sculptures, dancers, weavers, and model builders have come together in a lively and highly charged atmosphere of mutual exchange and encouragement. Important components of these conferences, apart from formal presentations, are gallery displays of visual art, working sessions with practitioners and artists who are crossing the mathematics-arts boundaries, and evening musical or theatrical events. Furthermore a lasting record of each Bridges Conference is its Proceedings, the latest of which you are holding now, – a beautiful resource book of the papers and the visual presentations of the meeting.

The Banff Centre is Canada's only leading center dedicated to the arts, leadership development, and mountain culture. The Centre is also home to a world-class conference facility. The convergence of the resources, multidisciplinary programming, and a spectacular physical location affords all the requirements for an inspirational learning experience. The Banff International Research Station (BIRS) is a component of the Pacific Institute for the Mathematical Science (PIMS) that is located at the Banff Centre. BIRS organizes over forty mathematics research workshops at the Banff Centre each year. Yet even at its inception, the directors of the PIMS and the Banff Centre were aware of the potential disconnection between this mathematics research station and the rest of the Banff Centre. They felt that they should go into a venture to connect all the different components at the Banff Centre. But how and what? The then Scientific Director of BIRS, Robert Moody, was left to struggle with this question.

As it turned out the catalyst for the conference was one of the founding members of BIRS, David Eisenbud (Director of MSRI and the President of AMS) who put the two editors of these Proceedings together. The chemistry matched and, voilà, the idea of bringing Bridges to Banff was born.

With the encouragement of Nassif Ghoussoub, who was Director of PIMS at the time, and Ivar Ekeland, its new Director, an organizing committee was struck that included the directors of PIMS and BIRS, and the creator and director of the Bridges conferences, Reza Sarhangi. When Christiane Rousseau, who was the President of the Canadian Mathematical Society, learned about the intention to have a mathematics-arts conference, she immediately came up with the idea of extending it to include a day devoted to Donald Coxeter, who was passionately devoted to the artistic side of mathematics and whose passing was still fresh on everyone's mind. With the addition of Christiane our Scientific Organizing Committee was complete. This is the first time a mathematics/arts event of this magnitude has been brought to Canada and in particular to the western Canadian community.

The conference title "Renaissance Banff" sums up its objectives in a nutshell. Renaissance Banff provides the first fulfillment of the expectations of the founders of the BIR-Banff Centre partnership in that it would foster a new era for drawing the worlds of the arts and the sciences closer together. In addition, the value of such a conference for teachers of mathematics in providing new ideas and methods for conveying the beauty, relevance, and ubiquity of mathematical ideas to their students cannot be overstated.

The four-day Renaissance Banff conference consists of two parts: A three-day Bridges Conference and a final day, organized in cooperation and with the support of the Canadian Mathematical Society, set aside for geometry-arts connections that are either related to or inspired by the life and work of Donald Coxeter. H.S.M. (Donald) Coxeter was one of the foremost geometers of the 20th century. His work and writing not only played a significant role in mathematics, but also touched innumerable people in the arts and other areas of science. A section of this Proceedings includes the articles that were presented in his honor. In order for the conference to meet the needs of K-12 teachers, a section of teacher workshops was scheduled. The last section of this book consists of the workshop articles that were presented in the meeting.

The refereed Renaissance Banff Proceedings has attracted even more quality authors from around the world than ever before. This forced us not only to be more sensitive to the selection of papers, but also to limit the number of pages for each article. Even with that we had to admit a significant growth in the number of papers accepted for publication. The increase in submissions, of course, caused more work for the referees. This Proceedings reveals not only the quality of work of its authors but also the hard work of our referees. No words can express our appreciation for the work the referees have done to enable publication of the proceedings you have in your hands. Please note that in order for the readers to locate an article in the book faster, an index of the author's names, which have been sorted alphabetically, has been added to the end of this publication.

The cover, *Van Gogh meets Riemann*, gives a view on the painting "Café Terrace at Night" by Vincent van Gogh (1853 - 1890) through a conformal transformation: the logarithm of the zeta-function of Bernhard Riemann (1826 - 1866). On the right we can see the pole at 1 and on the left a trivial zero at -2. The non-trivial zeros, which are the subject of the most important open problem in mathematics today, are outside the picture frame.

The *Bridges Visual Art Exhibit* is the result of Robert Fathauer's hard work in communicating with a large number of artists in order to carefully select the artwork and properly set them up for the exhibit. The CD that accompanies this book presents the images presented at the Bridges Visual Art Exhibit.

Special thanks must be given to the administrators and the staff at the Banff Centre for their key roles in organizing the conference in Banff. In particular we would like to acknowledge the support of the CEO of the Banff Centre, Mary Hofstetter and the then Vice-President for Artistic Programming, Joanne Morrow, as well as the on-going efforts of Luke Azevedo, who came especially to the previous Bridges Conference in Kansas as an observer and who has been our liaison with the Banff Centre throughout the development of this Conference. We also should thank Nicole Neubauer for her time and effort to organize the registration process, to Audrey Cutler of the Center for Instructional Advancement and Technology at Towson University for her technical support, and to Chris Palmer for his effort in updating the Bridges website, creating the 2005 Renaissance Banff CD, and for laying out the proceedings cover.

The Three-Day Bridges

Mathematical Connections in Art, Music, and Science

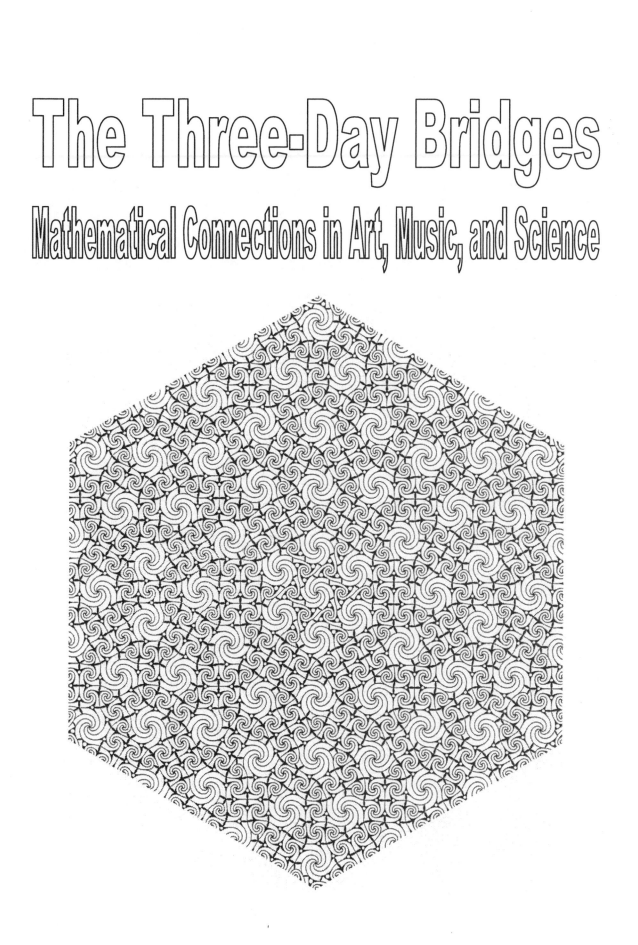

A curve of constant curvature is a circle, of course, and adding a constant, c, will bend the meander around a circle (Figure 4). If we require the curve to close after one circuit it must complete a whole number of cycles as it goes around, and the contribution to the total turn from the cosine term will be zero. The added constant, c, is determined by the number of steps, for example for a curve with symmetry order 5 there will be five cycles, and $c = 0.2$, if $b = 1$. If angles are in radians, with $b = 20.0535$, then $c = 0.2/b = 0.09973$, and the curve closes after $2\pi \times 20.0535 \times 5 = 630$ steps

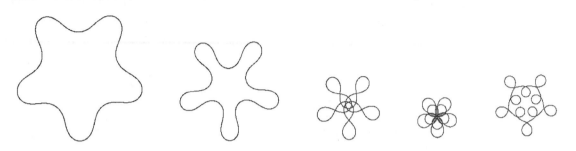

Figure 4: *A circular meander of symmetry order 5 as the parameter increases*

(a = 0.3, 0.4, 0.57, 0.715, 0.86).

An interesting variation occurs if the *cos(s)* term is replaced by *cos(s + cos(ks))*, with k close to unity. (Again suitable scaling parameters might be needed.) The whole meander curve itself meanders, suggesting the possibility of self-similar meander curves (Figure 5).

Figure 5: *A modified meander suggesting the possibility of self-similarity*

a = 2.2   k = 0.991

Meanders in Three Dimensions

In three dimensions there are three types of turn: *roll* around the direction in which the turtle is heading, *yaw* to left or right, and *pitch* up or down. Since we are not concerned with gravity there is no preferred up direction, so yaw and pitch are equivalent. Most versions of Logo include the possibility of three dimensional geometry but the better display available in VRML makes it worth writing scripts (in Java or JavaScript) to generate an extrusion along a turtle path. Abelson and diSessa [3] pp. 140-144 explains how to implement movement in three dimensions.

A sine-generated curve can be incorporated into a three dimensional space-curve in many ways. One of the most interesting has a constant pitch (so constant curvature), with the roll defined by a cosine function. A ribbon-like extrusion along this curve is a ruled surface of constant curvature.

The intrinsic equations of the curve are

$$\kappa = c$$
$$\tau = a\cos s/b,$$

where the curvature, κ, gives the pitch, and the torsion, τ, gives the roll. The constant curvature parameter, c, will be called the *bend*, and the torsion parameter, a, the *twist*. As before b is a scaling parameter.

Although things are more complicated than in two dimensions some of the same principles apply. If the curve is to close, the turtle's intrinsic axes should have an unchanged orientation when it returns to the start (although it might pass through the starting position several times before closing the curve). The roll must complete a whole number of cycles, so, as before, with $b = 20{\cdot}0535$ a curve with symmetry order 5 closes after approximately 630 steps. The total roll must be zero, so a ribbon along the curve is topologically equivalent to a cylinder.

A meander curve in three dimensions is defined (to similarity) by two parameters, the bend and the twist, and there is a range of possible space-curves as they vary. Considering only those curves with the same symmetry, say order 5, is sufficient to understand the full range of curves, since the same principles apply to curves of any symmetry, and any that does not close is arbitrarily close to one that does.

Begin by thinking about curves with twist = 0. They consist of some number of loops around a circle. What happens if the twist is increased? (See Figure 6.) The loops begin to separate, and in Figure 6 begin to curl inwards. The bend parameter needs to change to take account of this, but eventually the concave parts of the curve cancel the convex parts and any further increase in the twist parameter leads to a curve that cannot close after 630 steps, whatever the bend parameter.

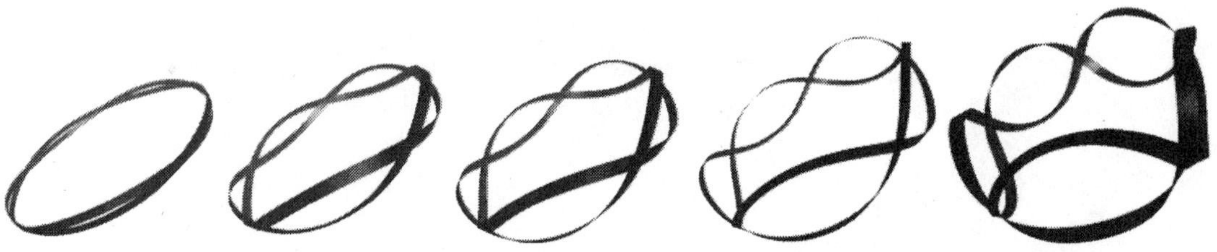

Figure 6: *Increasing the twist of a 3-D meander that starts with a 2 loop.*

Figure 7: *The 3-D meander from an 8 loop moves towards the same limit as twist increases.*

The same limiting case can arise starting with a different number of loops (Figure 7), allowing a smooth trajectory between the two starting points.

Figure 8 shows the values of bend and twist that give curves with 5-symmetry. Notice that a circle with five loops is equivalent to a single circuit, since each loop is identical, and it is a limiting case. It does not close for any non-zero twist. The dotted lines correspond to space-curves where the concave and convex parts exactly cancel, so they go to infinity (Figure 9). Curves on opposite sides of these lines have centres of symmetry on opposite sides

. Figure 8: *Values of bend and twist that produce 3-D meanders with 5-symmetry.*

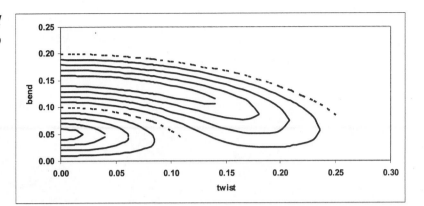

Figure 9: *Infinite 3-D meanders.*

These looping curves have an obvious aesthetic appeal, and many variations are possible. Figure 10 illustrates how changing the width of the ribbon can significantly alter their appearance. It is not surprising that some sculptors have produced works with similar features.

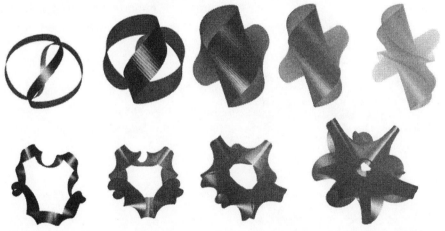

Figure 10: *Changing the ribbon width of two 3-D meanders (not to scale).*

Many pieces by Brent Collins [4] have the overall shape of 3-D meanders, but usually the twist maintains the same sign rather than oscillating, so they are not topological cylinders. His ribbon sculptures are exceptions [5], and Figure 11, *Pax Mundi* (Figure 22 in [5]), is a particularly obvious example, although it does not appear to be a ruled surface.

Figure 11: *Pax Mundi, by Brent Collins.*

Jan Zach's work [6] with stainless steel in the late 1960s inevitably expresses elastic curves, since the steel automatically takes on these shapes, although other forces are also at work, in particular gravity. *Windflower No.1 (*Figure 12) is a good example.

Figure 12: *Windflower No.1 (1967).*   **Figure 13**: *Flower of Freedom No.6 (1968).*

In *Flower of Freedom No.6* (Figure 13) the ribbon of steel has been cut into a more interesting shape, and it is obviously constrained near the centre. This illustrates an important point. The computer generated curves provide believable images of ribbons, but in reality an unconstrained ribbon of any elasticity will spring back to a circular cylinder.

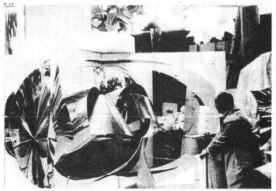

Figure 14 shows Jan Zach manipulating one of his sculptures, and the impression is very similar to some computer-generated images that use wide ribbons.

Figure 14: *Continuous Shape (1968).*

All the images of Jan Zach's work are reproduced by kind permission of Hallie Ford Museum of Art.

***

References

[1] Leopold, L. B. and Langbein, W.B., "River Meanders", *Scientific American", **214**, (Jun 1966), pp.60-70.

[2] Eagles, T.H., *Constructive Geometry of Plane Curves,* Macmillan, 1885, pp.348-354.

[4] Collins, B., Visualization: From Biology to Culture, *Bridges Proceedings 2000,* pp.309-315.

[6] Hall, R., *Intersections, The Life and Art of Jan Zach,* Hallie Ford Museum of Art, Willamette University, 2002.

An Introduction to the Golden Tangram and its Tiling Properties

Stanley Spencer
The Sycamores
Queens Road
Hodthorpe
Worksop
Nottinghamshire
England
S80 4UT
pythagoras@bcs.org.uk
www.pythagoras.org.uk

Abstract

The Author of this paper has developed a Tangram based upon the Golden Ratio. This introduction to the tiling properties of the Golden Tangram focuses upon the property called Preciousness and a Matrix called the Precious Matrix. It includes a discussion of some of the convex polygons that can be created and their non periodic tessellating patterns. It continues with examples of the unique way in which they can produce an infinite number of tiling patterns. It explains the iterative nature of the process as applied to designs for Mosaics and Quilts.

1. Introduction

This work follows on from previous work on Precious Triangles and Polygons [1],[2],[4], [5]. The idea has been expanded to include a set of polygons related to the Golden Ratio. The set of polygons introduced here have edges of only two dimensions. The ratio of the larger to the smaller being the Golden Ratio. Together, the tiles can be formed into a number of convex polygons, one of which is the regular Pentagon, see figure 1. Most people will be familiar with the standard Tangram puzzle [3] from which pictures and designs can be created. The normal Tangram rules are that all the tiles should be used and they should touch but not overlap another tile.

2. What are Precious Polygons?

Precious Polygons are sets of different polygons which can be used to form other sets of similar polygons. The necessary conditions for preciousness are that a larger version of each polygon can be produced using only the original polygons, secondly, the enlargement factor in each case must be the same and finally, all the elements of Nth power of the Precious Matrix must be non zero, where N is the number of different tiles [1]. This process is similar to that of Solomon Golomb's Rep-tiles [7],[8] but involving sets of polygons rather than a single polygon. Self similarity was also a feature of 14th and 15th Century Islamic Geometry [9].

3. Precious Polygons from the Golden Tangram.

There are six different polygons that form the Golden Tangram in figure 1, two triangles, one trapezium, two rhombi, and a pentagon. It also shows a scheme whereby each of the original polygons can combine together to form a similar but larger version of the original set. It can be quite easily shown that each large version is larger than the original by a factor known as the Golden Ratio or φ [4]. This enlargement factor must be a constant for the set to be Precious and is known as the Precious Ratio. Now that we have a Precious set then we can take any design made from the original Tangram shapes and produce a larger version using the scheme in figure 1. Since we end up with a design using only the original shapes, we can repeat the process ad infinitum. Each successive design is larger than the previous one by a factor of φ. Figure 2 shows the development of the series of designs based upon a cat design.

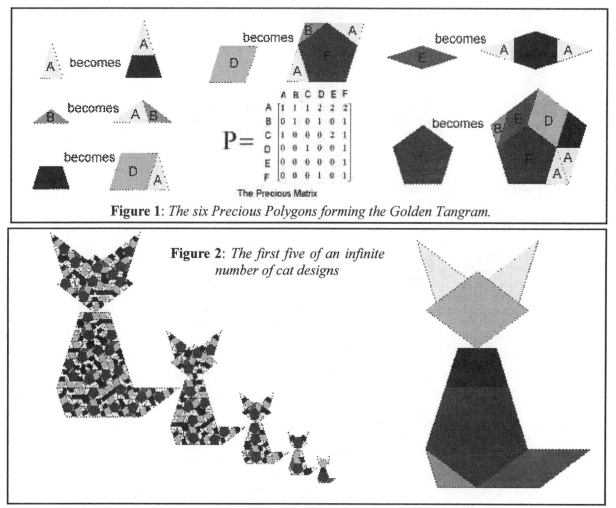

Figure 1: *The six Precious Polygons forming the Golden Tangram.*

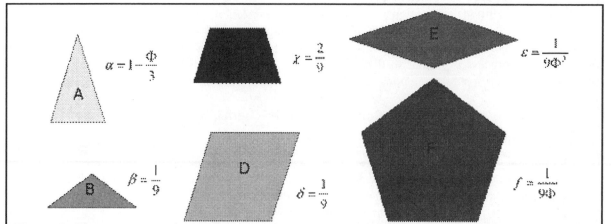

Figure 2: *The first five of an infinite number of cat designs*

4 Some interesting ratios.

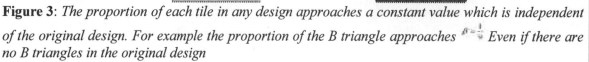

Figure 3: *The proportion of each tile in any design approaches a constant value which is independent of the original design. For example the proportion of the B triangle approaches $\beta = \frac{1}{9}$ Even if there are no B triangles in the original design*

The proportion of each tile in the final design seems to be independent of the number of tiles in the original design. This has been the case with other sets of precious shapes. Whether it is a design using all the tiles (figure 2) or a single tile, after 10 or so generations, the proportion of each tile approaches the constants shown in figure 3. Using a simulation exercise these conjectures are true to 5 or 6 decimal places after the tenth generation of design. There are proofs [1],[4] for other sets of shapes. The proof for the Golden Tangram are the subject of further research.

5 The Precious Matrix

The relationship between the original set of shapes and the enlarged set can be described with a Matrix. If you refer to figure 1 then it can be seen that each triangle A is replaced with a triangle A and a Trapezium C. B is replaced with A and B, C with A and D, D with 2 As, a B and an F and so on. Sometimes, one of the shapes will disappear after a few generations. A discussion of this related to the normal Tangram can be found at reference [1]. For a continuous scheme to infinity it is necessary for all the elements of the Nth power of P to be greater than zero. (Where N is the number of different tiles). It can be seen from figure 5 that all the elements of the 6th power of the Precious matrix are greater than zero, so the final condition for Preciousness is satisfied. It is, perhaps, worth pointing out that the Precious Matrix for a Reptile has a dimension of 1 by 1.

$$P = \begin{array}{c|cccccc|} & A & B & C & D & E & F \\ A & 1 & 1 & 1 & 2 & 2 & 2 \\ B & 0 & 1 & 0 & 1 & 0 & 1 \\ C & 1 & 0 & 0 & 0 & 2 & 1 \\ D & 0 & 0 & 1 & 0 & 0 & 1 \\ E & 0 & 0 & 0 & 0 & 0 & 1 \\ F & 0 & 0 & 0 & 1 & 0 & 1 \end{array}$$

The Precious Matrix

$$P^6 = \begin{bmatrix} 87 & 54 & 141 & 282 & 174 & 510 \\ 21 & 13 & 34 & 68 & 42 & 123 \\ 42 & 26 & 68 & 136 & 84 & 246 \\ 21 & 13 & 34 & 68 & 42 & 123 \\ 5 & 3 & 8 & 16 & 10 & 29 \\ 13 & 8 & 21 & 42 & 26 & 76 \end{bmatrix}$$

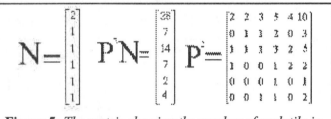

Figure 4: *The Precious Matrix P and its Nth power. N = 6 because there are 6 different*

6 Using the Precious Matrix to calculate the total number of tiles in a design.

The number of tiles in the original design can be represented by a Matrix. For instance the Matrix N for the cat in can be seen in figure 5. In the initial design there are 2 A tiles, 1 B tile and so on... The matrix $P^N N$ gives the number of each tile in the Nth generation of the picture.

$$N = \begin{bmatrix} 2 \\ 1 \\ 1 \\ 1 \\ 1 \\ 1 \end{bmatrix} \quad P^2 N = \begin{bmatrix} 28 \\ 7 \\ 14 \\ 7 \\ 2 \\ 4 \end{bmatrix} \quad P^2 = \begin{bmatrix} 2 & 2 & 3 & 5 & 4 & 10 \\ 0 & 1 & 1 & 2 & 0 & 3 \\ 1 & 1 & 1 & 3 & 2 & 5 \\ 1 & 0 & 0 & 1 & 2 & 2 \\ 0 & 0 & 0 & 1 & 0 & 1 \\ 0 & 0 & 1 & 1 & 0 & 2 \end{bmatrix}$$

Figure 5: *The matrix showing the number of each tile in generation 0 and 2 for the cat in figure 2.*

7 Convex polygons

The seven tiles from the normal Tangram based upon a square can be formed into only thirteen convex polygons. This was proved by Fu Traing Wang and Chuan-Chi Hsuing in 1942 [6]. A similar proof for this Golden Tangram is the subject of on going research. It is possible to show that there are no triangles, and that the maximum extent of the polygons is the decagon, even this is unlikely. A number of quadrilaterals, pentagons (including the regular pentagon), hexagons and heptagons have been identified. Not all of them will be discussed here. The quadrilaterals identified so far will tessellate in a regular fashion, as is normal for any quadrilateral. What is unusual is that they also tessellate in an non periodic fashion. Figure 6 shows a few of the convex polygons identified so far.

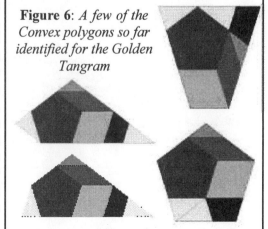

Figure 6: *A few of the Convex polygons so far identified for the Golden Tangram*

8 Tessellating Convex polygons

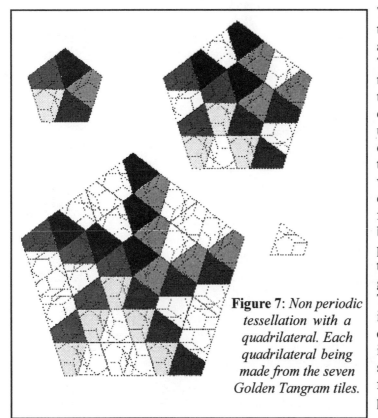

Figure 7: *Non periodic tessellation with a quadrilateral. Each quadrilateral being made from the seven Golden Tangram tiles.*

Tangrams that tessellate can often lead to a series of interesting patterns. An account of an approach using the normal Tangram can be found at [1]. It is easy to show that quadrilaterals will always tessellate in a periodic fashion. The convex quadrilaterals so far identified using the tiles from the Golden Tangram display some interesting non periodic tessellations. The one shown in figure 7 will cover the plain as a series of concentric pentagons. Five of the tiles form a pentagon . A larger pentagon can be made by copying the tiles in pairs and positioning them at the five corners of the original pentagon. The remaining gaps can be filled with the original tile. This process can be repeated ad infinitum producing a larger pentagon at each stage. Each of the quadrilaterals identified so far can cover a plane in a similar fashion. The design can be further expanded using the precious properties of the underlying tiles.

9 An interesting Precious Couplet.

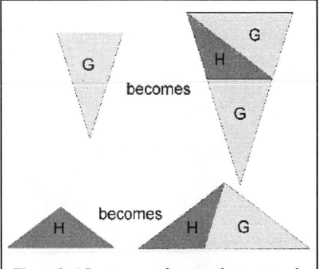

becomes

becomes

Figure 9: *A Precious couplet using the two triangles originally called A and B*

$$P=\begin{bmatrix} 2 & 1 \\ 1 & 1 \end{bmatrix} P^2=\begin{bmatrix} 5 & 3 \\ 3 & 2 \end{bmatrix}$$

Figure 8: *The Precious Matrix and its square for triangles G and H*

The two triangles A and B form a Precious set in their own right. They are shapes that are not similar, they can be used to create larger but similar shapes, each with the same enlargement and, because there are only two tiles, the second power of P should contain all non zero elements.

As before the enlargement factor is φ, the golden ratio. They are referred to in this paper as G and H because their relationship is different to that between triangles A and B. These triangles are the only triangles whose angles are multiples of 36 degrees. They are the basis of a range of interesting designs and are worthy of a paper in their own right. Section 11 shows an application of these designs in the area of patchwork quilting.

Malekula Sand Tracings: A Case in Ethnomathematics

Marcia Ascher
Mathematics Department
Ithaca College
Ithaca, New York 14850, USA
E-mail: aschaca@clarityconnect.com

Abstract

The Malekula sand tracing tradition is discussed as an exemplary case in ethnomathematics. The tradition evidences graph theoretic, geometric, and topological ideas. The sand tracings are placed within Malekula culture and the systematic procedures used to trace the figures are elaborated. Bridges to art and religion are noted.

Ethnomathematics

In this paper I discuss the sand tracing tradition of the Malekula of Vanuatu. But first I have several preliminary comments in order to put this into the contexts of ethnomathematics and of mathematics.

The basic tenet of ethnomathematics is that the expression of mathematical ideas is intimately related to culture; that ideas arise within cultural contexts and which ideas are emphasized and how they are expressed vary depending on the culture. My studies in ethnomathematics focus on the mathematical ideas of peoples in traditional or small-scale cultures.

Among mathematical ideas, I include those ideas involving number, logic, and spatial configuration, and, more significantly, their combination or organization into systems and structures. The need to clarify what is meant by mathematical ideas is an important issue raised by ethnomathematics. It is now generally recognized that what we refer to as *modern mathematics* is, in itself, the confluence of ideas from many cultures eventually merged through translation, media, and standardization of expression. But the term *mathematics* has no clear and agreed upon definition. More important, however, is that in most cultures, mathematics is not set apart as a separate, explicit category. Mathematical ideas, however, do exist with or without that explicit category and whether or not the ideas fed into or effected the mathematical main stream. As a result, mathematical ideas are found in contexts appropriate to the cultures in which they arise. These contexts could be, for example, what we might categorize as navigation, art, record keeping, religion, kinship, games, decoration, divination, construction, or calendrics.

By including the mathematical ideas of cultures previously ignored, we introduce considerable diversity and geographic breadth. The number of different cultures, using the criterion of mutually exclusive speech communities, that is, having different languages, has remained at about 5000 to 6000 during the past 600 years. (It is the number of people in the culture and the area they dominate that has changed considerably.) Although today there is an overlay of a few dominant cultures, traditional cultures still exist, even if in some cases blended with or blurred within the dominant culture as subcultures, part cultures, or composite cultures. The special contribution of ethnomathematics is elaborating the mathematical ideas of those traditional cultures while recognizing that the ideas are an integral part of the intricate web of language, beliefs, and life-ways that make up the culture. It is this focus that should make ethnomathematics of particular importance and relevance to people concerned with bridges that link mathematics to other cultural expressions. In ethnomathematics, we emphasize that mathematical ideas are embedded in cultural contexts and that, as we discuss the mathematical ideas, we *must* retain these bridges in order to properly and fully see the ideas for what they are.

Another important note is that until quite recently, over 90% of traditional cultures had no writing as we generally use the term. To learn about the mathematical ideas of cultures that had no writing systems and whose traditions are no longer extant, we must depend on information that can be extracted from artifacts or from the reports of observations left by others. Even where the ideas are recent or current, they may be part of an oral tradition and so must often be gleaned from observations and from the interpretation of material things. Thus, the study of ethnomathematics often interacts with or draws upon fields such as archeology, ethnology, linguistics, and culture history. This feature of ethnomathematics involves another set of bridges--bridges to disciplines and perspectives that are not the usual sources for mathematicians or mathematical investigations.

During the past 80 years, there have been vast changes in knowledge, understanding and theories about culture, language, and cognitive processes. We have come to understand that there is no single, universal path which all cultures or mathematical ideas must follow. When we learn about the varied and often quite substantial mathematical ideas of traditional cultures, we are not learning about some early phase in humankind's past. We are learning about pieces of a global mosaic. By incorporating expressions of different peoples, at different times, and in different places, we are enlarging our understanding of the variety of human expressions and human usages associated with the same basic ideas. (Recognizing that there is a plurality of paths, does not, of course, preclude that there was interaction, sharing or borrowing, but that would have to be specifically shown.)

Now, as we turn to the Malekula sand tracing tradition, we move beyond generalities and give more substance to many of the comments above about ethnomathematics. Within ethnomathematics, I am most interested in those cases for which analysis of structure can be combined with evidence that the people themselves were concerned with the structure. The Malekula sand tracings are one such case.

The Malekula and Graph Theoretic Ideas

The Malekula live in the South Pacific in the Republic of Vanuatu, which was formerly known as the New Hebrides. A particular idea evidenced by their sand tracing tradition falls within what Western mathematicians call *Graph Theory* and associated with it are other topological and geometric ideas. So, first let us collect some of our ideas on graph theory. Described geometrically, graph theory is concerned with arrays of points (we call them *vertices*) interconnected by lines (which we call *edges*).

A classical question in graph theory is "For a graph, can a continuous path be found that covers every edge once and only once? And, if such a path exists, can the path end at the point it started?" This is the question that is said to have inspired the founding of graph theory by the mathematician Euler. According to the story, there were seven bridges in Königsberg where Euler lived. The townspeople were interested in knowing if, on their Sunday walks, they could start from home, cross each bridge once and only once and end at home. Between Euler in the 1730s and Hierholzer about 130 years later, a complete answer was found. Before stating the result, I have to introduce the *degree* of a vertex. The degree of a vertex is the number of edges that emanate from it. A vertex is odd if its degree is odd and even if its degree is even. First of all, not all graphs *can* be traced continuously covering every edge once and only once. If such a path can be found, we call it, in honor of Euler, an Eulerian path. Such a path exists if the graph has one pair of odd vertices, provided you start at one of them and end at the other. And, if all the vertices are even, such a path can be traced starting anywhere and ending where you began. The cases in which there cannot be such paths are when the graphs have more than one pair of odd vertices.

Some examples of graphs are in Figure 1. In example (d), every vertex is of degree four--you can start anywhere and end where you started. In (b) (which some of you might recognize as a children's game if you grew up on the streets of New York City or London or Berlin), there are three vertices of degree four and two vertices of degree three. An Eulerian path can be found provided you start at one of the odd vertices and end at the other. Example (a) has one vertex of degree four and *four* vertices of degree three and so it cannot be done. Finally, example (c), a 19th -century Danish party puzzle, has eight vertices of degree three so it cannot be done. [(a) would require two lines or backtracking and (c) would require four lines or backtracking.] The philosopher Wittgenstein in his *Remarks on the Foundations of Mathematics* used this example of tracing a figure--with a figure very similar to (c)--as one that captures the essence of mathematics writing that "it is recognizable at once as a mathematical problem"[3].

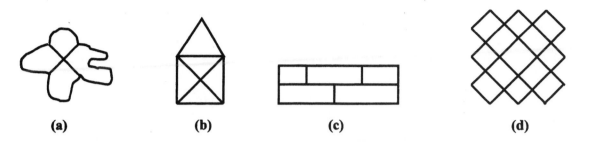

(a)   (b)   (c)   (d)

Figure 1: *Examples of graphs.*

Now back to the Malekula-----

In the 1920s, Bernard Deacon, a graduate student in ethnology at Cambridge University, studied among the Malekula. Deacon observed a tradition of tracing figures in the sand. Believing there was something quite important about it, he was meticulous in copying 95 figures and numbering the order in which *every* line on *every* figure was traced. While waiting for the boat home upon completion of his fieldwork, Deacon died of Blackwater fever. His doctoral mentor and a fellow graduate student published much of his work including his very detailed field drawings [2]. I think, perhaps, that his bad fortune led to the publication of this information (essentially raw data) that he might only have published in summarized form had he lived. Deacon, however, does seem to have had unusual insight combined with respect for the capabilities of the Malekula.

According to the Malekula, when a man dies, in order to get to the Land of the Dead, his ghost must pass a spider-like ogre who challenges him to trace a figure in the sand. The stipulation is that he must trace the entire figure without lifting his finger, without backtracking, and, if possible ending where he started. (These stipulations should be familiar--the Malekula are specifying what we discussed above as Eulerian paths.) If he does not meet the challenge, he cannot proceed to the Land of the Dead. They also have a myth about the origin of Death that involves figure tracing. The myth centers around two brothers Barkulkul and Marekul who have come to earth from the sky world. When Barkulkul leaves his wife to go on a trip, he places a vine in a certain configuration on the closed door of their house. When Barkulkul returns he sees that the vine has been disturbed. He goes to the men's house and challenges all the men gathered there to trace a figure in the ashes on the floor. Because Marekul cannot trace the figure *properly* (that is, with the stipulations previously stated), Barkulkul knows it was his brother who visited while he was away. The story goes on, but the important point here is that knowing the figures and tracing them *properly* is a serious matter. It is not a game and not just the concern of a few people. It is, however, restricted to men.

Tracing the Figures

The 95 figures range from simple closed curves to having more than 100 vertices and many having vertices of degree 10 or 12. Not only do we have the Malekula statement of an interest in tracing these figures continuously, covering every edge once and only once, and if possible, ending at the starting point, but we have the exact tracing paths that upon analysis bear it out. The Malekula refer to the figures as *nitus*. Figure 2 shows a few of them. In actuality the nitus measure about a square meter or more. We will now discuss some of these figures in greater detail.

(a)

(b)

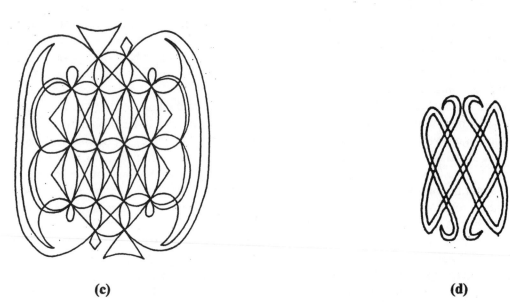

(c)

(d)

Figure 2: *Malekula sand tracings (nitus).*

In examining the tracing paths, I found more than just this graph theoretic concern. When an Eulierian path is possible, there can be many different ways to trace it. The Malekula tracing processes are very systematic within each figure but, even more important, the systems extend to groups of figures. There are three or four of these extended systems, one of which we'll look at in detail. First, for a large group of figures the system is what I call a *process algebra*. Namely, in the tracing of each figure there is some initial procedure (that is, an ordered set of motions) followed by a formal transformation of that procedure. And, for the group of figures, only a particular set of transformations is used. I'll expand on this using as an example a small, made-up initial procedure. Let us say that the initial procedure is the ordered set of motions A shown in Figure 3. It can be followed by itself--AA . It can be followed by each motion rotated through 90° --AA$_{90}$. There can be a reflection of each motion across a vertical axis (right and left interchange, up and down remain the same) --AA$_V$. The order for performing the motions can be inverted-- AA'. Notice that the transformed procedures do not yield the visual effects one usually associates with these words because, since the tracing is continuous, each procedure picks up where the last leaves off. In all, the set of transformations used by the Malekula are I (identity), rotate 90°, rotate 180°, rotate 270 °, reflect vertical, reflect horizontal, each with or without inversion.

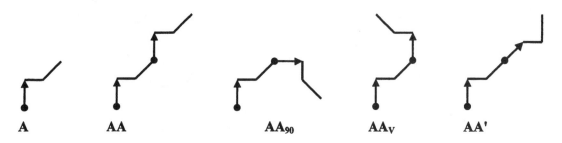

Figure 3: *Initial procedure A followed by some of its transformations.*

Now, let us look at some of the nitus to see how the Malekula traced them. Figure 4 shows a nitus and its initial procedure A. In terms of A, the complete tracing path can be described as AA$_{90}$A$_{180}$A$_{270}$. The visual fourfold symmetry results from successive rotations of the procedure. (The basic unit is not what I would have visualized from the end result.)

Figure 5 shows a tracing in three stages. Each stage is a procedure followed by its rotation through 180°. The visual effect is horizontal and vertical symmetry but it was created by rotation of the procedures. Usually discussions of symmetry rely only on after completion static effects. Here we have both that and the dynamic symmetry of construction.

Another nitus traced in three stages is one previously shown in Figure 2c. Here, too, each stage is a procedure followed by its transformation by a 180° rotation. In this case the procedures, the visual effect, and the nitus description all reiterate the 180° rotation. The Malekula description of the nitus is two of the same kind of fishes placed head to tail.

Next, Figure 6 shows a nitus traced in four stages--each stage is a procedure followed by its inversion.

In the last illustration, Figure 7, the complete tracing can be described as AA$_{180}$A$_V$A$_H$ which brings us to the need for a bit of algebra and which raises an important point about this use of modern symbolism.

In each description, such as AA$_{90}$A$_{180}$A$_{270}$ for the nitus in Figure 4, I described each subsequent procedure with reference to the initial procedure. These could be described differently. For example, if each procedure is referred to the one just before, it would be AA$_{90}$(A$_{90}$)$_{90}$(A$_{180}$)$_{90}$. Or, referring the last pair of procedures to the first pair, the result is (AA$_{90}$) (AA$_{90}$)$_{180}$. All of theses versions show successive rotations but with different emphases. For the last nitus (Figure 7), however, the different versions involve different transformations. Referring each procedure to the initial procedure, we had AA$_{180}$A$_V$A$_H$. Instead we'll refer each procedure to the one before it [AA$_{180}$ (A$_{180}$)$_?$ (A$_V$)$_{??}$] or we'll refer the last pair to the first pair if the pairing is possible [(AA$_{180}$) (AA$_{180}$)$_?$]. To solve this we need a product table for the transformations; that is, a table showing the result of one transformation followed by another. (See Table 1). Notice that the X and Y in the table are not in the set of transformations used by the Malekula and so the pairs that lead to them could not have occurred. Specifically, there could be no 90(V) or H (270). The transformations X and Y are, in fact, reflections across the diagonals and these were not present. Using the table, we have three different, but equivalent, symbolic representations:

$$AA_{180}A_VA_H = AA_{180}(A_{180})_H(A_V)_{180} = AA_{180}(AA_{180})_V.$$

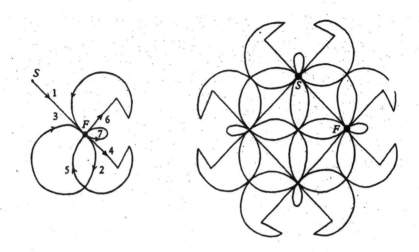

Figure 4: *The initial procedure A and the final figure* $AA_{90}A_{180}A_{270}$.

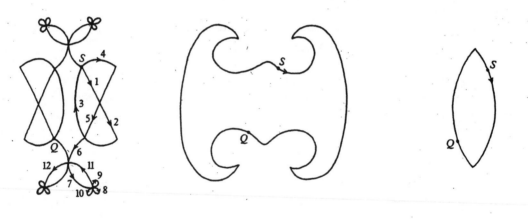

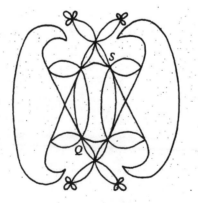

Figure 5: *A nitus traced in three stages. In each stage, the initial procedure (A, B, and C) starts at S, ends at Q, and is followed by the procedure rotated 180°. The final figure is* $AA_{180}BB_{180}CC_{180}$.

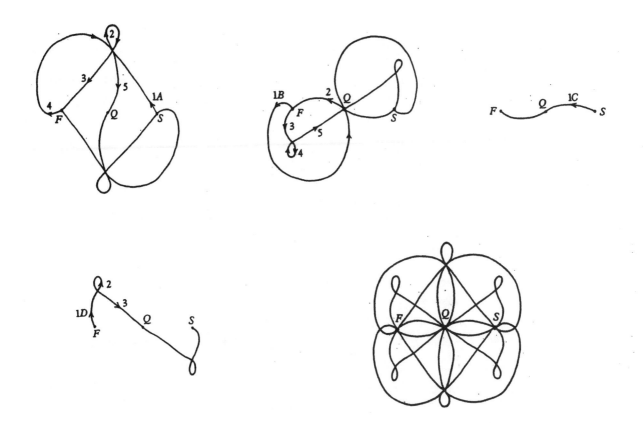

Figure 6: *A nitus traced in four stages. In the first and third stages, the initial procedures (A and C) start at S, end at Q, and are followed by the procedure transformed by inversion. For the second and fourth stages, the initial procedures (B and D) start instead at F. The final figure is AA'BB'CC'DD'.*

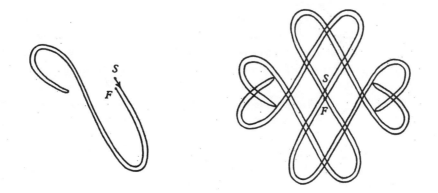

Figure 7: *The initial procedure A and the final figure $AA_{180}A_VA_H$.*

Each of these describes the structure of *what was actually done* but each version implies a slightly different conceptualization by the Malekula. That is, even though we know exactly what they did, we do not know exactly what they thought while they did it. But, being able to generate different versions can give us different insights. To me, the last version seems more in keeping with the overall procedures for the other figures, but that is just conjecture on my part.

	I	90	180	270	V	H
I	I	90	180	270	V	H
90	90	180	270	I	Y	X
180	180	270	I	90	H	V
270	270	I	90	180	X	Y
V	V	X	H	Y	I	180
H	H	Y	V	X	180	I

Table 1: *Transformation product table.*

These are just a few of the 95 tracings but in them you can see that in this sand drawing tradition there are:

1. A graph theoretic goal, which is carried out, of tracing figures continuously covering each edge once and only once and, where possible, beginning and ending at the same point.

2. There is the creation of visual symmetry in most of the figures.

3. Within these self-imposed constraints, the individual figures are traced quite systematically.

And 4. For different groups of figures, these systematic procedures are particular expressions of larger systems. For the system we have looked at, selections from a specific set of transformations are applied to different basic procedures.

Taken by themselves, simply as figures, the tracings are quite intricate and quite attractive. In fact, they have been compared to well-known works of Western art. In 1944, the eminent art historian, Ananda Coomaraswamy, who was curator of the Boston Museum of Fine Arts for some 30 years, wrote an article about Dürer's engraving entitled "Knots" and da Vinci's engraving "Concatenation". In his view, these are part of a worldwide tradition of single-line drawings. "But...", he says and shows one of the Malekula figures, "But it is, perhaps, in the New Hebrides that the one-line technique attains its fullest development"[1]. From their place in Malekula culture, the figures represent another, perhaps more important bridge, that is, they are clearly religious expressions, particularly related to Malekula myths about death. But above all, for those of us interested in mathematical ideas, as we consider the tracing goals, follow the tracing procedures, and view the tracing outcomes, they are a bridge to some understanding of an intellectual endeavor of the Malekula. In 2003, UNESCO included the Malekula sand tracing tradition on the World Heritage list proclaiming it 'A Masterpiece of the Oral and Intangible Heritage of Humanity'.

References

[1] A. Coomaraswamy, *The Icononograpy of Dürer's 'Knots' and Leonardo's 'Concatenation*, The Art Quarterly, Vol. 7, pp.109-128. 1944.

[2] M. Ascher, *Graphs in Cultures: A Study in Ethnomathematics*, Historia Mathematica. Vol. 15, pp.201-227. 1988. See this article for a more extensive discussion of these tracings, more illustrations of them, and numerous references.

[3] L. Wittgenstein, Remarks on the Foundations of Mathematics, G.H. von Wright, R. Rhees, and G.E.M. Anscombe, eds., Blackwell, Oxford, p. 174e. 1956.

Generative Art and Aesthetics

Susan Happersett
249 4th street
Jersey City, NJ 07302, USA
E-mail: fibonaccisusan@yahoo.com

As artists who choose mathematical principles as their theme, we are blessed with a never-ending stream of content. Many art, writing and film schools offer seminars in content generating. Whether it is basic numerical arithmetic, algebra, topology or other higher-level studies, there is an abundance of fertile areas of mathematical work to explore. The challenge is to take these ideas and create aesthetically artistic work, art that somehow speaks to others on a non-mathematical level as well.

By using mathematical laws, formulas, and algorithms, our work falls into the category of Generative Art. Philip Galanter offers one of the most accepted definitions for Generative Art:

> "Generative Art refers to any art practice where the artist creates a process such as a set of natural language rules, a computer program, a machine or other mechanism, which is then set to motion with some degree of autonomy contributing to or resulting in a complete work of art." [1]

By developing a grid work and mapping process, I have plotted various numerical properties. These graphs allow me to examine the aesthetic characteristics of functions, sequences and series in a visual language. I have deconstructed the placement of the strokes to eliminate any literal meaning. It is the number of strokes in each grid that holds significance. Although I do not use a computer in the production of my drawings, I do use mathematical algorithms to determine the number of markings drawn in each square of the grid. Each drawing is planned out mathematically ahead of time. The mechanism I use to make my type of generative art is manual mark making.

As an artist I must ask myself when does this generative process lead to a successful work of art. It seems to me that using an interesting formula and an algorithm to generate an image does not necessarily create art. There is an extra element, a hidden step in the decision-making that yields a work of art. In making the judgment of whether a process successfully initiates art, I am led to the thorny question, what is art?

In trying to grapple with this question, I decided to go outside of my comfort zone of art theory. Since my experience in art is based in modern and post-modern tenets, I looked to a philosopher that was pre-modern: Kant. I was particular intrigued by two statements from his "*Critique of Judgment*":

> When we judge free beauty (according to mere form) then our judgment of taste is pure. Here we presuppose no concept of any purpose for which the manifold is to serve the given object, and hence no concept [as to] what the object is meant to represent; our imagination is playing, as it were, while it contemplates the shape, and such a concept would only restrict its freedom. [2]

In his second Critique Kant says that the "beautiful and sublime agree on a point of pleasing on their own account. Further they agree in not presupposing a judgment of sense or one logically determinate, but one of reflection." [3] To me it seams that Kant is telling us that the aesthetic value of an art work is not necessarily determined by the content or the subject. It has more to do with how the viewer responds to the work, regardless of the generating concept of the work. When you take a mathematical principle or formula that you find astonishing or sublime, will it be as intriguing when it is translated into a visual image? Going a step further will the completed work of art be interesting with out the knowledge and comprehension of its basis in Mathematics. In other words: Will it engage a non-mathematics person?

Bringing these ideas back to the studio, I embarked on making some adjustments to my processes to test out the concepts of aesthetics in relation to my generative art. I tried three experiments. One challenges the visibility of my markings. Another experiment was displacing grids in the system, and then in the last experiment I applied my favorite mathematical sequence (Fibonacci) to a classic subject of aesthetics.

I hope to intensify the viewer's interaction with my work by making the markings subtler. I decided to make drawings in white ink on off-white paper. I could not actually see the markings while I was working. I just counted and stayed within the grid. It is not until the ink dries that the pattern is evident. These subtle white-on-white drawings take my work to a more intimate place, putting more emphasis on the meditation. It is as though the image comes out of the paper like magic.

The second new approach I incorporated into my drawing was inspired from nature. I have been saying all along that my use of the Fibonacci sequence was based on idealized growth patterns in plants, but plants rarely grow in idealized conditions, roots hit rocks, bugs eat leaves, etc. By displacing or switching grid spaces, I hope to express these imperfections. The plans for these drawings start just like all of my other drawings, but before I start the actual drawing process I select a few sections of the grid and alter them by trading one designated section for another. I am trying to create a sort of static energy and also make the viewer question whether this was a mistake.

Figure 1: *Fibonacci Flower, 2005*

The final experiment involves a complete change of parameters. I wanted to use the basic Fibonacci sequence to make a work of art that reflected one of the most accepted subjects in art - the flower. I created a series of eight concentric templates, the smallest with a 1" circumference, the second with a 2" circumference and each of the next consecutive circles having a circumference 2" larger than the previous circle. The first circle was kept whole and contains 1 petal within 1 petal. The next was divided into 2 equal chords and houses 2 petals. The next circle divided into 3 equal chords and 3 petals. The next circle divided into 5 equal chords and 5 petals. Then 8, 13, 21, and finally the largest circle divided into 34 chords and I drew 34 petals. The final structure is a type of Fibonacci-based, genetically engineered flower.

Working within a strict system to generate art, it becomes natural to continue to make art along the same process. I find it is important to step outside of the process and challenge one's work aesthetically. In doing so the artist may even discover new concepts.

References

[1] Philip Galanter, *www.philipgalanter.com*, Jan 2005.
[2], [3] Immanuel Kant, *The Critique of Judgment*, Trans. Werner Pluhar, Indianapolis: Cambridge, 1987.

Beauty in Art and Mathematics:
A Common Neural Substrate or the Limits of Language?

Daniel J. Goldstein
Departamento de Fisiología, Biología Molecular y Celular
Facultad de Ciencias Exactas y Naturales
Universidad de Buenos Aires
Argentina

Abstract

Mathematicians often refer to the aesthetic qualities of mathematical works using the same terms and expressions employed by artists and art critics to evaluate visually apprehensible objects. Does this reflect the limits of human language, or is it a subtle indication that vision is somehow connected with the process of understanding and inventing/discovering mathematics?

Gian-Carlo Rota and Freeman Dyson have written on the beauty of mathematics and refer to non-visual mathematics in visual terms. Rota discusses the phenomenology of the beauty of mathematics using words and arguments that are strongly reminiscent of those which are used to analyze the issues of beauty and aesthetic relevance in art. Do Rota's and Dyson's writings reflect the existence of a connection between mathematics and vision, or do they just reflect the limitations of the human language?

Dyson and the Visualization of the Invisible

Visual mathematics has become a very popular subject in contemporary mathematics. Ian Stewart's *Nature Numbers* deals with mathematical objects derived from many different fields of mathematics–e.g. non-linear dynamics, chaos theory, and complexity theory–which can be visually represented by means of computers [1]. In his review of Stewart's book, Freeman Dyson contrasts the "new visual style of mathematical thinking" with the "old fashioned non-visual mathematics, the mathematics of equations and exact solutions"[2]. Yet Dyson uses visual metaphors for criticizing Stewart's mathematical preferences, as well as for addressing his own perception of mathematics.

> The beauty of Maxwell's equations becomes *visible* only when you abandon mechanical models, and the beauty of quantum mechanics becomes *visible* only when you abandon classical thinking [...] Quantum mechanics runs counter to the two cardinal principles of the new wave of mathematics. (Italics mine)[3].

Dyson also asserts that the Van der Pol equation "illustrates vividly the *blindness* of mathematicians to discoveries in unfashionable fields," and finds "examples of mathematical description...that [he would not] consider *deep*" (Italics mine) [4]. Thus, the lack of appreciation of the "deep" meaning of mathematics that is impossible to visualize is attributed to "blindness."

These kinds of oxymorons and extreme metaphors are also frequent in critical inquiries, where language is often stretched beyond its literal meaning. For the poet Simonides of Ceos (c. 556-468 BC), the founder of the *ut pictura poesis* tradition, painting is mute poetry [5][6]. Leonardo considers poetry a speaking picture, a blind painting [7]. Wölfflin makes the metaphorical distinction between classical painting (tactile, sculpturesque, symmetrical, and closed) and the baroque painting (visual, "painterly," asymmetric, and open) [8].

Rota and the Phenomenology of Mathematical Beauty

Rota tries to "uncover the sense of the term 'beauty' as it is used by mathematicians." The issue, he argues, is relevant because beauty becomes a matter of contention in an intellectual discipline in which its practitioners "are fond of passing judgments on the beauty of their favored pieces of mathematics" [9]. Beauty is a fuzzy expression to denote a fuzzy sensation of pleasure that itself is the result of the combinations of other fuzzy appreciations such as "elegance," "surprise," "potency," and "opportunity," all of them conditioned by the ideological context–the historical stage–of the artist and the beholder. Mathematical beauty and artistic beauty are both cultural constructs and active societal work is required to impose the new cannons. "Beauty" and "elegance" are institutional facts, and change according the predominant ideology. There is not a uniform canon of beauty–e.g. the beauty of Picasso's cubist and surrealist portraits is different to the beauty of Filippo Lippi's *La Vergine*. The acceptance of new mathematical perspectives and new artistic perspectives is not immediate, and it is well known that mathematical theories and art styles became "objects of beauty" only after new generations are educated in them. Moreover, a given theory may induce pleasure in some mathematicians, and boredom and irritation in others.

Rota suggests that mathematicians use the word "beauty" to denote "the phenomenon of enlightenment"–i.e. the capture of the *sense* of a statement–"while avoiding acknowledgment of the fuzziness of this phenomenon" [10]. To appreciate mathematical beauty it is necessary to understand the mathematics involved–to force the brain to do mathematical work. Grasping the meaning of mathematical texts, not the aesthetic appreciation of its symbols or the sound of its phonetic reading, is what elicits the sensation of pleasure.

> Appreciation of mathematical beauty requires familiarity with a mathematical theory, and such familiarity is arrived at the cost of time, effort, exercise, and *Sitzfleisch* rather than by training in beauty appreciation. [11]

For Rota, "classical Euclidean geometry is often proposed by non-mathematicians as a paradigm of a beautiful mathematical theory [but not] by professional mathematicians"[12]. The fact that non-mathematicians often find Euclidean geometry pleasant proves Rota's argument. Euclidean geometry is probably the only tiny segment of the vast and expanding mathematical universe that (a minority) of high school students invest time and *Sitzfleisch* to understand.

Art appreciation is also based on understanding, and requires intellectual work and *Sitzfleisch*. Vision uninformed by previous knowledge and context means blindness. Bernard Berenson observed that "many see paintings without knowing what to look at" [13]. Mitchell, Gombrich and Nelson Goodman agree in that "the innocent eye" is blind [14]. An *oeuvre* is deemed "beautiful" and not merely elegant or technically accomplished when it makes sense–i.e. when it is enlightening. Moreover, significant images and icons–from prehistoric cave painting to cubism and concrete (abstract) art–are useful because they explain things, open new perspectives, and are symbolic resources. Picasso tried to understand the work of Matisse, his most important competitor [15].Yet the understanding of a picture does not mean deriving pleasure from it. Matisse understood Cubism and could "read" Picasso and Braque, although he disliked its aesthetics [16].

For Rota, mathematical beauty is associated with shortness and compactness [17]. The grasping of the representative essentials is one of the characteristics that are associated with beauty in the fine arts– e.g. the images depicting animals in the prehistoric caves, the drawings of Picasso and Matisse [18]. The notions of shortness and compactness are complemented with the appreciation of the beauty of "streamlined proofs." "Hilbert's original axioms were clumsy and heavy-handed, and required streamlining" [19]. Rota's use of the concept of streamlining underlines the historicity of the concept of beauty in mathematics. Streamlining began as a visual concept (the course of water and air currents as inferred by visual cues), which did not exist as an aesthetic concept until its invention by automobile and aeronautical designers in 20ᵗʰ Century USA [20]. The aesthetic canons of modernity, therefore, influence the aesthetic cannons of beauty in mathematics.

Mathematical beauty is often *partial*, in the sense that the mathematician often detects beauty in a small component of a much larger structure that is not perceived as beautiful as a whole. The portion that is deemed beautiful is "a brilliant step in an otherwise undistinguished proof" [21]. This is also well known in the fine arts, where isolated segments of an otherwise irrelevant picture (or sculpture) can impress as beautiful when considered in isolation. The photographic enlargements of portions of an *oeuvre* often disclose a hidden beauty that is lost in the whole. Different sectors of a painting have different meaning for different beholders. Jackson Pollock identified small areas in Picasso's paintings that justified his claim that the Spanish master was the direct precursor of abstract expressionism. These same areas are considered utterly irrelevant by other observers, which see them as technical accidents resulting from Picasso's sloppiness and speed.

G. H. Hardy and the Element of Surprise

G. H. Hardy believed that the beauty of a mathematical proof depends on the element of *surprise*. Rota concedes that "the beauty of a piece of mathematics is often perceived with a feeling of pleasant surprise [and] instances [can be found] of surprising results which no one has ever thought as classifying as beautiful." Still, Rota recognizes "instances of theorems that are both beautiful and surprising abound" and attributes the beauty of Galois theory of equations to "the once improbable notion of a group of permutations" [22]. Surprise is a central ingredient in the appreciation of a work of art, where the unexpected derives from leaps over conventional limits of theme, subject, and style, and humor. The works of Hyeronimus Bosch, Picasso, Dalí, and Magritte are a source of surprises, and the pleasure that they elicit is often related to their capacity of surprising the beholder. *La blague d' atelier* always lurks, with a touch of depravity and/or the inversion of the so called "natural hierarchies." In general, this is achieved by depicting conventional objects in new contexts, and things and circumstances that previously were confined to the fringes of artistic representation (where they were mostly unseen), or were not represented at all, suddenly became central and are in the spotlight.

In Courbet's *The Burial* and *The Vagina*, the artist jumps over all the conventions of representation of his time. The visual depiction of a group of minor landowners in an obscure French village and the scrupulous anatomical rendition of a body part that is normally hidden suddenly acquire aesthetic relevance. Until Courbet, small landowners and rural personages were not the adequate subject for high art, and the representation of the woman sexual organs unthinkable. Manet's *Olympia*, the rendition of an inexpensive prostitute, shocked a French public used to an art that represented haughty courtesans. Nan Goldin's photographs were revolutionary because they exposed domestic violence and physical degradation in all its magnitude and horror. Duchamp's urinal shocked and surprised because the functionality of the object (the collection of urine) had so far determined its automatic exclusion from the realm of aesthetics. Courbet, Manet, Goldin, and Duchamp produced abrupt discontinuities in the realm of visual narratives by bringing things peripheral into the central point of attention.

Does something similar to this occur in mathematics? In the 18th Century, sines and cosines, although they were standard methods for analyzing waves–e.g. harmonics–did not belong to the advancing edge of the mathematical sciences of the time. When Fourier, half a century later, showed that any function could efficiently approximated by using the summation of a series of sines and cosines he suddenly put trigonometric functions in the center of mathematical inquiry. Fourier's discovery led Dirichlet to the precise definition of the concept of function, and Riemann to invent the Riemann integral to deal with situations that could not be tackled with the Cauchy integral. Fourier, Dirichlet, and Riemann brought to the center of mathematical inquiry objects and anecdotes that had been considered to be just useful algorithms or plain curiosities, and showed that they are endowed with extraordinarily interesting and useful mathematical attributes. These were mathematical surprises.

Rota also refers to *elegance*, although he recognizes that "mathematical elegance has to do with the presentation of mathematics, and only tangentially does it relate with its content" [23]. Like beauty, elegance is an age-and context-dependent attribute. Mathematics that was considered elegant in the past may be seen as dull now, in the same way that aesthetic preferences change with time. One hundred and fifty years ago, Botticelli's women, the paradigms of feminine beauty in the Twentieth Century, were described as swallow semi-skeletons stricken by consumption. "Heavy," "clumsy," and "massive" mathematics could also have been aesthetically appealing in the past, as once were *à la* Rubens nudes.

The Aesthetics of Authority

Canons of beauty in mathematics and in the fine arts are institutional facts, human-made constructs based on complex metaphysical assumptions than change with time and context [24]. Institutional facts are shaped by a power structure that defines those resources that conform a culture and its attributes in a given moment [25]. This power structure establishes an ideology, namely a systems of normative precepts that establishes the canons of value, and informs both the practitioner of a craft and the beholder[26][27]. Successive ideologies impose paradigmatic definitions of beauty that become the golden rule of the times, establishing which forms of discourse are substantive, beautiful, trivial, or merely decorative. Each one of the successive power structures (in mathematics and in the fine arts) determines the values and the content of the prevailing culture, defining its classicism–the language of authority–and controlling its social perpetuation.

In the realm of the fine arts, influential critics, patrons, *marchands*, museum directors and curators, impose the genres and styles that are worthy of exhibition at museums and galleries. Then, these genres and styles receive acclaim by the media, and are enthroned as the mainstream imagery of a generation. Many artists have painted apples, mountains, and men playing cards, yet Cezanne's apples, Mount Saint Victoire, and men playing cards have became the canonical representation of these objects. The Analytic Cubism of Picasso, Braque, and Gris is the exclusive paradigm of Cubist representation, while the Scientific Cubism of Lohte and Metzinger is deemed trite and uninteresting. Selection implies preferences and omissions; preferences lead to the establishment of paradigms, and omissions result in the suppression of alternative art forms. The preferred art is consecrated at canonical temples of high culture, is covered by the media, and becomes the object of the art market. The art omitted becomes an item in obscure specialized art encyclopedias.

Is there an equivalent power structure in mathematics, ruling which theorems are interesting and worthwhile, and which are not? Do the intellectual leaders of the mathematical community impose to the mathematicians of their generation their styles and preoccupations, and suppress alternative avenues of research? Cultural trend-setters in academia define the fashionable topics and methodologies of the day and displace from the limelight other subjects and trends. In every intellectual and scientific discipline, each generation of trend-setters determines what is mainstream, and what is "out." Research grants, publications, prizes, appointments, editorial boards of professional journals, and graduate students follow.

Yet usefulness, and not beauty, is what matters in mathematics. Beauty *per se* is not the aim of the mathematician, who is primarily interested in proving theorems and finding solutions to mathematical problems [28]. Mathematical truth–within its very limited and precisely defined context–is not a matter of opinion. Mathematicians prove theorems, and sometimes the mechanics of the intellectual process of asserting the logical truth of a proposition strikes other mathematicians as being "elegant" and "beautiful." Yet mathematical beauty is an epiphenomenon unrelated to the intrinsic value of a piece of mathematics, defined by its capability to solve mathematical problems.

For tens of thousands of years, pictorial beauty was an epiphenomenon of visual representation–the very concept of "visual art" is a very recent acquisition in human cultural evolution. Visually perceived objects impress and can be understood without the need of language, and this makes iconic representation an extraordinarily effective medium of communication. This is why images and visually apprehended objects, imbued with strong formulaic and symbolic content, were developed as tools for ideological propaganda and psychological warfare thousands of years before the invention of written languages. The control of images and imagery is still today one of the most tightly regulated elements in politics [29].

Yet Rota warns that "the beauty of a mathematical theory is independent of the aesthetic qualities, or the lack of them, of the theory's rigorous expositions" [30]. Something analogous happens in art. For the great masters of the modernist revolution in the visual arts, beauty was also an epiphenomenon of their search for "realism" in representation. Courbet search for "realism" led him to bypass the canons of beauty of the 19th Century. Picasso and Braque tried to grasp visual "reality" through Cubism. For them, conventional beauty was contingent, something that was not deliberately looked upon. Picasso's masterpiece *Les demoiselles d'Avignon*, the most revolutionary picture of modernity, is a frontal assault against conventional taste– childishly rude, spiked with silly depravity, and a smatter of elemental sexual symbolism [31].

Conclusion

The fact that mathematicians can *see* the beauty of the visually unrepresentable,   unseen and unseeable, suggests at least three different interpretations.

1.   *All mathematics is visual, in the sense that is elaborated by some module of the visual brain* [32]. Between 80 to 90 per cent of the cortex of the brain and numerous subcortical neuronal structures are involved in processing visual stimuli. We are a very visual species and can absorb very fast–in the microsecond range–a vast amount of visual information. This extraordinarily complex and rapid visual equipment endows humans with the almost instantaneous capacity of apprehension by sight. Michael Atiyah suggests that "instantaneous visual action" provides a wealth of spatial information that geometry perfects. He considers that geometry, concerned with *space*, and   algebra, concerned with *time*, provide us with two orthogonal perceptions of the world. For Atiyah, the comparative easiness with which we grasp visible structures could explain the tendency of mathematicians to "geometrize" algebraic problems [33].

Yet the sensorial inputs from the retina that recruit the brain visual system are not needed for the understanding and the invention/discovery of mathematics—as demonstrated by the fact that there are blind mathematicians. Therefore, to understand and create mathematics other cues must be involved in the activation of the visual processing system. In this restricted sense, the creation of a mathematical inner world could be considered a type of visual hallucination. It is a fact that the brain images of visually detected regular solids, and those produced through mathematics seem to coincide. The mental image of visual perception is consistent with that generated by the manipulation of abstract elements according to an arbitrary set of operational rules. On the other hand, the assumption that the operational logic of the brain must necessarily be equivalent to that of human mathematics is highly debatable. The brain is a "brute" fact, the product of hundreds of millions of years of chaotic evolution through adaptive and non-adaptive selection [34][35][36]. Mathematics is an institutional fact, a human-designed system operating with a human-designed arbitrary logic. Even if mathematics can be used to model some brain phenomena, this does not mean that we are reproducing the way in which the brain functions [37][38][39]. However, if the same brain structures are involved in processing visual stimuli and understanding and inventing/discovering mathematics, it would be plausible to assume that understanding mathematics could generate the same sensations that we feel when *seeing* something that we deem pleasurable or rewarding.

2. *The visual system is not involved in the creation and understanding of mathematics, but the activation of whatever brain regions are involved in that process gives raise to the same sensation of pleasure that is generally associated with visual perception.* Anecdotal evidence suggests that the activation of sensorial systems can elicit paradoxical sensations–e.g. visual perception is sometimes translated in melodic impressions, and vice versa. The association between surprise and pleasure in arts and mathematics does not in itself prove that art and mathematics have anything in common, beyond the fact that innovations elicit sensations of pleasure.

3. *The use of visual metaphors to discuss mathematical beauty indicates the limits of language*. Human language is distinctly limited in its capacity to convey sensations and affective tones—feelings themselves being non-transferable. Therefore, to describe what they feel about mathematics, mathematicians must convey these sensations through metaphors. The vision-related words they use are just "pieces of meanings" transferred from one descriptive discourse to another, used primarily as a literary devise to increase the power of conviction of their argument [40].There is nothing wrong with the use of metaphors in science, if one remembers that *they are* metaphors [41].

References

[1]   I. Stewart, *Nature Numbers*, (London: Weidenfeld & Nicolson, 1995).

[2]   F. Dyson, Book review of Ian Stewart's Nature Numbers, *The Mathematical Intelligencer* Vol. 19, pp. 65-67. 1997.

[3]   *Ibid.*

[4]   *Ibid.*

[5]   W.J.T. Mitchell, *Picture Theory: Essay on Verbal and Visual Representation*, (Chicago:University of Chicago Press, 1994), p 116.

[6]   R. Debray, *Vie et Mort de l'Image: Une Histoire du Regard en Occident* (Paris, Gallimard, 1992).

[7]   *Ibid.* p. 117.

[8]   A. Sokal and J. Bricmont, Intellectual Impostures, (London: Profile Books, 1998).

[9]   G.-C. Rota and F. Palombi (Editors), Indiscrete Thoughts, (Boston: Birkhäuser, 1997), p.121.

[10] *Ibid.* pp. 126, 36-37.

[11] *Ibid*. p. 128.

[12] *Ibid*. p. 122.

[13] B. Berenson, *Essays in Appreciation*, (London: Chapman & Hall, 1958).

[14] Mitchell, p. 118.

[15] J. Richardson. *A Life of Picasso*, (New York: Random House, 1991).

[16] *Ibid*.

[17] *Ibid*. pp. 121-122

[18] J.-P. Kahane and P. G. Lemarié-Rieusset, *Séries de Fourier and ondelettes* (Paris: Cassini, 1998).

[19] Rota p. 123.

[20] J. Heskett, *Industrial Design*, (New York: Oxford University Press, 1980).

[21] Rota p. 122.

[22] *Ibid*. p. 123.

[23] *Ibid*. p. 128.

[24] J.R. Searle, *The Construction of Social Reality* (New York: Free Press, 1995).

[25] W. Sewell, *A Theory of Structure: Duality, Agency and Transformation*, American Journal of Sociology, Vol. 98, pp. 1-29, 1992.

[26] See Henri Zerner, *L'Art de la Renaissance en France: L'Invention du Classicisme*, (Paris: Flammarion, 1996).

[27] Charles Rosen and Henri Zerner, *Romanticism and Realism: The Mythology of Nineteenth-Century Art*, (New York: Viking Press, 1984).

[28] Rota p. 126.

[29] C. S. Goldstein, *The Political Control of Images: Iconoclasm and Indoctrination in American Occupied Germany, 1945-1949*, Ph. D. Dissertation, University of Chicago, 2002.

[30] Rota p. 24.

[31] Richardson.

[32] D. J. Goldstein, "Do we do mathematics with our visual brain?" *The Mathematical Intelligencer*, Vol. 20, pp. 5-10, 1998.

[33] M. Atiyah, *Mathematics in the 20th Century*, The American Mathematical Monthly, Vol. 108, pp. 654-666, 2001.

[34] S.J. Gould, *The exaptive excellence of spandrels as a term and prototype*, Proceedings of the National Academy of Sciences, U.S.A., Vol 94, pp. 10750-10755, 1997.

[35] S.J. Gould, Darwinian Fundamentalism, New York Review of Books, 12 June 1997.

[36] S.J. Gould and R.C. Lewontin, *The Spandrels of San Marco and the Panglossian Paradigm: A Critique of the Adaptationist Programme,* Proceedings of the Royal Society, Series B, Vol. 205, pp. 581-598, 1979.

[37] Paul C. Bressloff, Jack D. Cowan, Martin Golubitsky, Peter J. Thomas, and Matthew C. Wiener, *Geometric visual hallucinations, Euclidean symmetry and the functional architecture of striate cortex,* Phil. Trans. R. Soc. London. B Series, Vil. 356, pp. 299-330, 2001.

[38] M.C. Reed, *Why is Mathematical Biology so Hard?* Notices of the American Mathematical Society, Vol. 51, pp. 338-342, 2004.

[39] D. J. Goldstein, *If mathematicians do not do it, who will?*,The Mathematical Intelligencer Vol 23, pp 11-12, 2001.

[40] S. Maasen, E. Mendelsohn, and P. Weingart, *Biology as Society, Society as Biology: Metaphors,* (Boston: Kluver Academic Publishers, 1995), pp. 1-2.

[41] R. Lewontin, *The Triple Helix: Gene, Organism, and Environment*, (Cambridge: Harvard University Press, 2000).

Correspondence: Daniel J Goldstein, 1615 Q street NW. Apt T-6, Washington DC 20009, USA. E-mail: cs@scs.howard.edu

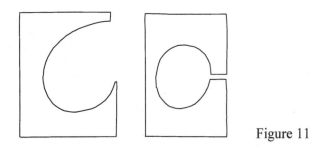

Figure 11

"To construct a complete developable surface in two sheets from its edge of regression. lay one piece of perfectly flat, unwrinkled, smooth-cut paper on the top of another. Trace any curve on the upper, and let it have no point of inflection, but everywhere finite curvature. Cut the two papers along the curve and remove the convex portions. If the curve traced is closed, it must be cut open (see second diagram). Attach the two sheets together by very slight paper or muslin clamps gummed to them along the common curved edge. These must be SO slight as not to interfere sensibly with the flexure of the two sheets. Take hold of one corner of one sheet and lift the whole. The two will open out into the two sheets of a developable surface, of which the curve, bending into a curve of double curvature, is the edge of regression. The tangent to the curve drawn in one direction from the point of contact, will always lie in one of the sheets, and its continuation on the other side in the other sheet. Of course a double-sheeted developable polyhedron can be constructed by this process, by starting from a polygon instead of a curve."

If only they had not cut the curve open and rotated it slightly, they would have discovered anti-D-Forms, which would probably have taken them on the path to D-Forms some 120 or so years ago. Their method is also described in Koenderik [5] who says to take a series of circles on two sheets of paper. These form the tangential developable helicoids of a helix which is the edge of regression. He shows how the two halves of the tangents to the circles form the two surfaces which meet at the edge of regression (figure 12).

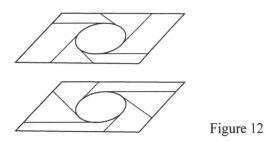

Figure 12

The helicoids are not as prominent as in the anti-D-Forms of figure 5. Tangential developables are easy to program as ruled surfaces. If you have a space curve, you can just extend the tangents. Figure 13 shows a D-Form which has been created by the intersection of two elliptical cylinders. The edge curve was then extracted from this and the two tangential surfaces created as shown as two views of figure 14.

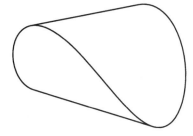

Figure 13: *simulated D-Form*

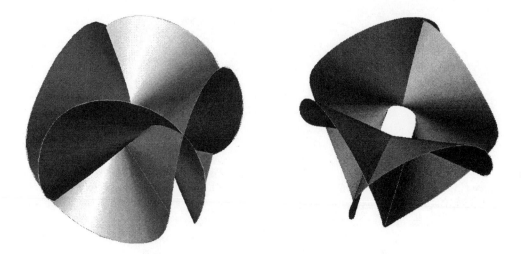

Figure 14: *tangential developable*

The two surfaces result from the two halves of the tangent of the space curve. Thompson and Tait and Koenderik's example of figure 12 took two separate circles and produced the edge of regression by twisting to form the space curve. When you take a space curve as in the edge curve extracted from the example of figure 13, the two tangent halves create the surfaces. This is not an intuitive result, and like constructing D-Forms, needs to be performed to be understood. What is interesting in this case (and also counter-intuitive) is that the two tangential developable surfaces intersect one another.

Concluding thoughts

The more you explore this simple concept the more you wonder why it was not thought of before. There has only been space to touch on the fundamentals of the subject in this paper. It has also not been possible to show the dynamic way a D-Form takes on a life of its own as is constructed. The only way you can understand this is to make one for yourself. The subject raises many questions and suggests many avenues to explore.

References

1. Tony Wills has examples of his D-Form work at
   www.wills-watson.co.uk/proj_street_01.html
   Figure 1 is copyright Tony Wills 2004 as is the Squaricle shown in figure 4.
2. Paul Bourke http://astronomy.swin.edu.au/~pbourke/surfaces/dform/. He may reorganise his site, so this may change.
3. John Sharp, "D-Forms: surprising new 3D forms from flat curved shapes", Tarquin 2005
4. Jun Mitani, Pepakura Designer, www.tamasoft.co.jp/pepakura-en
5. Sir William Thomson (Baron Kelvin) and Peter Guthrie Tait, "A Treatise on natural philosophy", 1888
6. Jan J. Koenderik, Solid Shape. MIT 1990
7. W Abbott, "Practical Geometry and Engineering Graphics" Blackie London1943

(Vector) Fields of Mathematical Poetry

Carla Farsi
Department of Mathematics
University of Colorado
395 UCB
Boulder, CO 80309-0395, USA
E-mail: farsi@euclid.colorado.edu

Abstract

In this note we will look at some artwork inspired by the mathematics of vector fields on surfaces.

1.1. The Art Work. My installation "(Vector) Fields of Mathematical Poetry" will be shown at the Core New Art Space Gallery in Denver from June 2 to June 18, 2005. This exhibition is part of the "2005 CU Special Year in Art and Mathematics" at the University of Colorado/Boulder. This installation was inspired by some beautiful results on vector fields on surfaces that I am going to describe. (All our surfaces are assumed to be orientable.)

1.2. Mathematical Vector Fields on Surfaces. For rigorous definitions, see [1], [3].

a)   Surfaces are mathematical objects such as the sphere, and the doughnut's outer shell or a "doughnut with more than one hole"

b)   A local vector bundle on a surface is a local assignment of a linear space. Its elements are called vectors and in the easiest cases can be represented by arrows.

c)   Local vector bundles patch together to form globally defined vector bundles on surfaces.

d)   A vector field on a surface is a smooth assignment of a vector for each point.

e)   Vector fields have a well defined index at any of the points at which they are zero. This index denotes the total number of vector field loops around the zero point.

1.3. The Euler Characteristic. The Euler Characteristic X(S) of a planar geometric object S can be computed in the following way. First, subdivide S into triangles (or generalized triangles, triangles which curved edges). Define Then X(S)=T-E+V, where T is the number of triangles, E the number of edges, V the number of vertices in the subdivision. Euler characteristic is additive. The Euler characteristic of the sphere, thought of as a tetrahedron, is 2, while the Euler characteristic of the doughnut is 0.

1.4. Theorems. The following two theorems are classical results

1)   The sum of the indices of a vector field on a surface equals the Euler Characteristic.

2)   If a surface admits a nowhere zero vector field, then its Euler Characteristic is zero.

The second theorem is a straightforward consequence of the first one, as there is no point at which the index can be computed. Also, as the Euler Characteristic of the sphere is 2, every vector field on the sphere must vanish at least one point, or, more intuitively, it is not possible to "comb" a sphere without a bold spot. (See Image 1.)

1.5. Proof of Theorem 1. [1], [2], [3]. We will restrict our proof to the sphere and the doughnut. (For general surfaces the proof is similar to these two cases.) Firstly, one can show that Theorem 1 is independent of the vector field chosen. By Morse theory, surfaces are built from the bottom up by performing surgery operations at vanishing points of Morse vector fields. An artistic rendering of Morse vector fields can be obtained by pouring colored viscous liquid from the top of the surface. (See Figures 2 and 3.)

For the sphere, the North and the South Poles are the only zeros of the given Morse vector field. At the South Pole, we attach a half sphere, whose Euler characteristic is 1 (1 is also equal to the index of the Morse vector field at the South Pole). At the North Pole, we also attach a half sphere. The two half spheres are joined together at the equator. Then the Euler characteristic of the sphere, 2, computed by adding the Euler characteristics of the two given halves. And 2 is also equal to the sum of the vector field indices at the North and South Poles.

For the doughnut, the North and the South Poles together with the two points A and B of Figure 3 are the only zeros of the given Morse vector field. At the North and South Poles the situation is similar to the sphere case. At the two points A and B we attach a "pair of pants," i.e., two cylinders glued together along a point. The Euler Characteristic of a pair of pants is -1, the same as the index of our Morse vector field on it. The Euler Characteristic of the doughnut is therefore 0, computed by adding the Euler characteristic of the two given half spheres to the Euler Characteristic of the two pairs of pants. And 0 is also equal to the sum of the Morse vector field indices at the four zeros.

Illustrations

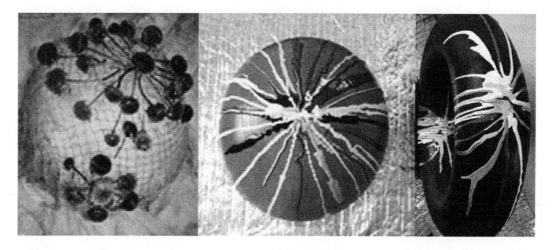

Figure 1: *It is not possible to "comb" a sphere without a bold spot*
Figure 2: A *Morse vector field on the sphere* **Figure 3**: A *Morse vector field on the doughnut*

References

[1] Victor Guillemin and Alan Pollack, *Differential Topology*. Prentice-Hall, Inc., Englewood Cliffs, N.J., 1974.
[2] J. W. Milnor, *Morse Theory,* Annals Studies 51, Princeton University Press, Princeton, 1961.
[3] J. W. Milnor, *Topology from the Differential Viewpoint,* The University Press of Virginia, Charlottesville, 1981.

Aspects of Symmetry in Arpachiyah Pottery

Duncan J. Melville
Dept. of Mathematics
St. Lawrence University
Canton, NY 13617
dmelville@stlawu.edu

Abstract

Arpachiyah is one of the most well-known and extensive sources of Halafian pottery (ca. 5500 – 5000 BC). In this paper, we apply symmetry analysis in the style of Washburn and Crowe to analyze symmetries underlying central motifs in bowls and dishes from Arpachiyah. We note that while there is a great variety in the degree of symmetry, there is an overwhelming preponderance of dihedral patterns.

1. Introduction

Arpachiyah is a small site in northern Mesopotamia a few kilometers east of Nineveh. It was excavated briefly by Mallowan in 1933 [7] and again by Hijara in 1976 [4,5]. Despite the brevity of the excavations, a large number of important finds were excavated at the site. The main part of the site itself formed a small tell or debris hill, built up over perhaps as many as fifteen occupation layers. Additionally, there were some less well-preserved outlying locations in the surrounding area. Among the finds were many pottery objects from the Ubaid and preceding Halaf periods (ca. 5500 – 5000BC). The Ubaid-era occupation seems to have been quite poor – Mallowan commented on the low quality of the house construction and many of the pottery and stone-ware finds were unpainted and in many cases poor manufacture. However, the earlier levels produced finer ware, including a series of painted bowls and dishes incorporating complex designs from the last Halaf occupation layer. Although most of these bowls were badly broken, and in fact appeared to have been deliberately smashed, it was possible to reassemble the sherds sufficiently to study the overall design. This was an immense labor – one bowl (A748) was reassembled from 76 pieces [7].

Due to their abundance and clear stratification, the finds from Arpachiyah are important in linking archaeological levels of different sites in the Near East and demonstrating their connections. For this reason, they have been subject to various types of stylistic and physical analysis. For example, Davidson and McKerrell used neutron activation analysis to show that there was a considerable transfer of ceramics produced in Arpachiyah to Tepe Gawra [3]. However, despite a propensity for geometric decoration, the material has not been subjected to a thorough symmetry analysis. This paper represents the first step in such a study.

2. Symmetry Analysis

Ceramics break, but they don't decay. Once abandoned and buried in the ground, pottery will survive without much additional damage for hundreds, even thousands, of years. Over the same period many other goods, especially organic artifacts such as those made from cloth, leather or wood will largely vanish without trace. Their survivability ensures that the study of ceramics plays an important role in the archaeologist's approach to the past.

Another aspect of ceramics that makes them important is their extreme variability. Pottery comes in a vast array of different shapes and sizes, with plates, dishes, bowls, cups, beakers, vases, urns, all ranging from small to large, sometimes extremely large. They may be finely or crudely made, from a wide variety of clays with different characteristics and fired with varying degrees of skill. They may be decorated or undecorated. If decorated, there are an unlimited number of ways for the painter to design the decoration.

Archaeologists use all these factors to glean information from pottery. While form and location of find can indicate function and thus say something about the lives of those who lived there, changes in type and style can provide a chronological framework for understanding not just the site under investigation, but via linkages with similar ceramics elsewhere, show correlations between levels at different sites. Assemblages of the same types of pottery show that peoples in different places were contemporaneous, and also that there was some form of contact between them. As pottery plays such an important role on scales from the micro investigation of the inhabitants of a single building to the macro level tying together cultures encompassing huge areas, it is vital that precise delineation of the characteristics of pottery assemblages be obtained. In this regard, it is important that analysis of pottery be objective and reproducible. That is, different researchers viewing the same collection of objects should reach the same conclusions. Although desirable, this is manifestly not the case with many aesthetic criteria and interpretations of style. It is, however, a feature of symmetry analysis.

Symmetry analysis restricts itself to a study of the formal symmetries of the designs on pottery (or other wares). It is thus limited to decorated pottery, and requires enough of the piece to survive that the overall design can be viewed; it is of little use on the vast numbers of individual sherds typically uncovered in an excavation. Symmetry analysis does not concern itself with interpretation of motifs or designs, only with their abstract symmetry. Where sufficient decorated pieces survive, it presents an objective analysis. For a more detailed evaluation of the strengths and limitations of symmetry analysis, see Irving [6]. Modern symmetry analysis is largely due to the efforts of Washburn, and the clearest accessible description of the technique is in the classic Washburn and Crowe [9]. It has been successfully applied in several cases where there was suitable material, for example by Crowe studying Ghanaian clay pipes [2], Washburn in the Aegean [8] and Washburn and Matson in the American Southwest [11]. The recent book [10] includes a number of more recent case-studies, including one by Washburn on patterns in Ica Valley ceramics.

Whenever an element of a design is repeated, there is the possibility of some sort of regular, orderly repetition, that is, some symmetry. There are several systems of classifications for symmetries. If the design allows translations in one dimension, the resulting patterns are called 1-dimensional, or frieze patterns; if there are translations in two dimensions, the designs are referred to as 2-dimensional, or wallpaper patterns; if there are no translations the designs are termed finite. The standard notation for 1- and 2-dimensional patterns derives from crystallography, where the concern was for describing the regular placements of atoms. The regions between the atoms did not require special handling. However, in a decorated design, one has to account for the use of multiple colors in the regions, and there are extensions to the notation to handle these cases, (see Washburn and Crowe [9] for details). In this paper, we confine ourselves to finite designs, and it will turn out that in the pottery we consider, there is no symmetry-breaking through use of color.

For finite designs, there are two types of symmetries with which we have to be concerned, rotations and reflections. A design has rotational symmetry of order n if a rotation of $\frac{1}{n}$th of a turn, or $\frac{360}{n}°$, leaves the pattern unchanged. Additionally, a pattern may have reflection, or mirror, symmetry. The symmetry group, or type, of a finite design is determined by the largest n such that it has rotational symmetry of order n. Following the notation of Washburn and Crowe, we say a design has symmetry type cn, if it has n-fold rotations but no reflections, and type dn if it does have reflections. Types cn and dn are the only possibilities for finite patterns.

3. Bowls from Arpachiyah

The finds from Mallowan's excavation were divided between Iraq and Britain; those from Hijara's remain in Iraq. In this paper, we concentrate on the central designs of the Halaf-ware bowls from Mallowan's level TT6, principally from the single location, the Burnt House. Hijara was mostly interested in the earlier Halaf occupation phases and none of his finds from this level are complete enough to be included in this analysis. Consequently, we use Mallowan's record numbers to identify each object. Recently, Campbell made an extensive study of all the artifacts discovered in the Burnt House with a view to interpreting its function and subsequent destruction [1]. As part of his study, Campbell published a catalog of artifacts relevant to his discussion. Mallowan did not publish a complete record of finds and since excavation many pieces have been scattered among museums and collections, although the bulk of the important bowls are in either the British Museum or the Iraq Museum. Those in the British Museum I was able to view in July 2004 and March 2005; those in Iraq were unavailable to me and conclusions have to be drawn from published illustrations.

Figure 1: A 745

There are about 20 bowls of assorted shapes and sizes of which enough survives to be able to interpret the symmetry of the central design. Others, such as A 746 are too badly damaged to attempt a reconstruction with confidence, even though some of the design survives. For convenience, we divide the bowls into three groups based upon central design: those with a cruciform design; those with a central rosette, and a miscellaneous group.

Among the most well-known pieces from Arpachiyah is A 745, a delicate small bowl currently on display in the British Museum and featured on the Museum's Compass website (see Figure 1). The design features a central Maltese cross in black paint with the corners drawn together in a sweeping curve. The curve is emphasized by two exterior parallel lines and the interior spaces so created are filled with red paint with a small reserve area setting off the red and black. Unsurprisingly, for a design based on a Maltese cross, the bowl has symmetry type $d4$. A similar design, but with only the cross and exterior lines painted, occurs on A 754 and A 514 (the latter not illustrated by Mallowan and Rose, and unfortunately not included in Campbell's catalog). Both bowls thus have $d4$ symmetry. The piece labeled A 1003 by Campbell may also have had a similar design, but the bowl is too damaged to be certain. Table 1 summarizes this information.

Number	Museum Number	Central motif	Symmetry
A 514	BM 127503	Maltese Cross	$d4$
A 745	BM 127585	Maltese Cross	$d4$
A 754	IM 14720	Maltese Cross	$d4$
A 1003	I of A 53/337	Maltese Cross?	$d4$

Table 1

The first group was defined by having a central Maltese cross. However, it is clear from A 514 and A 745 that the space between the arms of the cross was also considered important. These petal-shaped pieces, taken as a motif in their own right, form rosettes that make up the largest class of bowls. Figure 2 shows an illustrative example.

Figure 2: A 752 central rosette

In this group, the number of petals varies widely, from eight upwards, and although there is some clustering around powers of two, there are examples that fall outside that tendency, as A 750, with 13 petals. The petals vary in design, whether rounded or pointed, filled or hatched, but in all cases they maintain mirror symmetry so that each is of dihedral type, but with no obvious emphasis on the number of petals. Some of the bowls, such as A 529, have too much fire-damage to be absolutely sure how many petals there were originally in the rosette. These bowls include the very fine large bowls that make up some of the most spectacular early pottery from any Halaf site.

Number	Museum Number	Central Motif	Symmetry
A 511	Louvre 1973	Rosette	$d8$
A 529	BM 127504	Rosette	$d15$?
A 746	IM 17836	Rosette	damaged
A 747	IM 14741	Rosette	$d8$
A 748	IM 17837	Rosette	$d32$
A 750	BM 127507	Rosette	$d13$
A 752	BM 127508	Rosette	$d16$
A 753	IM 14753	Rosette	$d8$
A 755	IM 14724	Rosette	$d8$

Table 2

The last group comprises a miscellaneous collection of designs. There are two bowls with sets of triangles pointing together, A 742 and A 743. Mallowan and Rose illustrated A 742 and stated that A 743 was a smaller duplicate, but no illustration is available and the dish is in the Iraq Museum. This is the only example of duplication in the entire Arpachiyah corpus, and even then the bowls are not of the same size. A 742 has dihedral symmetry of order 6, and if A 743 is identical in design, then we can assume it has $d6$ symmetry, too. A 751 is an example of a Maltese square design and so is constrained to have $d4$ symmetry. A 763 has a curious design of crossed lines and dots. Mallowan said the design was on the underside of the bowl; Campbell suggested it might be a lid. Whatever the purpose, or the significance of the design, it is again of type $d4$. A very unusual design is that on A 524 (see [7, Plate XIX]). The design has two chequered bands crossing in the center, and the alternating motifs in the small squares appear to allow a dihedral symmetry, so that the design is of type $d2$.

The final example from the miscellaneous group is A 515, a coarse bowl with a bukranium (bull's head) design formed by four bukrania with heads at the center of the bowl. Hence, the design has a dihedral four-fold symmetry, and we label it as $d4$, although the symmetry has been deliberately broken by the placing of a red dot, perhaps symbolizing the sun, in the horns of one of the bulls. The symmetries of this group are summarized in Table 3.

Number	Museum Number	Central Motif	Symmetry
A 515	BM 127511	Bukrania	$d4$
A 524	IM 15702	Checkered arms	$d2$
A 742	BM 127583	Triangles	$d6$
A 743	IM 14726	Triangles	$d6$
A 751	IM 14733	Maltese Square	$d4$
A 763	IM 14762	Crossed lines	$d4$

Table 3

4. Conclusions

The most notable result of this study is that every single piece, regardless of motif, has dihedral symmetry. There is a clear preference for even numbers, although there are some exceptions, but only among the rosettes. Apart from the rosettes, most pieces have low-order symmetry, with $d4$ and $d6$ the most common. These are in contrast to earlier and later phases and the types of decorations found at other sites. A detailed comparison is beyond the scope of this paper, but the conclusions determined here will form part of a larger study. Another important feature that is not always sufficiently stressed is that all these pieces are different. There is no standardization, rather there appears to be a requirement that every piece be individual.

Acknowledgements

I wish to thank the staff of the British Museum, especially Christopher Walker and Sally Fletcher for their help and support while I was visiting. This work was supported in part by a Faculty Research Grant from St. Lawrence University. Figures 1 and 2 are reproduced by kind permission of the Trustees of the British Museum.

References

[1] S. Campbell, 'The Burnt House at Arpachiyah: A Reexamination, *Bulletin of the American Schools of Oriental Research* 318 (2000) 1-40.

[2] D.W. Crowe, 'The geometry of African art. Part 3. The smoking pipes of Begho.' In *The Geometric Vein: The Coxeter Festschrift* (C. Davis, B. Grünbaum, F.A. Sherk, eds.) New York, Springer, 1982, pp. 177-189.

[3] T.E. Davidson and H. McKerrell, 'The neutron activation analysis of Halaf and 'Ubaid pottery from Tell Arpachiyah and Tepe Gawra', *Iraq* 42 (1980) 155-167.

[4] I. Hijara, *The Halaf Period in Northern Mesopotamia*. London, NABU Publications, 1997.

[5] I. Hijara et al., 'Arpachiyah 1976', *Iraq* 42 (1980) 131-154.

[6] A.C. Irving, *Approaches to style in Near Eastern ceramics*, U. of Manchester diss., 1988.

[7] M.E.L. Mallowan and J.C. Rose, 'Excavations at Tall Arpachiyah, 1933', *Iraq* 2 (1935) 1-178.

[8] D.K. Washburn, 'Symmetry analysis of ceramic design: two tests of the method on Neolithic material from Greece and the Aegean.' In *Structure and Cognition in Art* (D.K. Washburn, ed.), Cambridge, Cambridge University Press, 1983, pp.138-164.

[9] D.K. Washburn and D.W. Crowe, *Symmetries of culture: theory and practice of plane pattern analysis*. Seattle, University of Washington Press, 1988.

[10] D.K. Washburn and D.W. Crowe (eds), *Symmetry comes of age*. Seattle, University of Washington Press, 2004.

[11] D.K. Washburn and R.G. Matson, 'Use of multidimensional scaling to display sensitivity of symmetry analysis of patterned design to spatial and chronological change: Examples from Anasazi prehistory.' In *Decoding Prehistoric Ceramics* (B.A. Nelson, ed) Carbondale, Southern Illinois University Press, 1985, pp. 75-101.

Abstract Art from a Model for Cellular Morphogenesis

Gary R. Greenfield
Department of Mathematics & Computer Science
University of Richmond
Richmond, VA 23173, U.S.A.
ggreenfi@richmond.edu

Abstract

In this paper, we modify a mathematical model for differential gene expression introduced by Eggenberger for simulating cell morphology in order to evolve aesthetic imagery from grids of cells. We focus upon investigating fitness criteria to use so that genetic learning can effectively guide the evolution of the underlying cellular processes that lead to aesthetic results. In the model, cellular processes are governed by regulatory genes and transcription factors in such a way that cells with identical genomes exhibit differences during development. By associating certain cell products with color channels, images obtained from grids consisting of only two types of interacting cells are shown to yield a rich generative framework for artistic exploration.

1. Introduction

Modeling cellular development for aesthetic purposes first received attention thanks to Fleischer's doctoral thesis [4] and his subsequent work [5] [6]. More recently, Hoar et al [9] used a model for the life cycle of a bacterium to make images visualizing the simulated evolution of bacteria colonies which they referred to as "creative bacteria patterns." Complex models such as these that are used for aesthetic pattern generation from cellular processes supersede earlier reaction-diffusion models based on Alan Turing's seminal paper [12]. Reaction-diffusion models for generating aesthetic patterns have also been considered by many other authors [14] [13] [7] [2]. In this paper we investigate an evolutionary framework for pattern formation arising from cellular processes based on cell genomes that use regulatory genes. The genomics and cellular developmental model follow [3]. After presenting our model, our principal focus is on the problem of formulating aesthetic fitness criteria needed for implementing genetic learning in such as a way that it maximizes the aesthetic potential of the evolved imagery. Due to its subjective nature, the problem of non-interactively guiding evolution for aesthetic purposes is not well-studied. Previous approaches that are of interest include those using neural nets [1][10], co-evolution [8], and statistical analysis [11].

2. Cell Genome

In this section we give a formal description of the genomes we use for our cells. The key idea is that a genome consists of structural genes and regulatory genes, and that sequences of regulatory genes affect, and are affected by, immediately adjacent sequences of structural genes. Formally, we define a *gene* to be a string $g_0 g_1 \ldots g_7$ of digits. The last digit g_7 is called the *marker* of the gene. Markers may assume any of the values zero through six, but all other digits are constrained to lie in the range zero through four. For each gene, we calculate an *offset* $o = g_0 + g_1$ mod 3, a *diffusion coefficient* $d = (g_2 + g_3)/9$, and a *type* $t = g_4 + g_5 + g_6$ mod 5. A *unit* is a sequence of one or more genes whose final gene has marker five *concatenated* with a sequence of one or more genes whose final gene has marker six. Genes within the first segment are designated *regulatory* genes while genes within the second segment are designated *structural* genes. The purpose of this definition is to make it possible to "read" any sequence of genes and identify functional units simply by scanning the sequence, segmenting on the basis of markers, and locating adjacent regulatory and structural segments. Formally, then, a gene *unit* is a sequence of genes of the form $R_1 R_2 \ldots R_u S_1 S_2 \ldots S_v$ where each R_i is a regulatory gene, and each S_j is a structural gene, but only R_u and S_v have the requisite markers. Later we will restrict our attention to genomes with a fixed number of gene units, each consisting of precisely two regulatory genes and one structural gene, but for the time being we continue to maintain full generality in order to describe how cellular processes depend on gene units.

In nature, individual cells maintain concentrations of transcription factors denoted TF's. When a structural gene is activated, or expressed, its type determines the resulting cell "products," or morphogens, that it produces. Cell products, by affecting the concentrations of TF's, lead to higher order cellular processes. Due to our incomplete understanding of the underlying effects of chemical reactions within cells, and in light of the inherent complexity of modeling chemical reactions, following [3], for the purpose of simulation we introduce a simplification by using a structural gene's type to directly initiate higher order cellular processes when it is expressed. In [3] examples of higher order processes included cell division, cell death, creation of special molecules, creation of new TF's, etc. However, in our model when a structural gene is expressed the result is a change in the concentration of one, and only one, of its cell's TF concentrations and, as will be explained shortly, in some situations a change in the concentration of that same TF in its neighboring cells.

3. Gene Activation

Given a gene unit $R_1 R_2 \ldots R_u S_1 S_2 \ldots S_v$, in order to determine whether a structural gene S from the unit is active, consider a fixed gene R_j from the regulatory sequence of the unit and the i-th TF of the cell. Using the offset o of S, first extract the five digit string from R_j beginning at position o, perform a base five conversion, and then subtract the result from the *weight* w_i of the TF thereby obtaining the *affinity* f_i of R_j for the i-th TF. The weight w_i an environmental quantity that for us is constant across all cells. Note that since weights are allowed to be negative, f_i is a signed quantity. Now, multiply the affinity f_i by the concentration c_i of the i-th TF, and then sum over all TF's to obtain the activity level r_j for R_j. Next, sum r_j over all regulatory genes to associate to S the quantity, $a = 1/(1 + \exp(\Sigma_j r_j))$. Finally, determine the activity level γ for S by setting

$$\gamma = \begin{cases} -1.0 & \text{if } a < 0.2 \\ +1.0 & \text{if } a > 0.8 \\ 0.0 & \text{otherwise} \end{cases}.$$

To make allowances for the inherent complexity, we make a further simplification by saying that the structural gene S is expressed in an *excitory* state if $\gamma = +1$, expressed in an *inhibitory* state if $\gamma = -1$, and not expressed otherwise. This simplification makes it easier to simultaneously manage both the increases and decreases of TF concentrations within cells. With reference to [3], we should point out that it is not clear precisely how Eggenberger makes use of the three different values γ assumes, and also point out that his model is more sophisticated than ours because his calculation for r_j sums only over a "current list" of TF's and his cell products are capable of dynamically adding and removing TF's from this current list.

4. Cell Development

In this paper we use four TF's named Red, Blue, Green, and Communication. We devote one structural gene to each TF and two regulator genes to each structural gene. Thus a cell consists of a genome constructed from four gene units, with three genes per unit, together with concentrations of each of the four TF's. When expressed, a structural gene either increases or decreases the concentration of the TF it affects. The extra feature in our model is that if the concentration in the cell of the *communication* TF is sufficiently high then the concentrations in neighboring cells of the TF under consideration will also change. It is under these circumstances that the diffusion coefficient d of the structural gene comes into play. It is used to determine what proportion of the increase (respectively decrease) of the affected TF's concentration the structural gene's cell will receive, and what proportion of the increase (respectively decrease) in the affected TF's concentration all the neighboring cells will receive. More precisely, if structural gene S with diffusion coefficient d is required to change the concentration of a TF by the amount Δ, then the cell's allotment of that change will be $100(1-d)\%$ while the remaining $100d\%$ of that change will be equally distributed among the eight neighboring cells. When cells are organized in a grid, cellular development occurs over time by initializing TF concentrations for all cells and then simulating the gene activation, TF concentration update cycle for all the cells for a prescribed number of time steps.

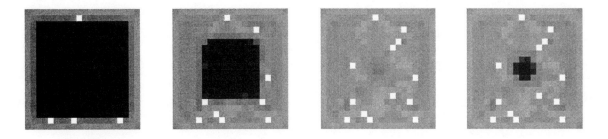

Figure 1: *An example showing the outside-in development of the cell pattern obtained after 50, 150, 250, and 350 time steps.*

5. Aesthetic Cell Development Patterns

By strategically locating a few cells with different genomes in the grid of cells and by strategically initializing the TF concentrations of those cells, the simulation of the cell development algorithm will yield a matrix of cells that can be visualized by interpreting the Red, Green, and Blue TF concentrations as color channel values. Our objective is to control the factors responsible for creating such cell patterns in such a way as to yield aesthetic imagery. To make this task more manageable, we consider only square grids and permit only two different genomes to be assigned to the cells within the grid. The two genomes are used to distinguish between cells that are either *specialized* cells or *substrate* cells. A small, but fixed percentage of specialized cells are randomly scattered in the grid and then the grid is filled in with substrate cells. Initial TF concentrations for the cells are determined by imagining that a morphogen gradient is being applied to the grid. This means that edge cells receive small, but fixed nonzero initial concentrations for their TF's, while interior cells have all their TF concentrations set to zero. The result is that cellular development occurs slowly starting at the edges and working towards the center as shown in the time series for a 20×20 cell example in Figure 1. This further simplifies our task by only requiring us to decide what genomes to use for the two different cell types and deciding how many time steps cellular development should be allowed to proceed for. Since a suitable number of time steps can be quickly determined experimentally once the grid dimensions are fixed, this only leaves the problem of finding appropriate cell genomes. Our approach to this problem is to use a genetic algorithm and let genetic learning participate in the solution.

6. Genetic Learning

To implement genetic learning using the simple genetic algorithm we consider a population of grids. The genotype of a grid is determined by the genomes for its two cell types, and the phenotype of a grid is the visualization of the matrix of cells following cellular development as described above. Initial populations use randomly generated genomes. At the start of each run of the genetic algorithm a randomly generated placement scheme for locating cells on a grid is fixed so that all grids in the population will have their specialized cells and substrate cells identically positioned. To mate two grids, we mate their two cell types — specialized cell genomes to specialized cell genomes and substrate cell genomes to substrate cell genomes — by invoking one-point crossover followed by point mutation on a gene by gene basis. To form breeding pairs of grids, we make random selections from a breeding pool consisting of the most fit grids, typically the top four. Due to the computational load, population sizes are small, typically 6-12, and the number of generations allotted for genetic learning to occur is short, typically 5-20.

To determine grid fitness, we make use of quantities measured during the final cycle of cell development. To help define these quantities we use the subscripts R, G, B, and C when referencing the four TF's. Let μ_i and σ_i denote the mean and standard deviation calculated over all the cells in the grid of the concentration for the TF subscripted by i. Let N_a denote the number of cells that had a change in the activation status of at least one structural gene during the final development cycle, and let N_b denote the number of cells in the grid that are dormant, meaning their R, G, and B concentrations are all below trace levels whence they appear black in the visualization.

Figure 2: *Examples using fitness functions: (a) F_1 with $\delta = 1$ which rewards both communication among cells and variability within all color channels, (b) F_1 with $\delta = 0$, (c) F_2 which rewards patterns exhibiting variability within at least one color channel, and (d) F_2 giving rise to a pattern that is unusual because it has both dormant and active substrate cells on its border.*

Initial tests revealed that the fundamental obstruction to achieving aesthetic imagery using the genetic algorithm was the presence within the population of grids with either too many dormant cells or with monochrome colorings. Denoting by $F(P)$ the fitness of grid P, the first reliable fitness function we discovered calculated fitness using

$$F_1(P) = \sigma_C{}^\delta \cdot \min(\sigma_R, \sigma_G, \sigma_B),$$

where δ is zero or one. This fitness function rewards grids that exhibit various communication behaviors between neighboring cells and that possess highly variable color channels. It was used to evolve the 25×25 cell patterns in Figure 2a and Figure 2b. In fact, patterns such as those found in Figure 2c and Figure 2d, obtained by changing the fitness function to

$$F_2(P) = \max(\sigma_R, \sigma_G, \sigma_B),$$

showed that by ignoring the communication TF and rewarding those grids where *at least* one color TF showed significant variability we could obtain promising results.

The principal drawback to the two fitness functions introduced so far is that although they consistently produce interesting results, they do not exert sufficient evolutionary pressure on initial populations of grids where a preponderance of grids have large numbers of dormant cells. This is explained by the fact that a grid with a large number of black cells (indicating no TF activity) or white cells (indicating maximal TF activity) that are set off against a background color produced by active substrate cells can lead to misleading standard deviation measurements. Various fitness functions we designed incorporating color channel averages and the "activity" measure N_a failed to alleviate this problem. To overcome this difficulty we used the dormancy measure N_b to introduce a term for penalizing such patterns. This led us to formulate our two most successful fitness functions

$$F_3(P) = \frac{N_a \cdot \min(\sigma_R, \sigma_G, \sigma_B)}{1 + N_b},$$

and

$$F_4(P) = \frac{\sigma_C \cdot N_a \cdot \min(\sigma_R, \sigma_G, \sigma_B)}{1 + N_b}.$$

Figure 3: *(a) An example using fitness function F_3, which incorporates a penalty term for black, dormant cells, and (b) a high resolution example using fitness function F_4, which also incorporated a penalty term for black, dormant cells.*

Not only did these two functions lead to an increase in the number of interesting patterns that were evolved, but they allowed us to increase the dimensions of our images while simultaneously decreasing the percentage of specialized cells we used. This, in turn, led to a better understanding of how the underlying cellular processes that were occurring within our cells functioned. The images in Figure 2 used 20% specialized cells. Figure 3a shows an example of a 40×40 pattern with only

5% specialized cells after only 300 developmental time steps that was evolved using the fitness function F_3, while Figure 3b shows a 50 × 50 pattern, also using only 5% specialized cells, after only 400 developmental time steps that was evolved using the fitness function F_4.

7. Conclusions

We have adapted a model for simulating cellular morphogenesis in order to generate aesthetic cell patterns and we have investigated automating the search for such patterns using a genetic algorithm. Initial results are encouraging. Given that random placement of only two different types of cells within a grid was used to initiate the pattern formation process, future work will consider the use of "template" placement schemes using additional cell types and the use of other grid geometries so that cell interactions between tissue types can be simulated and visualized.

REFERENCES

[1] Baluja, S., Pomerleau, D., and Jochem, T., Towards Automated Artificial Evolution for Computer-Generated Images, *Connection Science*, **6**, 1994, 25–354.

[2] Behravan, R., and Carlisle, R., Interactive organic art, *Proceedings of the Seventh Interantional Conference on Generative Art*, AleaDesign, 2004, Vol. 1, 239–246.

[3] Eggenberger, P., Evolving Morphologies of Simulated 3d Organisms Based on Differential Gene Expression, *Proceedings of the Fourth European Conference on Artificial Life (ECAL97)*, Springer Verlag, 1997, 205–213.

[4] Fleischer, K.W., *A Multiple-Mechanism Developmental Model for Defining Self-Organizing Structures*, Ph.D. Dissertation, Caltech, Department of Computation and Neural Systems, 1995.

[5] Fleischer, K.W., Laidlaw, D.H., Currin, B.L. and Barr, A.H., Cellular Texture Generation, *SIGGRAPH 95 Conference Proceedings August 6-11, 1995*, ACM Press, 239–248.

[6] Fleischer, K.W., Investigations With a Multicellular Developmental Model, *Artificial Life V Conference Proceedings*, MIT Press, 1996, 229–236.

[7] Greenfield, G.R., Case Study: A Sculptor - Programmer Collaboration, Technical Report TR-94-03, Dept. of Mathematics & Computer Science, University of Richmond, 1993.

[8] Greenfield, G.R., Art and Artificial Life — A Coevolutionary Approach, *Artificial Life VII Conference Proceedings*, eds. M. Bedau et al, MIT Press, 2000, 529–536.

[9] Hoar, R.M., Penner, J.K., and Jacob, C., Transcription and Evolution of a Virtual Bacteria Culture, *2003 Congress on Evolutionary Computation Proceedings*, IEEE Press, 2003,54–61.

[10] Machado, P. and Cardoso, A., Computing Aesthetics, *Proceedings XIV-th Brazilian Symposium on Artificial Intelligence SBIA'98, Porto Allegre, Brazil*, ed. F. Oleiveira, Springer-Verlag, 1998, 219–229.

[11] Staudek, T., Computer-Aided Aesthetic Evaluation of Visual Patterns, *ISAMA/Bridges 2003 Conference Proceedings*, eds. J. Barrallo et al, University of Granada, 2003, 143–150.

[12] Turing, A.M., The Chemical Basis of Morphogenesis, *Philosophical Transactions of the Royal Society of London Series B*, **237**, 1952, 37–72.

[13] Witkin, A. and Kass, M., Reaction-Diffusion Textures, *SIGGRAPH 91 Conference Proceedings*, ACM Press, 1991, 299–308.

[14] Young, D.A., A Local Activator-Inhibitor Model of Vertebrate Skin Patterns, *Theory & Application of Cellular Automata*, ed. S. Wolfram, World Scientific, 1986, 320–327.

The Complexity of the Musical Vocabulary of the Nzakara Harpists

Barbra Gregory
Catawba Valley Community College
Hickory, NC 28602, USA
Email: bgregory@cvcc.edu
http://www.musicandmath.com

Abstract

We present a new method for evaluating the complexity of music. We explore this method as it applies to the Nzakara harpists of Central Africa. In particular, the movement of the harpist's hands is measured for short, repeated patterns. Longer harp patterns are then compared to shorter patterns to determine a measure of the difficulty level of the piece based upon the amount the player's hands must move. Following explanation of the structure of the patterns, the method of measuring complexity is described. We then give a table of measurements for various harp patterns, some of which fit the grammatical rules of the Nzakara and some of which do not. We give an evaluation of some of these results and discuss the difficulty of achieving a whole picture of the difficulty or complexity of a musical structure.

Introduction

In contrast to our modern language full of symbols and definitions to describe mathematics, cultures have often relied upon the arts to express mathematical ideas and principles. Following a series of researchers including Simha Arom, Eric de Dampierre, Marc Chemillier, and Klaus-Peter Brenner, we examine the mathematical principles at work in the traditional harp music of the Nzakara people of Central Africa. In [3], Chemillier presents an in-depth review of his experiences with the practitioners of this art. Though there are few practitioners left, Chemillier has found unique mathematical structure in the harpists' language. In 2004, Brenner and Gregory each examined Chemillier's work. In [1], Brenner gave an ethnomuscological review of Chemillier's approach to harp pattern analysis. In [5] and [6], Gregory counted the number of patterns that fit the observed grammatical structure of the tunes.

The following section discusses the patterns Chemillier observed among the Nzakara harp tunes and develops the vocabulary which refers to various aspects of the tunes. The third section presents the definition of our complexity measure as it applies to the harp patterns. Next we give examples of one type of complexity of several harp tunes, some following Chemillier's observed patterns and some not. Finally, we conclude with a discussion of the difficulty of gaining a complete picture of the complexity of music because of the multidimensionality inherent in musical structure.

The language of the harps

The traditional harps have 5 strings. The strings are played in pairs as dyads, which Chemillier terms *bichords* and which can be viewed as the letters in the alphabet of the Nzakara harpists. There are five allowable bichords: those consisting of neighboring strings are disallowed, as is the pair of the lowest and highest strings. Each harp tune is a succession of bichords repeated over and over again to accompany chant and dance. The smallest repeated set of bichords is the *core* of the harp tune. Within each core, the same letter never appears twice in succession, and the core does not begin and end with the same letter (to avoid repeating the letter upon repeat, or concatenation). Further, the core will not "factor" into repeated smaller words since it is defined to be the smallest repeated word. Chemillier encoded the five allowable bichords into $\mathbb{Z}_5$, ordering them from lowest-pitched to highest by the lower note of the bichord and using the upper note to break ties as shown in Figure 1. He found that each allowable core is made up of a generator followed by four successive translations of the generator modulo 5. Since for any translation in $\mathbb{Z}_5$ the pattern returns to the beginning of the core at the fifth translation, each harp tune is a never-ending cyclical "ladder" created by perpetually translating a word in $\mathbb{Z}_5$. An example is shown in Figure 2. We should note that harpists often improvise their own variations on these base themes, and there may be rules governing these variances that are susceptible to mathematical or grammatical analysis. However, such variations are not recorded or documented at this time.

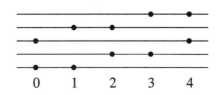

Figure 1: The five allowable bichords of the Nzakara harpists

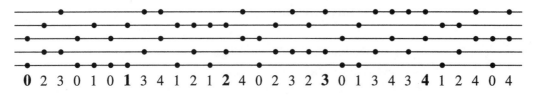

Figure 2: Example of a *limanza* canon

Measuring the complexity

One way to evaluate the complexity or richness of the vocabulary is to examine the number of cores following the grammatical rules outlined by Chemillier, as done in [5] and [6]. Here we examines another measure of the complexity, inspired by Jeffrey Pressing's method of measuring rhythmic complexity [7],[8]. It is impossible to capture the multi-dimensional nature of music in a single, simple mathematical procedure. Therefore, any measurement of the complexity of these tunes is limited to one aspect or one dimension of the tunes. The measure described below examines the difficulty of playing the harp tune due to the movement of the harpist's hands.

According to Pressing's algorithm for the cognitive complexity of rhythms, each rhythm is divided into subparts of equal length repeatedly until we reach subdivisions of the smallest prime length. Then the rhythm as a whole and each subdivision are examined for certain properties which contribute to the syncopation of any western-style rhythm. Each of these properties has a certain cognitive cost, or difficulty level assigned. For example, playing only on the upbeat, or the last pulse of a subdivision, would be more difficult or more costly than playing only on the downbeat. The cognitive complexity is calculated by summing each of the cognitive costs, weighted by the proportion of the total pattern of the subdivision.

We follow a similar model and formulate a definition of complexity for these tunes based upon the amount of movement by the hands between bichords. To begin we establish a base set of patterns which have complexity zero. We then build a catalog of complexities for cores of different length by comparing each new core with shorter cores.

Consider the five allowed bichords and their labelling in $\mathbb{Z}_5$, as shown in Figure 1. The least complex (in our sense of complex) string of notes to play is a single repeated bichord since the hands will not move among the strings. The complexity of such a string (e.g., ...000000... or ...222222...) is defined to be zero.

Notice that to move from bichord 0 to bichord 1, the player must move one finger one string. So bichords 0 and 1 are considered to have distance equal to 1. To move from bichord 4 to bichord 1, the player must move one finger down one string and the other down two strings. So we say bichords 1 and 4 have a distance of 3. Thus we define the *distance between bichords* to be equal to the total number of strings which the fingers must move to change from one bichord to the other. Because of the way the labelling has been defined, we can see that the distance between two bichords is the absolute value of the difference between the numbers which represent them in $\mathbb{Z}_5$: $\text{dist}(B_1, B_2) = |B_1 - B_2|$.

As in Pressing's definition of cognitive complexity, the complexity of each harp core is defined through comparison to more basic patterns. In this case, the more basic patterns are the shorter cores. This definition applies to both allowable harp patterns and those which are disallowed, allowing comparison between "grammatical" harp patterns and those which do not follow the observed rules. We define three measures of complexity, denoted C_1, C_2, and C_A. C_1 and C_2 are variations on the same theme of comparing the core in question with a single "closest" core of a smaller size. C_A will use an "average" over the smaller cores.

Each complexity measure relies upon a definition of the distance between two words. We define a distance closely related to the Hamming distance or $\bar{d}$-distance of information theory and to the swap distance described in [4]. Let l and d be positive integers. Let $u = u_1 u_2 ... u_l$ and $v = v_1 v_2 ... v_l$ be two finite strings of elements of $\mathbb{Z}_d$, each of length l. If $\text{dist}(u_i, v_i) = |u_i - v_i|$ is the distance between u_i and v_i as defined above, then the distance between u and v is defined to be

$$\text{dist}(u, v) = \frac{1}{l} \sum_{i=1}^{l} \text{dist}(u_i, v_i). \tag{1}$$

In short, the distance between two finite words of the same length is the average distance between their corresponding letters.

Since the cores used in the harp patterns are repeated over and over in a cyclical pattern, there is a straightforward definition of the distance between two finite cores of different lengths. Consider u and v of positive lengths s and t, respectively. Define u' to be u concatenated upon itself $\text{lcm}(s, t)/s$ times to create a word of length $\text{lcm}(s, t)$, and define v' to be v concatenated to itself $\text{lcm}(s, t)/t$ times to create another word of length $\text{lcm}(s, t)$. Then the distance between u and v is defined to be the distance between u' and v'.

We define the *nearest-neighbor complexity* of a core of length 2 as the minimum of the distances to cores of length 1. Both the C_1 and C_2 complexities of cores of length 2 are defined this way. For example, the complexity of the core 01 is 0.5, since its distance from 0 and 1 is equal to 0.5: $C_1(01) = C_2(01) = 0.5$. Similarly, $C_1(03) = C_2(03) = 1.5$, demonstrating that the player must move both fingers between the 0 bichord and the 3 bichord further than between the nearby 0 and 1.

The nearest-neighbor complexity of a core of length longer than 2 takes into account all shorter cores which are "close to" the core under consideration as well as their complexities. There are many reasonable variations on this theme, two of which are discussed here. In the first version, C_1, finding a nearby neighbor is considered of more importance than the complexity of that nearby neighbor: the set of words of minimum distance is found and then complexity is minimized within that set. In the second version, C_2, complexity and distance are minimized together by finding the minimum of their product.

More precisely, given a word u of length $k > 2$, let V_i be the set of words of length i which have the minimum distance to u for all $i < k$:

$$V_i = \{v | v \text{ is of length } i, \text{dist}(u,v) \leq \text{dist}(u,w) \text{ for all words } w \text{ of length } i\}.$$

If $i = 1$, then let $s_1(u) = \text{dist}(u,v)$ for any v in V_1. (Note that $s_1(u)$ is well-defined since every element of V_i has the same distance to u.) For $i > 1$ we define

$$s_i(u) = \min\{\text{dist}(u,v) \cdot C_1(v) | v \in V_i\}.$$

Then the C_1 complexity of u is defined to be

$$C_1(u) = \sum_{i=1}^{k-1} \frac{s_i(u)}{\omega_i},$$

where ω_i is a weighting term.

Some possible weighting variables ω_i are i, 5^i, 5^{i-1}, or $i!$. We have chosen to use $\omega_i = 5^{i-1}$. Since we are working with an alphabet of size 5, the number of possible words of length i is given by 5^i. Thus with this choice of ω_i, the weight on each sum term approximates the number of choices among which we minimized. Furthermore, because of computing resource limitations, the summations resulting in Table 1 are truncated at 5. (Note that the distance function is bounded by 4, so as i increases, the weight variable we chose will quickly dominate and the contribution from the i'th term becomes inconsequential.)

Our second version of the nearest-neighbor complexity of a core u of length k minimizes both the distance and complexity of the comparison words with equal importance:

$$s_1(u) = \min\{\text{dist}(u,v) | v \text{ is a word of length } 1\}$$

for $i > 1$, $s_i(u) = \min\{\text{dist}(u,v) \cdot C_2(v) | v \text{ is a word of length } i\}$

Then C_2 is the weighted sum of the s_i's, as before:

$$C_2(u) = \sum_{i=1}^{k-1} \frac{s_i(u)}{\omega_i}.$$

The calculations in Table 1 use the same weighting variable as the first version and truncate the summation term in the same location.

The final complexity measure in the table, the *complexity over averages*, is calculated using the average of distance times complexity over all the smaller v. In other words,

$$C_A(u) = \sum_{i=1}^{k-1} \text{mean} \frac{(\text{dist}(u,v_i) \cdot C_A(v_i))}{\omega_i}, \tag{2}$$

where the arithmetic means are taken over all V_i with length i.

The effectiveness of the measure

As we see in Table 1, the C_2 complexity measure appears to do the best job of finding the distance a player's hands must travel to play any pattern of bichords. For example, a harpist's hands can never move

Table 1: The computed complexities of selected bichord patterns

Bichord pattern	C_1	C_2	C_A
...01010101010101...	0.5	0.5	1.7
...02020202020202...	1	1	1.6
...03030303030303...	1.5	1.5	1.7
...04040404040404...	2	2	2
...010010010010010...	0.38	0.38	2.38
...012012012012012...	0.75	0.75	2.03
...013013013013013...	1.12	1.12	2.12
...024024024024024...	1.48	1.48	2.29
...000010000100001...	0.26	0.26	2.67
...000020000200002...	0.48	0.48	2.62
...012340123401234...*	1.35	1.35	2.29
...024130241302413...*	1.35	1.35	2.29
...031420314203142...*	1.35	1.35	2.29
...021340213402134...**	1.35	1.35	2.29
...113231132311323...**	0.91	0.91	1.95
...034140341403414...**	1.58	1.58	2.51
...00000000010000000001...	0.54	0.15	2.74
...013412402301341240023...*	3.00	1.35	2.06
...021324304102132430041...*	3.05	1.35	2.06
...014034231201403423121...*	3.00	1.35	2.06
...013402431401340243141...**	3.27	1.55	2.07
...042414144204241414421...**	3.25	1.53	1.85
...011204402101120440211...**	2.70	1.24	2.27

* These patterns follow the grammatical rules of the harp tunes.
** These patterns were generated randomly for comparison.

more than 4 strings with each succeeding note, yielding a "tune" alternating between bichords 0 and 4, or ...040404040.... This tune does indeed have the largest C_2 complexity in the table, with a measure of 2. However, it has among the lowest complexities with averages. In contrast, a harpist playing the "tune" ...00000000010000000001... moves his hands very little, and this pattern has the lowest nearest-neighbor complexity in the table (0.15), while it has the highest complexities with averages (2.74).

C_A seems to be a poor measure for hand movement, as demonstrated by a simple example. The hands of a harpist playing a sequence of bichord 0 alternating with bichord 1 should move the same amount between each bichord no matter the number of total strings on the harp (i.e., the size of the alphabet). Consequently, the complexity of 01 should remain constant across alphabet sizes. However, as the size of the harp grows, $C_A(01)$ will also grow as it is compared to words farther and farther away. In general, cores far away from the word in question with high complexity have at least as much influence as close cores with near complexity. We might try to counteract this problem by dividing by the distance instead of multiplying so that cores further away would have less influence over the complexity of the core in question.

The two nearest-neighbor complexities give similar results, and we begin to see differences for cores of length 10 or more. The values given by C_1 are naturally higher, since the minimum is being taken over a smaller set. Within each set of period lengths, C_1 and C_2 demonstrate similar ratios among the patterns. However, we can see a telling difference between the two when we examine 00001 and 0000000001. We see that $C_1(00001)$ is actually smaller than $C_1(0000000001)$, indicating that 00001 is less complex than the string with more zeros. It may indeed be mentally less complex in that the musician has to keep track of a smaller number of 0's before he plays a 1. However, in terms of the complexity we are trying to measure, namely the movement of the hands, C_2 gives a more satisfying conclusion with $C_2(0000000001) < C_2(00001)$.

Conclusion

Our goal was to find a complexity measure to evaluate the total amount of movement of the harpists' hands. Other factors that impact the difficulty of learning and playing a piece might include the speed at which the piece is played, the positioning of the hands (for example, whether the piece is played with one hand or two – a choice which varies by harpist – or whether fingers or hands must cross over each other), the length of the period of the piece (i.e., the memory required), the care with which the player has to count rhythms, finger fatigue, and many other factors. The particular dimension of hand movement seems to be measured well by the two nearest-neighbor complexities. Other measures may satisfactorily evaluate these other aspects. With enough such complexity measures and an understanding of what each one means, we might be able to combine them to gain a reasonable profile to understand the overall complexity of a piece of music.

References

[1] Klaus-Peter Brenner, *Die kombinatorisch strukturierten Harfen- und Xylophonpattern der Nzakara (Zentralafrikanische Republik) als klingende Geometrie eine Alternative zu Marc Chemilliers Kanonhypothese* , Holos-Verlag, Bonn, 2004.
[2] Marc Chemillier, *Ethnomusicology, ethnomathematics. The logic underlying orally transmitted artistic practices*, Mathematics and Music: a Diderot Mathematical Forum (G. Assayag, H.G. Feichtinger, and J.F. Rodrigues, eds.), Springer, Berlin, 2002, pp. 161183.
[3] Marc Chemillier, *La musique de la harpe*, Une esthetique perdue (Eric de Dampierre, ed.), Presses de lEcole Normale Superieure, Paris, 1995, pp. 99208.
[4] J. Miguel Díaz-Báñez, G. Farigu, F. Gómez, D. Rappaport, G. Toussaint, *El Compás Flamenco: A Phylogenetic Analysis*, Proceedings of Bridges: Mathematical Connections in Art, Music, and Science (Wichita, Kansas) (Reza Sarhangi and Carlo Séquin, ed.), Central Plain Book Manufacturing, 2004, pp. 61-70.
[5] Barbra Gregory, *Entropy and Complexity in Music: Some examples*, Masters thesis, University of North Carolina at Chapel Hill, 2004.
[6] Barbra Gregory, *The Musical Vocabulary of the Nzakara Harpists*, Proceedings of BRIDGES: Mathematical Connections in Art, Music, and Science (Winfield, Kansas) (Reza Sarhangi and Carlo Séquin, ed.), Central Plain Book Manufacturing, 2004, pp. 339-340.
[7] Jeffrey Pressing, *Cognitive complexity and the structure of musical patterns*, `http://www2.psy.uq.edu.au/CogPsych/Noetica/OpenForumIssue8/Pressing.html`, Accessed on August 16, 2004.
[8] Godfried Toussaint, *A Mathematical Analysis of African, Brazilian and Cuban Clave Rhythms*, Proceedings of Bridges: Mathematical Connections in Art, Music, and Science (Wichita, Kansas) (Reza Sarhangi, ed.), Central Plain Book Manufacturing, 2002, pp. 157168.

Acknowledgments

I thank Karl Petersen of the University of North Carolina at Chapel Hill for his help in brainstorming and developing the tools and techniques you read here and for his expertise and advice in maintaining the mathematical viability of these methods.

A Computerized Environment for Learning and Teaching 3-D Geometry

Irit Wertheim, Emzar Panikashvili, Gershon Elber and Nitsa Movshovitz-Hadar
Technion – Israel Institute of Technology
Technion City
Haifa, 32000, ISRAEL
E-mail: weririt@tx.technion.ac.il, nitsa@tx.technion.ac.il

Introduction

This is a presentation of a project in progress at Technion – Israel Institute of Technology. The ultimate goal of this project is a computerized environment integrated in a program for learning and teaching 3D Geometry in high schools, focusing on the morphology of solids. 3D Geometry is an area of mathematics that most country's curricula almost totally neglect, yet it is of utmost importance due to its applicability to other mathematical areas, to many professions, to the arts and to daily life.

The computerized environment we have started to develop will combine, in an interactive mode, the teaching and learning of spatial geometry issues, and the development of spatial capabilities. The environment will allow users to analyze, to investigate, and to animate solids, to carry out geometric constructions, and to perform upon them operations such as dissection and truncation, using a friendly graphical user interface. The interface will facilitate presenting solids and space relations in various representations simultaneously: a verbal representation, a graphical dynamic representation, and a vector representation.

This paper presents Platonic III, a computer program developed by the project team that allows the visualization and examination of the splendid features of a special class of five geometric solids – the so-called *Platonic solids*.

1.	Tetrahedron	
2.	Cube	
3.	Octahedron	
4.	Dodecahedron	
5.	Icosahedron	

This computer program demonstrates many capabilities that will become a part of the computerized environment envisioned by the project's team.

Polyhedra and the Arts

Symmetric figures of solid geometry fascinated people since ancient times. Their aesthetic value kept attracting artists' attention during the Renaissance, the Enlightenment, and up to modern time. For some artists, Polyhedra simply provided challenging models to demonstrate their mastery of perspective. For other artists, Polyhedra provided inspiration and an inventory of forms with various symmetries, while for some Polyhedra were symbolic of deep religious or philosophical truths (Hart, 1998). For example, Plato in the Timateus, associated Platonic solids with the 4 elements.

The mere observation of the regular Polyhedra, with their perfect symmetries and relationships, makes one perceive the implicit information and identify patterns on their complexity. This process integrates mathematical visualization with the beauty of art. Oftentimes, human brain finds this combination very fulfilling. As Coxeter put it: "The chief reason for studying regular Polyhedra is still the same as in the time of the Pythagoreans, namely, that their symmetrical shapes appeal to one's artistic sense." H.S.M. Coxeter.

Platonic III

Platonic III provides the user with a program that allows two main options: (i) The performance of actions in 3D upon the five Platonic solids, and (ii) the examination of the results of these actions. The user interface of the program was designed to be as intuitive as possible in order to serve as an educational tool that helps young users get an insight into the special features, of the five *Platonic solids*, their inter-relationship, and their relationship with some other solids
Platonic III provides users with five modes of action:

1. **Truncating vertices or edges mode**
User can perform vertex truncation and/or edge truncation by one truncating plane per vertex and one truncating plane per edge. The vertex truncation plane is perpendicular to the rotation axis through the center of the solid and that vertex. (Clearly, all five Platonic solids have a well-defined center-point.) The edge truncation plane is perpendicular to the rotation axis through the center of the solid and the midpoint of that edge.

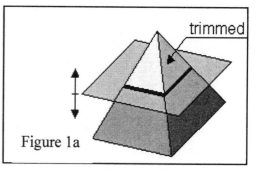

Figure 1a

Each truncation plane divides the whole space into two half-spaces – one half-space contains the center of the Platonic polyhedron and the other contains the vertex (or edge) to be truncated. The part of the solid located in the latter half-space is trimmed away (see Figure 1a).

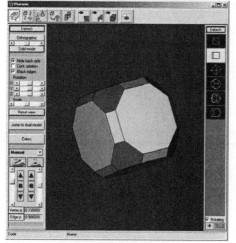

These truncation operations allow the user to produce new polyhedra as derivatives of the Platonic solids (See screen-shot in Figure 1b). For instance, by applying the edge / vertex truncation on the Platonic solids one can generate the so-called ***Archimedean solids***. (Archimedean solids like Platonic, are symmetrical geometric polyhedra with regular polygonal faces. Unlike Platonic solids, the regular polygonal faces of Archimedean solids, do not all necessarily have the same number of edges. For example, Archimedean solids can be constructed from equilateral triangles and squares or from regular pentagons and regular hexagons, and so on.). Any newly created solid can be added to the inventory of solids and operated upon using the various modes of action the software makes available.

Figure 1b - A solid obtained by truncating the vertices and the edges of a cube.

2. Planar intersection mode

In this mode the user can examine planar dissection of a Platonic solid as well as of any solid obtained by truncation as described above. The intersection is highlighted on the 3D. In addition it is shown in a separate window as a 2D polygon (Figure 2).

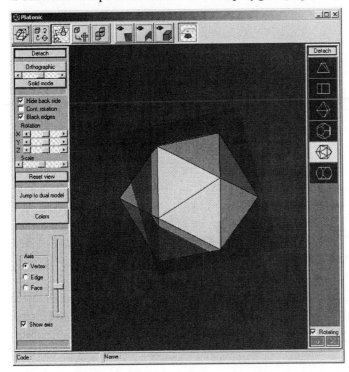

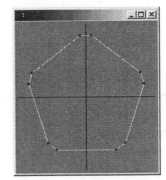

Figure 2 - Planar intersection

The cut is an intersection of the solid with a cutting plane that the user can move. The cutting plane has three possible directions. Each direction coincides with an n-fold rotational axis (which is a normal to this plane) and passes through the center of the polyhedron. The three options are:

- The axis passes also through a vertex.
- The axis passes also through the center of an edge.
- The axis passes also through the center of a face.

The user selects the desired direction by clicking on an appropriate radio button.

3. Net layout mode

In this mode, the user can "unfold" a Platonic solid (and of some of the derived solids as well), to obtain a planar net of its faces. User can then "close" the solid observing how the faces fit together. Users can use a print-out on cardboard, in order to construct a physical model of the polyhedron.

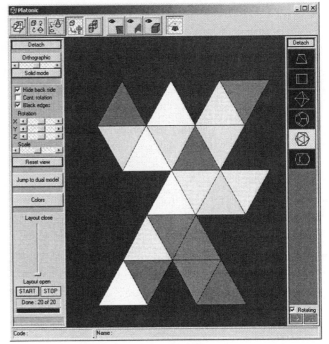

Figure 3 – Net layout

4. Duality visualization mode

One of the remarkable properties of the five Platonic solids is their pairwise dual relationship: the cube and the octahedron, the dodecahedron and the Icosahedron, and the self-duality of the tetrahedron to itself. In this mode, the software allows the user to observe and manipulate two dual Platonic solids with coinciding centers. The user can slide the control button, making one of the two, gradually more transparent, while the other becomes less transparent and consequently more visible. In the process a vertex of one solid replaces a face of the other and vice-versa.

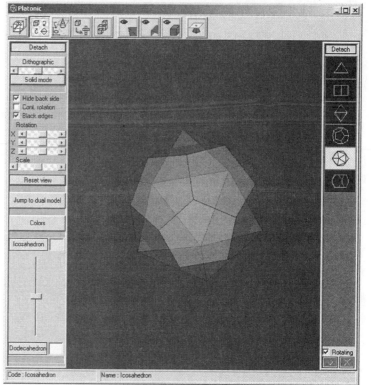

Figure 4 – Duality

5. Space filling mode

The space filling mode allows the user to examine the possibility of filling the space with a single solid (Platonic polyhedra or a truncated one), or using a combination of solids. The whole process is divided into three steps:

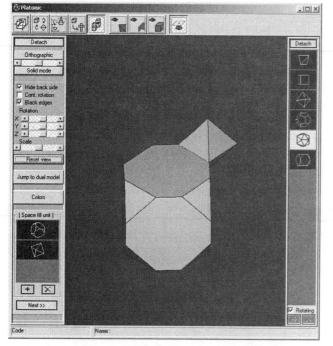

a. In the first step user constructs a space-filling unit, to be used in attempting to fill the space. (See Figure 5a) In order to attach two polyhedra to form one space-filling unit, user needs to manipulate one of the two polyhedra so that congruent polygonal faces of the two polyhedra touch one another. When they do, the automatic snapping is activated and the two polyhedra "stick" together.

Figure 5 a – Creation of space filling unit

b. The second step is creating a space fill pattern according to which the space will be filled using the space-filling unit created in step a. The pattern defines the way space-filling units will be arranged to fill the space. Patterns are created automatically and (at the moment) cannot be changed manually (See a screen shot in Figure 5b).

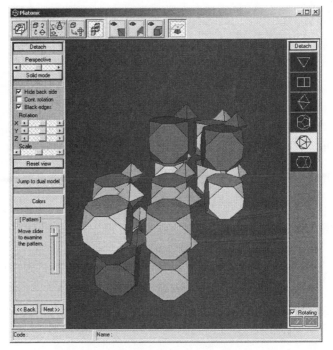

Figure 5 b: Space-filling pattern

c. The final step is an animated space filling. Here user can observe space fill units "flying" to the unit in the center of the screen to fill the space (See a screen shot in Figure 5c.).

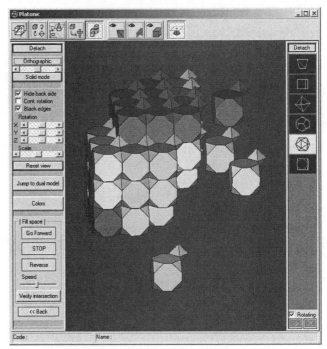

Figure 5 c – Space-filling animation.

A Few Words about the System in General

The system can process any predefined geometry and not just the regular polyhedra and the polyhedra derived from them. The system constructs the true geometry of the (semi) regular and other polyhedra, which enables further and future arbitrary processing and analysis of the models. For example, the volume of the model is now quite easy to compute. The system can also be used as a WEB oriented environment (having an Active X control for Explorer), providing the 3D graphics support for remote teaching via the Internet.

Platonic Vs. Alternative Software

Platonic is a non-commercial software development project, as a part of a whole curriculum development in morphological 3-D geometry. In this framework special attention is given to improving visualization. Consequently it focuses on interactive processes such as solid truncation gradually yielding new solids, interactive cutting of a solid moving the cutting plane in certain directions, gradual transition between a solid opening into its net and folding back, and packing the space by identical solids, or by a combination of solids. These interactive processes seem to be unique to this program, as far as we were able to examine other available 3-D software e.g. 'Stella[1]'. This interactivity feature was chosen initially in order to make the software of value for pedagogical use, assisting in building up students' understanding of abstract processes, as well as improving students' ability to associate and connect properties and forms.

Empirical implementation of this curriculum in classrooms is characterized by self-exploration performed by students in small groups or individually. Teacher's role is more of a mentor than a source of knowledge.

Final Remarks

The project we have been working on is highly demanding. It combines mathematical tools, pedagogical tools and computing tools in order to provide educational systems with an integrated environment enabling the introduction of an area in mathematics that is known to be difficult to grasp for a wide range of students. The technology is available to make this happen, our team is committed to this project however the resources needed are scarce. We hope to be able to cope with the challenge we set forth, and complete our program in the near future. Future work plan includes adding of quantitative information, and presenting it adjacent to each solid or its components, improving the duality representation, and making the cuts more flexible in terms of choice of direction by the user, and manual control of the process.

Reference

Hart, G. W. (1998). Virtual Polyhedra. http://www.georgehart.com/virtual-polyhedra/copyright.html

---

[1] Stella: Polyhedron Navigator, http://www.software3d.com.

Symmetry and the Sacred Date Palm in the Palace
of
Ashurnasirpal II, King of Assyria

Sarah C. Melville
Box 5750
School of Arts and Sciences
Clarkson University
Potsdam, NY, U.S.A.
melville@clarkson.edu

Abstract

This paper examines the use of mathematical symmetry in the stylized depiction of the date-palm on the sculptured stone wall reliefs decorating the royal palace of the Assyrian king, Ashurnasirpal II in the 9th century BC. Although the significance of the date palm in Neo-Assyrian iconography is still debated, the frequency of its appearance on the palace walls indicates that it played an important role in Assyrian apotropaic ritual. We argue that one of the keys to unlocking the mystery of the ritual is to understand the principles underlying the formal depiction of the date palm.

The Assyrians were a Semitic people who inhabited the northern part of what is now Iraq and had profound cultural connections with their southern neighbors and hereditary enemies, the Babylonians. For the three centuries between approximately 900 and 600 BC, Assyria was the major power of the Near East, ruling over the largest empire the world had ever seen. The Assyrian king, Ashurnasirpal II (883-859 BC), who was instrumental in founding the empire, commemorated his achievements by rebuilding and expanding the city of Nimrud (ancient Kalhu). The focal point of the project was a massive royal palace, which the king had lavishly decorated with carved orthostats, most of which depicted apotropaic *apkallu* and *utukku* demons, the stylized date palm, or the king undertaking various ritual activities usually involving the demons and the tree. Although archaeologists have not yet excavated the entire palace, more than eighty rooms have yielded hundreds of relief panels and more than two hundred representations of the sacred tree [5].

The date palm played an essential role in the daily life of ancient Mesopotamians, who relied on the fruit of the tree for sustenance and used the palm fronds and other parts of the tree for things as disparate as furnishings (matting or roofing) and exorcistic rituals. Artistic representations of the date palm or its flower appear in all periods of Mesopotamian history on all types of objects including cylinder seals, furniture, jewelry, and monumental art [2; 4]. What is especially curious about the prevalence of the image at Ashurnasirpal's palace is that the date palm is not indigenous to Assyria, and will not thrive there because of cold winter temperatures [7, p.17]. The emphasis on the date palm in the decorative scheme of Ashurnasirpal's palace cannot be a simple reference to the productivity of Assyrian husbandry, but must have some more symbolic meaning.

In fact the tree does not usually stand alone, but appears as part of a larger scene in which the demons seemingly pollinate the female flower clusters on the tree with a male flower which they carry (figure 1) [7, p.15]. In the throne room, the king takes part in the scene, but he stands in the standard pose of worship between the demons and the tree (figure 2). The demons, who appear with the tree, were supernatural and belonged to the sphere of the divine. It had to be immediately apparent to the viewer that the world depicted on the walls was not the mundane one he/she inhabited, but the domain of power and magic. The king could appear in that world because he was the intermediary between the divine and the terrestrial.

The tree is always rendered schematically rather than naturalistically in these scenes because it represents, not a real tree, but a special, divinely perfect tree. Assyrian artists were capable of rendering a naturalistic date palm, but they did so only when they meant to evoke the natural world. The so-called Black Stone of Esarhaddon (ruled 680-669 BC) depicts the date palm in each of its different realms (figure 3). The bottom register shows a date palm as it appears in the real world, but on the top register where the king is shown worshiping before an altar, the date palm has become stylized because it is part of the ritual world.

Attempts to determine the sacred significance of the stylized tree in Assyrian art have been frequent and sometimes controversial. Generally, scholars understand the pollination scene to represent, "a symbolic cross-pollination of the tree by supernatural beings, and thus the gods' gift of abundance to mankind" [7, p. 5; 4, p. 125]. Recently, the Finnish scholar, Simo Parpola, has suggested that the positions of the date palm flowers on the tree correspond to the mystical numbers that are sometimes associated in Assyrian esoteric literature with the key deities of the pantheon. According to Parpola, the tree image was chosen to depict metaphorically the relationship between individual divinities (flowers and branches) and an overarching divine whole or godhead (the tree) [6]. His arguments concerning numerology and inchoate monotheism are problematic [3], but the notion that there is meaning in the spatial arrangement and decorative organization of the tree itself is borne out by an examination of the design principles – including mathematical symmetry – which underlie all depictions of the tree.

No two trees from Ashurnasirpal's palace are exactly alike, yet all trees share certain features: a central trunk capped with a palm spray, intertwining branches, and linked (mostly) seven-petaled palm flowers. The number of flowers, branches, and central joins to the trunk can vary substantially, as can the tree's height and proportions. Some trees are short and squat, others tall and narrow, depending on the space to be filled. Trees in the same room are usually homogeneous up to a point. That is, they all tend to have the same general structure. For example, all the trees in room F have a double row of flowers (figure 4), while the trees in room L have the more common single row. There is usually some variation in the number of flower clusters on different trees in the same room. The number of flowers on trees in room L ranges from twenty one to thirty five. At this point it is impossible to determine whether the tendency to visual uniformity within a room fulfilled a ritual purpose or only aesthetic requirements. Nor can we tell if relief scenes depicted in a room were tied to the room's function in any way.

Although the arrangement of the orthostats on the palace walls was not strictly symmetrical, it is clear that the ancient sculptors and architects made an effort to achieve an overall coherence and balance in their decorative program [5]. Likewise, the pollination scenes give an impression of symmetry without actually being symmetrical. At first glance the demons look identical, but neither they nor their positions are true mirror images of one another. This is also true of the sacred tree itself. Each one has an overall approximate symmetry; the trunk and palm spray of each tree are symmetrical. However the sculptor has taken care to break – delicately – the actual symmetry of the intertwining branches, the arrangement of the flowers, and sometimes even the flowers themselves (figure 1). There is often subtle variety in the number and positions of the central branches (figure 4). Although each side of any given tree has the same number of flowers, they may not be placed exactly opposite each other. If we analyze the ring of flowers as a frieze, then we see that (usually) each flower has vertical symmetry and so the flower ring has, according to standard notation, symmetry type $pm11$, or vertical reflection only.

One might be tempted to ascribe such sculptural variation to general inconsistency on the part of the ancient artists. After all, many different sculptors worked on the reliefs and there is a detectable range in artistic technique [8, p. 17]. The fact that examples of design symmetry executed with near perfect regularity appear elsewhere in Ashurnasirpal's palace belies such a conclusion. Figure 5, a floor slab sculpted to mimic a carpet, offers a good example of the types of symmetry sometimes employed. The "carpet" slab depicts a central two-dimensional pattern with 60 degree rotation and reflections, type p6m. Considered as linear patters, the two rosette bands have both horizontal and vertical reflection (type pmm2), while the two remaining bands, one of palm flowers and the other of lotus flowers, each only have vertical reflection (type pm11). Importantly, each band does have translational symmetry; that is, each of the rosettes, palm flowers and lotus flowers is identical. Assyrian artists were perfectly capable of depicting different types of symmetry with fine precision, but in the case of the sacred trees they chose not to. It is the deliberate manipulation of symmetry – not just its use – that is particularly significant.

The ancient sculptors of Ashurnasirpal's palace, who clearly intended to give an overall impression of balance and symmetry, also found it necessary to disrupt that balance through careful management of individual design components. Both the symmetry and its violation were, in fact, essential to the proper depiction of these ritual scenes, and were inextricably bound up with the Near Eastern concept of the *salmu* (usually translated "image"). In ancient Mesopotamia every image could be an individual being.

> "That is, rather than being a copy of something in reality, the image itself was seen as a real thing. It was not considered to resemble an original reality that was present elsewhere but to contain that reality in itself. Therefore, instead of being a means of signifying an original real thing, it was seen as ontologically equivalent to it, existing in the same register of reality." [1, p. 127]

Since there could be no real duplicate of the king, for example, each portrayal of him had to be individually charged with the royal character, and thus each image had to be unique in order to be efficacious.

Compositional symmetry expressed the order inherent in the divine; subtle shifts in balance rendered each figure (including the king) unique, and therefore uniquely imbued with the proper attributes. Had all trees and all demons been identical, their power would have been dangerously diluted. Had the king's images been mere duplicates, they would have been lifeless, powerless cartoons. As a result of the ancient concept of the function of the image within reality, their art always manifested a certain tension between uniformity, which was necessary to convey the correct image category – "king", "sacred tree", "supernatural being" – and uniqueness, which was essential to the activation of the image. A properly rendered image, therefore, existed in perpetuity; hence, the correct depiction of rituals represented ongoing, continuous sacred activity.

The decorative program of Ashurnasirpal II's palace at Nimrud contained a complex message, all the nuances of which have yet to be decoded. However, our study has shown that artists cleverly manipulated symmetry in order to fulfill the required tenets of their art. The image of the stylized date palm, so prevalent in the palace, offers a perfect example of the principles underlying the sacred art of Assyria. Not only was the tree always depicted in abstract form so as to be recognizably of the divine sphere, but artists also chose to regulate its depiction through symmetry, which could be easily and delicately altered in order to create the necessary individuality for each tree.

Illustrations

All illustrations appear courtesy of the Trustees of the British Museum

Figure 1: *Female demons pollinating the sacred tree. From room I.*

Figure 2: *Demons, the king (shown twice), the divine disc and the date palm. Throne room relief.*

Figure 3: *The Black Stone of Esarhaddon.*

Figure 4: *Tree from room F. Note the double row of branches and the slight asymmetry of the the interior flowers*

Figure 5: *Stone "carpet" from Ashurnasirpal's palace*

References

[1] Zainab Bahrani, *The Graven Image: Representation in Babylonia and Assyria.* Philadelphia: University of Pennsylvania Press, 2003.

[2] Hélène Danthine, *Le Palmier-Dattier et les Arbres Sacrés dans l'Iconographie de l'Asie Occidentale Ancienne.* Paris: Geuthner, 1937.

[3] Ithamar Gruenwald, "'How Much Qabbalah in Ancient Assyria' – Methodological Reflections on the Study of a Cross Cultural Phenomenon," in S. Parpola and R. Whiting (eds), *Assyria 1995: Proceedings of the 10th Anniversary Symposium of the Neo-Assyrian Text Corpus Project, Helsinki, September 7-11, 1995.* Helsinki: Neo-Assyrian Text Corpus Project, 1997, pp. 115-128.

[4] Andrew MacDonald, "Botanical Determination of the Middle Eastern Tree of Life," *Economic Botany* 56 (2002), pp. 113-129.

[5] Janusz Meuszynski, Samuel Paley and Richard Sobolewski, *Die Rekonstruktion der Reliefdarstellungen und Ihrer Anordnung im Nordwestpalast von Kalhu (Nimrud).* 3 volumes, Baghdader Forschungen 2, 10 and 14. Mainz am Rhein: Philipp von Zabern, 1981-1992.

[6] Simo Parpola, "The Assyrian Tree of Life: Tracing the Origins of Jewish Monotheism and Greek Philosophy," *JNES* 52 (1993), pp. 161-208.

[7] Barbara N. Porter, *Trees, Kings, and Politics: Studies in Neo-Assyrian Iconography.* Orbis Biblicus et Orientalis 197. Fribourg: Academic Press, 2003.

[8] Julian Reade, *Assyrian Sculpture.* London: The British Museum, 1983.

Three-Dimensional and Dynamic Constructions Based on Leonardo Grids

Rinus Roelofs
Sculptor
Lansinkweg 28
7553AL Hengelo, the Netherlands
E-mail: rinusroelofs@hetnet.nl

Abstract

Leonardo grids is the name I gave to my bar grid construction system with which I was able to construct domes and spheres out of simple elements using one constructing rule. Most of the constructions I made where planar and static.
In this paper I want to focus on the nonplanar and dynamic possibilities of the Leonardo grids.

1. Definition of the bar grid system

The Leonardo grid construction system is a way to make constructions using simple line shaped elements, like rods or beams. The system can be described as follows: on each element we define four connecting points, two at or near the ends and the other two somewhere in the middle at a certain distance from each other. We call these points respectively endpoints and interior points. In this kind of constructions endpoints of one rod may only be connected to midpoints of another rod and vice versa. An example can be seen in Figure 2, a dome structure also represented in the drawing by Leonardo da Vinci in Figure 1 at the left. The drawing of the stucture (Figure 3), which we shall call a Leonardo grid, can be seen as a graph. And this graph has the property that every vertex has degree 3. For the domes the representing graph is always a planar graph. The name Leonardo grid was chosen because his drawings are the only references I found.

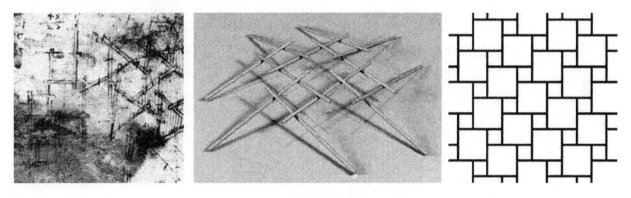

Figure 1: *Drawing by L. da Vinci.*   **Figure 2**: *Dome construction.*   **Figure 3**: *Graph.*

2. From 2D to 3D

Also the spheres built with the Leonardo grid construction system can be represented by a planar graph. So in fact the sphere is a 2D object. It is no more than a bent surface. In the example (Figure 4) you can see that the elements don't have to be straight sticks. The four connecting points and the connection rule can be recognized in the model, of which the graph is presented in Figure 5. I found many patterns that can be used as Leonardo grids and all these patterns can be used as basic designs for domes and spheres.

Figure 4: *Sphere - 12 elements.*

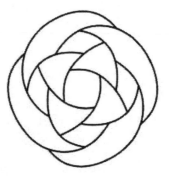

Figure 5: *Graph.*

Figure 6: *Sphere in sphere.*

The question arose whether it would be possible to make real 3D constructions based on the Leonardo grids. Is it possible to make multi layer objects using the Leonardo grids? Or even can we make 3D space frames built out of simple elements just like in the domes? So mathematically speaking instead of planar graphs I had to look for non-planar graphs now.

A first example of a real 3D construction is the double sphere in Figure 6. In this object you can see a sphere within a sphere. Each of the 24 elements is half in the inner sphere and half in the outer sphere. The design was made by starting with two layers of Leonardo grids. The layers were placed above each other in such a way that after cutting each element in two parts, half elements from the upper layer could be connected to half elements of the under layer. The resulting structure again has all the properties needed for a Leonardo grid: each element is connected to 4 other elements in the right way: all endpoint connected to midpoints and all midpoints connected to endpoints. Half of the connecting points are on the surface of the inner sphere, the other half on the surface of the outer sphere. A first non-planar or real 3D result. And surprisingly enough the total structure appeared to be stable.

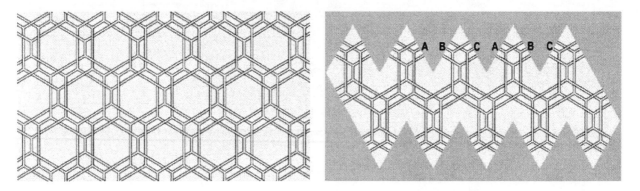

Figure 7: *Three interwoven patterns.*   **Figure 8**: *Icosaherdon - plan.*

Another approach is to start with interwoven patterns (Figure 7). A simple way to transform a flat pattern into a spherical construction is to use a polyhedron. When the pattern is hexagonal, the net of a icosahedron can be used. In the special case of the three interwoven patterns of Figure 8 the cut off elements of pattern A will be connected to the cut off elements of pattern B when folding the net to an icosahedron. And so with the cut off elements of B and C and of C and A.

The result is real 3D Leonardo grid construction. And now all the connecting points are laying in the same spherical surface. In the pictures (Figure 9, 10 and 11) you can see some variations.

Figure 9: *Interwoven sphere - A.*   **Figure 10**: *Interwoven sphere - B.*   **Figure 11**: *Interwoven sphere - C*

Although this is a good approach it is hard to find a good set of interwoven patterns that can be used for this method.

3. Infinite double layer structures

To go one step further towards the Leonardo grid space frames I first tried to find a way to construct infinite double layer structures. Space frames can be built by connecting polyhedra in systematic way. Cubes stack so as to fill space completely. And when you look at the graph that represents the cube you will notice that all vertices have degree 3, which was a condition for the Leonardo grids. A cubic frame can be made as a Leonardo grid construction in three different ways (Figures 12, 13 and 14; only in Figure 14 the ends point to the X, Y and Z-direction).

 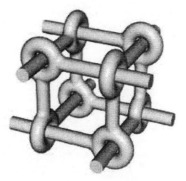 

Figure 12: *Cubic frame - A.*   **Figure 13**: *Cubic frame - B.*   **Figure 14**: *Cubic frame - C*

A way to make a double layer structure is to connect these kinds of cubes as in Figure 15. This will result in a non-planar infinite construction that has also dynamic properties. The elements can slide between certain boundaries and the total construction can be pressed together or stretched.

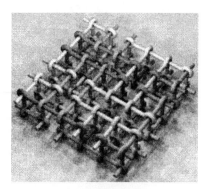

Figure 15: *Double layer structure*   **Figure 16**: *Pressed together.*   **Figure 17**: *Stretched*

4. Rings and strings

In the double layer structures the basic elements, the rods with the 4 connecting points, are linked together to form bigger units. We can distinguish two kinds of these bigger units: rings, a closed concatenation of a finite number of basic elements, and strings a (open) concatenation of an infinite number of basic elements. Some examples of both categories are shown in Figures 18, 19 and 20 (rings) and Figures 21, 22 and 23 (strings).

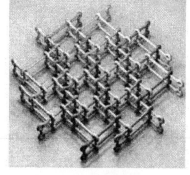

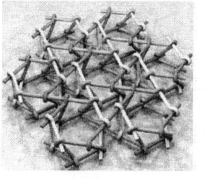

Figure 18: *Double layer structure*   **Figure 19**: *Pressed together.*   **Figure 20**: *Stretched*

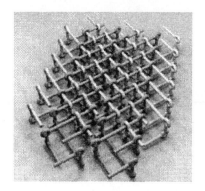

Figure 21: *Double layer structure*   **Figure 22**: *Pressed together.*   **Figure 23**: *Stretched*

And the constructions don't have to be limited to 2 layers as can be seen in Figures 24, 25 and 26. Here an infinite 3D construction is built with one type of string, which is a concatenation of basic Leonardo grid elements.

The question still is whether it is possible to make space frame constructions out of basic elements which are not linked.

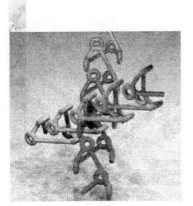

Figure 24: *Strings 3D*

Figure 25: *String structure 3D.*

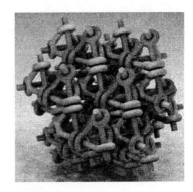

Figure 26: *String structure 3D*

5. Grid transformation

Another, and perhaps even better way to construct real 3D structures based on Leonardo grids appeared to be the use of transformation of the basic Leonardo grid from 2D to 3D. The process can be described as follows: we can start with any pattern in which we can find a hexagonal hole. We now keep the 6 sticks around this hole connected and change the hexagon from flat to skew. This change will cause a transformation of the sticks, which are connected to the first 6 sticks. The six parallelogram shaped holes in the pattern will also be parallelogram shaped at the end of the process. But one of the connections around the triangle holes will get loose. The resulting structure now can be used as a layer with which we can create space frames.

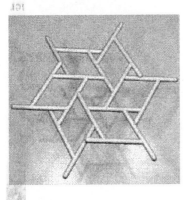

Figure 27: *Leonardo grid 2D.*

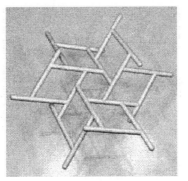

Figure 28: *Halfway between .*

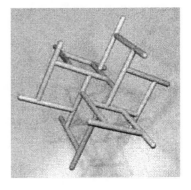

Figure 29: *Leonardo grid 3D.*

The discovery of this process lead to many designs of Leonardo grid space frames because the process could be applied on all the flat basic patterns. We can also start with a square hole in a pattern. In the same way the flat hexagon is transformed into a skew hexagon, a flat square can be transformed into a skew squre. The over a hunderd different patterns that I had drawn as possible designs for the domes can now be transformed to Leonardo grid space frames. In the illustrations you can see some examples of the resulting space frames.

Figure 30: *Space frame grid A*

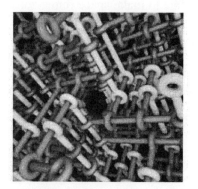

Figure 31: *Space frame grid B.*

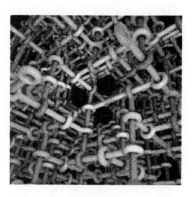

Figure 32: *Space frame grid C.*

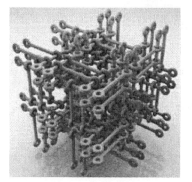

Figure 33: *Space frame grid D*

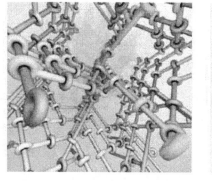

Figure 34: *Space frame grid E.*

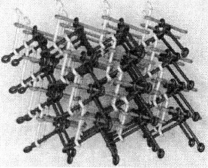

Figure 35: *Space frame grid F.*

6. Dynamic space frames

Just as in the double layer structures the Leonardo grid space frames also have dynamic properties. The sticks can be slid along each other and so the total construction can be pressed together or stretched. To show this we will go back to the skew hexagon first. In Figures 36, 37 and 38 you see three stages of the sliding process. And we can extend that to a complete layer as in Figures 39, 40 and 41. In the total movement it looks as if there is some twist in the structure. The shrinking and growing of the structure is in a way a spiral movement. This can be best viewed in animation.

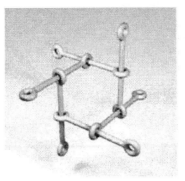

Figure 36: *Sliding first stage.*　　　**Figure 37**: *Sliding second stage.*　　　**Figure 38**: *Sliding third stage.*

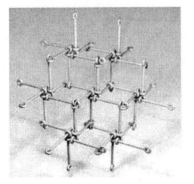
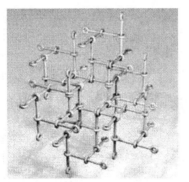
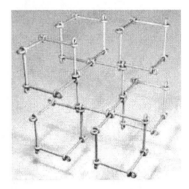

Figure 39: *Sliding first stage.*　　　**Figure 40**: *Sliding second stage.*　　　**Figure 41**: *Sliding third stage .*

7. Dynamics in 2D

While studying dynamics in the 3D Leonardo grid constructions I also discovered an interesting new way of translating 2D Leonardo grids into dynamic structures. Looking again at the basic grids you will realize that there are two possible interpretations: you can either look at it as a construction built out of rods or as a tiling, a pattern built with a set of tiles. The dividing lines then form the Leonardo grid.

One line in this grid represents the edges of 4 tiles: 2 big tiles and 2 small tiles. So this one gridline can be seen as a set of 4 edges. And because the edges are alternating long-short-long-short, the set of edges can be seen as a collapsed parallelogram. In the original grid the tiles are close to each other so the described has area zero. But what will happen when we 'open' the parallelogram? The set of tiles then turn out to be a dynamic hinged construction. The Leonardo grid lines transform from line to parallelogram to rectangle and back via parallelogram to Leonardo grid line again. And as a result of this process is that a left-hand orientation of the Leonardo grid has changed into a right-hand orientation.

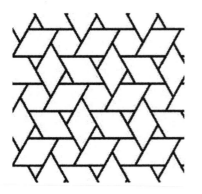
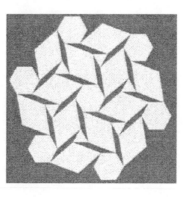

Figure 42: *Transforming first stage.*   **Figure 43**: *Second stage.*   **Figure 44**: *Third stage.*

And because this process can be applied on any Leonardo grid this lead to an enormous collection of hinged tile constructions. Most special is that this process also works on Leonardo grids with distortions, Leonardo grids in which more than one pattern is used, and on Leonardo grids in which more than one length of grid lines is used. Some examples can be seen in the figures.

Figure 45: *Transforming first stage.*   **Figure 46**: *Second stage.*   **Figure 47**: *Third stage.*

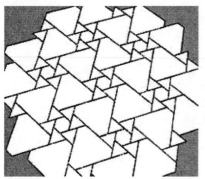
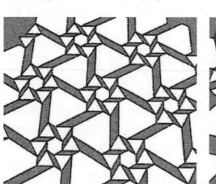

Figure 48: *Transforming first stage.*   **Figure 49**: *Second stage.*   **Figure 50**: *Third stage.*

Of course this can be better viewed in animation.

The creation of the solid wireframe consists of two main steps. The first one involves creation of the 3D joints at each of the vertices in the input wireframe. The second step involves connecting the joints to create the 3D pipes corresponding to each edge in the input wireframe. The following paragraphs describe these two steps in more detail. The term "wireframe" will be used to refer to the input mesh, while the term "solid wireframe" will be used to refer to the output mesh.

2.1. 3D Joints   In the first step of the process, 3D joints are created at every vertex of the input wireframe. The shape of the 3D joint at a vertex depends on the number of edges incident on that vertex, and the desired thickness and cross-sectional shape of the 3D pipes. There are three steps in the joint creation process as described below.

2.1.1. End-faces   For every edge in the wireframe, we compute a *virtual 3D pipe* of user-specified thickness and cross-section, with the axis of the pipe aligned with the edge. At this stage we are only interested in obtaining the end-faces of each 3D pipe. We also establish a link between each vertex of the wireframe and the end-faces that will be used to create the 3D joint at that vertex.

The centroid of the end-faces lies on the original edge, with the normal to the face aligned with the edge. All the end-faces linked to a vertex are positioned at the same distance from the vertex. This distance is computed in such a way as to avoid intersection with the other end-faces linked to this vertex. To do this, we take end-faces linked to a vertex in pairs and find the minimum distance at which there is no intersection. We then take the maximum of these minimum distances and use that distance for all the end-faces linked to that vertex. If the thickness of the pipe is large, this approach can produce incorrect joints in situations where the mesh has very short edges near a sharp corner. We ignore this special case since the user can adjust the thickness of the pipes to avoid such situations.

2.1.2. Convex Hull   For every vertex of the original mesh, we collect end-faces that correspond to the edges incident on the vertex. Using the vertices of these end-faces we then calculate a convex hull which defines the shape of the 3D joint. The distance of the end-faces from the vertex affects the shape of the convex hull. Since we avoid intersections between end-faces when computing the distances, the points making up each end-face are guaranteed to be a part of the convex hull.

2.1.3. Convex Hull Clean-up   Figure 2A shows a close-up view of the convex hull for one vertex of a wireframe cube. As can be seen, the convex hull algorithm creates a triangulated mesh. In order to create 3D pipes of user specified cross-section and thickness, it will be necessary to clean up the triangulated mesh so that we have a face on each 3D joint which can serve as the end of a 3D pipe. By keeping track of which vertices came from which end-face we can remove edges which were not part of the end-face, in effect recreating the end-faces on the 3D joint. Note that we restrict this clean-up to edges between vertices from the same end-face. Figure 2B shows the convex hull after the end-faces have been recreated.

The convex hull can be cleaned-up further by removing edges which are adjacent to co-planar faces. That is, if two adjacent faces have the same face normal, the shared edge can be removed. This produces a cleaner 3D joint by removing edges which do not add any extra visual detail. Figure 2C shows the result of the additional clean-up.

2.2. 3D Pipes   Once the 3D joints have been created, the creation of the 3D pipes is fairly straightforward. It involves insertion of a handle between matching faces of the joints. The connectivity information in the original mesh is used to determine the matching faces. The actual handle creation is done using the CREATEPIPE operator which is one of the operators provided by our mesh modeling system [1, 10, 9]. Figure 3 illustrates the main steps of the above algorithm using a wireframe cube as the initial shape.

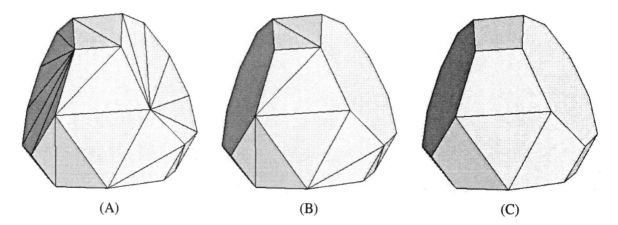

(A)   (B)   (C)

Figure 2: *A closeup view of the 3D joint creation at one corner of a dodecahedral wireframe. (A) shows the joint after the initial convex hull has been created, (B) shows the joint after the end-faces have been recreated and (C) shows the joint after the additional clean-up.*

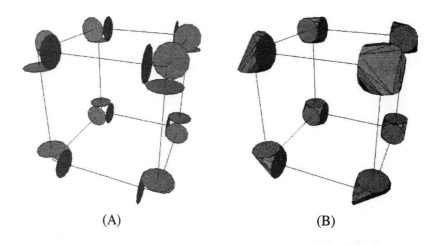

(A)   (B)

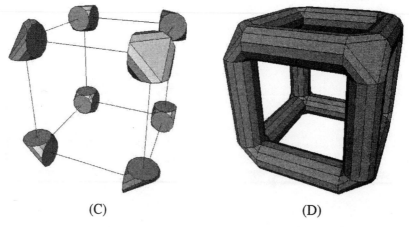

(C)   (D)

Figure 3: *Creating a solid wireframe from a cube. (A) Creation of the end-faces. (B) Creation of convex hulls. (C) The 3D joints after clean-up of the convex hulls. (D) Final mesh obtained by inserting handles between the 3D joints.*

3. Results

Our solid wireframe modeling method has been incorporated as an interactive tool into the three-dimensional mesh modeling system that we have developed [1, 2, 9]. Our system includes other features such as extrusions and re-meshing schemes, which when used in combination with the solid wireframe modeling tool, can create very interesting and complex shapes. The re-meshing schemes are particularly useful since they allows users to create several types of solid wireframe structures from the same initial mesh.

Figure 4 shows an example of applying the solid wireframe modeling tool to a dodecahedron with different values of thickness and cross-sectional shape. As can be seen, increasing the number of sides in the cross-section of the pipes, produces smoother looking pipes. Having a smaller number of sides produces angular pipes. By varying the thickness we can create thin wire-like structures or thick pillar-like wireframes.

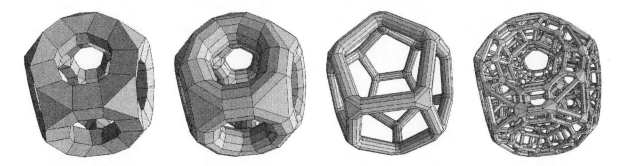

Figure 4: *The solid wireframe modeling tool applied to a dodecahedron with varying thickness and cross-section. The final model was created by applying the tool twice in succession.*

The solid wireframe modeling tool provides a simple, intuitive and easy-to-use interface for creating very complex structures in a few steps. It is well suited for use by architects and artists, and has been used to create conceptual models as well as stylized depictions of existing architectural models. Figure 5 shows an example of a model created using the solid wireframe modeling tool and its use in a conceptual sketch. Figure 6 shows a rendered model of a cathedral created using our new method.

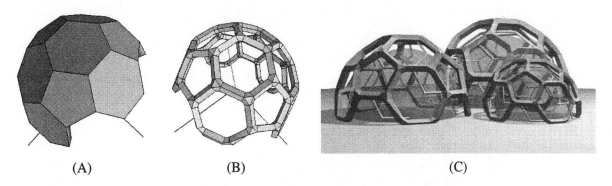

(A)   (B)   (C)

Figure 5: *Example of a frame structure created using the solid wireframe modeling tool. (A) shows the initial mesh and (B) shows the end result. (C) is a rendered image from a conceptual sketch (created by Ozan Ozener).*

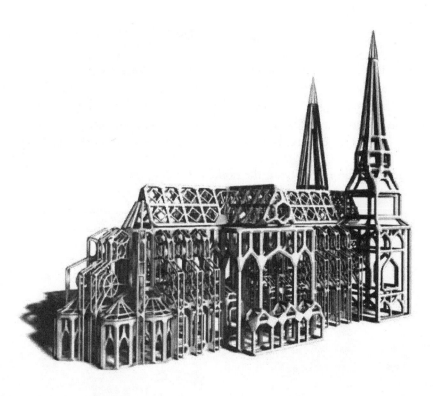

Figure 6: *Model of a cathedral created using the column modeling tool.*

4. Conclusions

In this paper we have presented a new method for converting a regular wireframe mesh into a mesh in which the edges of the wireframe are replaced by cylindrical pipes of finite thickness and volume, a process we refer to as "solidifying" the wireframe. Our method allows users to create *solid* wireframes. The resulting model conveys 3D information about the object, including interior structures, much better than a traditional wireframe rendering or a surface rendering.

Our algorithm works on any set of input edges – they need not be connected to each other, nor do they have to represent a manifold surface. The fact that models created using our new tool can be fabricated (using 3D printers or rapid prototyping machines) is particularly pertinent for architects who want to create conceptual sketches and produce real 3D models from them.

The tool has been used to create real and virtual environments, artistic depictions of known objects and architectural conceptual models. It can also be used to easily and quickly create complicated artistic shapes that would be difficult to generate using traditional modeling methods. Figures 7 and 8 show some more examples of conceptual design projects which make use of the solid wireframe modeling tool

Our new method makes available a powerful tool for end users. However there is still room for improvement. For example, it would be useful if users could create spherical joints. This would add the ability to create models of molecules and other chemical structures, which when fabricated could be used as educational aids. Another useful addition would be the option to have symmetric but non-circular cross-sections, such as elliptical cross-sections, which are found in several engineering structures in the real world.

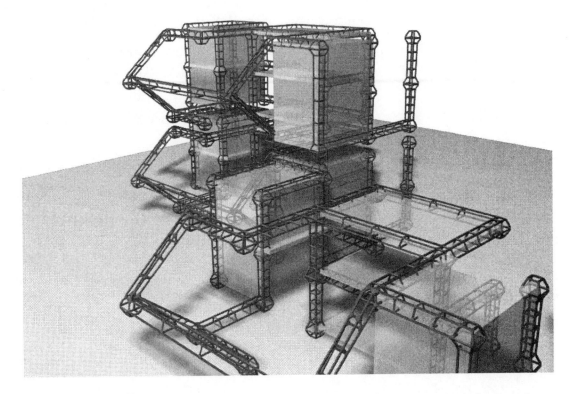

Figure 7: *Conceptual work done using the column modeling tool. Design and modeling by Ozan Ozener.*

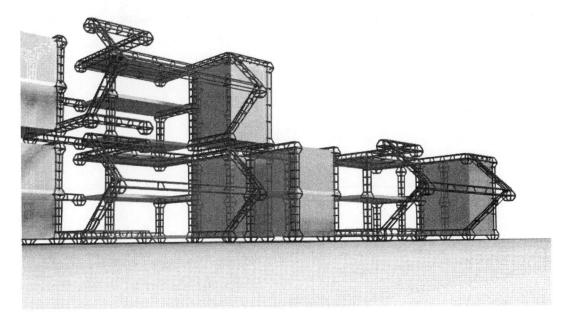

Figure 8: *Conceptual work done using the column modeling tool. Design and modeling by Ozan Ozener.*

References

[1] AKLEMAN, E., CHEN, J., AND SRINIVASAN, V. An interactive shape modeling system for robust design of functional 3d shapes. In *Proceedings of ACADIA 2001* (Oct. 2001), pp. 248–257.

[2] AKLEMAN, E., CHEN, J., AND SRINIVASAN, V. A prototype system for robust, interactive and user-friendly modeling of orientable 2-manifold meshes. In *Proceedings of Shape Modeling International 2002* (Banff, Canada, May 2002).

[3] AKLEMAN, E., SRINIVASAN, V., AND CHEN, J. Interactive rind modeling. In *Proceedings of Shape Modeling International 2003* (Seoul, Korea, May 2003).

[4] CATMULL, E., AND CLARK, J. Recursively generated B-spline surfaces on arbitrary topological meshes. *Computer Aided Design 10* (1978), 350–355.

[5] CATURANO, U., AND SANSEVERINO DI MARCELLINARA, C. Solid modelling by low-cost hardware and software: the crystal palace's node. In *Proceedings of eCAADe Conference* (Eindhoven (The Netherlands), Nov. 1993).

[6] DOO, D., AND SABIN, M. Behavior of recursive subdivision surfaces near extraordinary points. *Computer Aided Design 10* (1978), 356–360.

[7] MANDAL, E. Wire and Column Modeling. Master's thesis, Texas A&M University, 2004.

[8] MANDAL, E., SRINIVASAN, V., AND AKLEMAN, E. Wire modeling. SIGGRAPH 2003, Sketches and Applications, July 2003.

[9] SRINIVASAN, V. *Modeling High-Genus Surfaces*. Ph.D. dissertation, Texas A&M University, 2004.

[10] SRINIVASAN, V., AKLEMAN, E., AND CHEN, J. Interactive construction of multi-segment curved handles. *Pacific Graphics 2002* (Oct. 2002).

[11] VAN KEMPEN, A., KOK, H., AND WAGTER, H. Design modeling. *Automation in Construction 1* (May 1992), 7–13.

[12] ZORIN, D., AND SCHRÖDER, P. Subdivision for modeling and animation. ACM SIGGRAPH 2000 Course Notes, 2000.

Splitting Tori, Knots, and Moebius Bands

Carlo H. Séquin

Computer Science Division, EECS Department
University of California, Berkeley, CA 94720
E-mail: sequin@cs.berkeley.edu

Abstract

A study of sculptures and puzzles resulting from splitting lengthwise, tori, Moebius bands, various knots and graphs, illustrated with many models made on rapid prototyping machines.

Figure 1: *"OUSHI ZOKEI 1999," sculpture by Keizo Ushio, created at ISAMA'99.*

1. Introduction

The inspiration for this study originated from the participation of Keizo Ushio [5] at Isama'99 [2] in San Sebastian, Spain. At that conference, he carved an intriguing sculpture consisting of two intertwined loops from a single solid block of granite (Fig.1). He started out by carving a massive torus with a relatively small hole. He then split that torus into two parts with a cut that sliced around the whole ring, and while doing so, twisted through 360° (Fig.1a). This cut the torus into two identical linked loops, each having a twisting cross section in the form of a half-circle. Once the two pieces had been pried apart, the constellation was reconfigured to make a dramatic figure-8 shape composed of the two loops placed into a position where portions of their original toroidal surfaces became coincident over a significant stretch (Fig.1b).

This process inspired me to start my own investigation to find out in what other intriguing ways a torus could be split. A straight-forward extension of the above geometry readily led to sets of more than two mutually interlocking rings (Section 2) and to multi-loops (Section 3) and Moebius space configurations (Section 4). Subsequently, I experimented with the splitting of Moebius bands (Section 6) and twisted knots (Section 7), which eventually led to a design for a snow sculpture (Section 8). Most recently, I gave myself the challenge to see whether a torus could also be split into a configuration of Borromean rings (Section 5), and how the splitting of these 1-manifold loop structures could be extended to more complex branching graph structures (Section 9). These concepts are illustrated with models made on a rapid prototyping machine.

2. Interlocking Rings

While Keizo Ushio's sculpture had to be created in painstaking hard labor by drilling some hundred holes into the hard granite torus, conceptually this operation amounts to sweeping a "knife" once around the torus, and in doing so, letting it execute one full twist around the curved toroidal axis. This separates the torus into two identical parts which however remain interlocked. If the two radii of the torus are suitably chosen, then the two rings can be re-arranged so that the outer curvature of one fits snugly into the inner curvature of the toroidal swept loop. In this constellation, the two rings seem to form a new symbiotic structure. A model of this configuration (Fig.2a) can easily be made on a rapid-prototyping (RP) machine. These two rings were made in a single run on a Fused Deposition Modeling (FDM) machine [4], depositing thin, 0.01" thick layers of ABS plastic. A tiny twisting gap was left in the part description of the torus, which was then filled in by the FDM machine with some scaffolding of filler material. This material, being differently colored and more brittle than the material that forms the actual part, can easily be removed with a scalpel after the two halves of the torus have been pried apart.

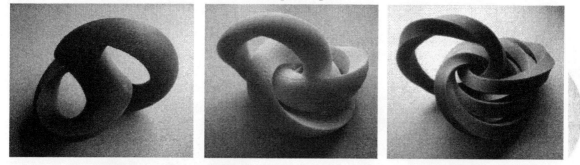

Figure 2: *Interlocking congruent rings cut from a single toroid: (a) 2 loops representing Keizo's sculpture; (b) 3 loops cut from a similar torus; (c) 4 loops cut from a twisted square toroid.*

It seemed only natural to ask whether the torus could also be split into three congruent parts and how these parts might be arranged. It was quite obvious, that the cutting "knife" now had to have the shape of a three-spoked star where three straight blades join together at angles of 120° at the points of the toroidal axis; and again this 3-blade knife would be rotated through 360° as it swept once around the toroid. The result can be seen in Figure 2b; this structure forms a puzzle that is very satisfying to manipulate and to play with. However, so far I have not found any good sculptural constellation that matches the dramatic harmony of "OUSHI ZOKEI 1999" (Fig.1b).

Similarly, if the cutting "knife" has four "spokes" (equivalent to two cuts at right angles), then four interlocking loops would result (Fig.2c). The above configuration makes it quite clear how this paradigm can be extended to more than four parts. N interlocking rings can be generated by a knife with N blades coming together at angles of 360°/N at the points of the toroidal axis. The partitioning into 4 and into 6 parts is particularly attractive. In the first case, the cross sections of the individual rings can be made square, which then leads to a torus also with a square cross section. In the second case, if the individual rings have cross sections equal to an equilateral triangle, then the assembled torus would have a hexagonal profile. The symmetry of the cross sections of the individual rings makes these puzzles particularly intriguing   and for some people quite challenging   to put back together again, since it is not immediately obvious what faces need to be joined against one another.

3. Multi-Loops

The torus can also be cut by twisting a single straight "knife" through angles other than 360°. Keizo Ushio has explored many possibilities in his early work. Figure 3 shows what happens when the cut is rotated through 180°, 360°, and 540°, respectively. The second option represents the case discussed above, which later lead to "OUSHI ZOKEI 1999." But for the other two twisting angles something new happens: the torus is no longer cut into two parts, but remains connected as a single strand that loops twice around the central hole, and while doing so executes either a single twist of 360° (Fig.3a) or three full twists (Fig.3c). Figure 4a shows the first case more schematically.

Figure 3: *Split tori by Keizo Ushio: (a) 180° twist (1989), (a) 360° twist (1992), (a) 540° twist (1996).*

Again we can generalize this cutting action by using a "knife" that has three or more blades joining on the toroidal axis, and which executes twists of various amounts as it is swept around the toroidal loop. Figure 4b and 4c show the results for a 3-blade knife executing twists of 120° and 240°, respectively. In both cases the result is a single connected strand looping around the central hole three times. If we use a 4-blade knife, we can generate a quadruple loop for twist amounts of ±90° or ±270°. But if we use ±180° of twist, then the torus is actually divided into two double loops (Fig.4d). These two loops, however, are tightly nested and, unlike the case of Figure 2a, cannot be separated and put into an interesting sculptural configuration. Of course, in all those cases, in order to make the individual branches quite visibly distinct, one should use a "thick knife" that produces sizeable gaps between the individual branches of the multi-loop.

In summary, if we use a knife with n blades and apply a total twist angle of $t*360°/n$, the cut line on the surface forms a (t,n)-torus link, and so do the solid parts after the cut has been executed. The solid parts form g connected components, where g is the greatest common divisor of (t,n), and each link component is a $(t/g, n/g)$-torus knot. When t and n are relatively prime, there is only a single connected component.

Figure 4: *Connected multi-loops cut from a toroid: (a) n=2, t=1; (b) n=3, t=1; (c) n=3, t=2; (d) n=4, t=2, resulting in two linked, inseparable double loops.*

4. Moebius Space

When building maquettes of potential sculptures, and peering into the gaps of some of the split tori, I often found myself agreeing with Nat Friedman, who has repeatedly pointed out at these conferences that for some abstract geometrical sculptures the spaces where material is missing may be even more important visually than the actual material itself. Thus, in my sculpture "Moebius Space" (Fig.5a) presented at Bridges 2000 [3], I hollowed out this space more dramatically and enhanced its visual impact by giving it a shining, silvery, almost mirror-like surface, while the outer torus surface was left dark and more textured. I am convinced that the effect will be quite dramatic if this sculpture is ever realized at a larger-than-human scale. In his 2004 implementation of such a Moebius cut through a torus Keizo Ushio has also dramatically enhanced the visibility of this inner space by coloring it orange (Fig.5b). In both these sculptures the material cut out from the torus has the shape of a Moebius band (hence the name of my sculpture). Figure 5c shows what happens when this space is equivalent to a Moebius band with three half-twists (Séquin 2005).

Figure 5: *Moebius Spaces: (a) Séquin (2000), (b) Ushio (2004), (c) triply twisted: Séquin (2005).*

5. Borromean Rings

We have seen that the torus can be split into many intertwined rings. In all the above situations, every pair of rings is mutually interlocked. Can we also find an elegant way by which a torus is cut into a set of three Borromean rings (Fig.6a), in which no two individual rings are actually linked?

Figure 6: *Borromean rings: (a) basic configuration, (b) 3 playdough rings squashed into a toroidal configuration, (c) 3 suitably interlinked loops cut from a torus.*

To get some insight into this problem, I modeled the three Borromean rings from colorful playdough, placing the three differently colored links into the three main coordinate planes. I then compressed the configuration parallel to the {1,1,1} axis, while at the same time enlarging the central hole along this axis, and massaged the result to become a roughly toroidal configuration (Fig.6b). Inspecting the result made it clear that this is no longer just a torus link configuration. The three colors form a regular 3-strand braid around the toroidal loop, and each strand has to squeeze between the other two strands at two opposite positions in the toroidal loop. The main question now becomes how to best administer suitable cuts to achieve the necessary braiding of the three strands, while creating a geometry that still allows the three rings to be separated and put at right angle with respect to one another.

In a first phase I examined the relative positions of the three strands in the toroidal loop and created corresponding cross-sectional cuts in the form of a "Y", a "V", or a "| |". Then adjacent cross sections were morphed into one another. This did indeed create a geometry that trisected the torus into three pieces that had the desired topological linkage and which could be placed into the desired orthogonal Borromean configuration (Fig.6c). In order to obtain unobstructed movements of the three pieces from their resting position in the torus to the desired orthogonal constellation, one must take into account the relative motions of the three parts and fine-tune the cutting surfaces to follow the swept surfaces generated by these motions.

6. Splitting Moebius Bands

We have seen above that if the cutting knife is rotated by the right amount when slicing the torus, then we get Moebius-like results. This entices us to explore what happens when we start with a more typical Moebius band and then split this ribbon lengthwise. Most readers probably have done the experiment to cut lengthwise a Moebius band made from a simple paper strip, and then were fascinated when they obtained a single loop of twice the size and with a 360° twist. Splitting a Moebius band also has a lot of potential for aesthetically pleasing geometrical sculptures. M.C. Escher has made an attractive rendering of a split Moebius loop (Fig.7a). I also have been fascinated by this shape and have built various realizations of it on our rapid prototyping machine (Fig.7b,c). It should be pointed out, that the Moebius band cannot only be split sideways, but could also be split into two thin layers (Fig.7d); this configuration is most suitable for a realization in metal. Such a sculpture is available from Conrad Valett in Germany [6].

Figure 7: *Split Moebius bands: (a) sketch by M.C Escher, (b), (c) corresponding FDM models, and (d) a different way to split a Moebius band.*

The split Moebius band is another one of Keizo Ushio's signature shapes (Fig.8a). Over the last 15 years he has sculpted dozens of variations; a few of them also result from splitting triply twisted bands (Fig.8b).

Figure 8: *Split Moebius bands by Keizo Ushio: (a) half-twist (1990), (b) three half-twists (2001).*

7. Splitting Knots

Splitting a simple Moebius band produces a single connected component that can be unfolded into a loop of twice the length of the original band. However, when we split a Moebius band with three half-twists, as depicted in Figure 7, then we obtain a knotted configuration corresponding to a trefoil knot. In Section 4 we have seen that when the torus is cut with the right combinations of n and t, one obtains a single torus knot. The simplest such torus knot is again the trefoil knot. If the sweep along the knot curve does not use a circular cross section but rather forms a "band" with distinctly different "width" and "thickness" values, then two other degrees of freedom appear in this shape: twist and azimuth. Changing them can dramatically alter the look and feel of a sculpture. In particular, there are only some twist values that maintain the three-fold symmetry of the trefoil knot, and only very few choices will make the ribbon seem to curve smoothly and organically around each other. If we try to form a trefoil knot from a flat ribbon, we find that the tightest configuration forms a one-sided loop, but it does not maintain 3-fold symmetry. In order to obtain a 3-fold symmetrical shape, we may give the ribbon either zero twist (seen in a projection along the symmetry axis) or impose three half-twists, as depicted in Figure 9a. Now we can split this ribbon, by letting the knife follow the curving and twisting of the band. Because of the built-in one-sidedness, the cut will not result in two separate components, but will produce a more complicated knot formed by a half-ribbon with twice the original length. Figure 10 shows a more artistic version of this same topology.

Figure 9: *Trefoil knot split into 2, 3 and 4 strands.*

If we try to form a tight and compact trefoil knot from an *n*-sided prism, we find that for *n*=4 we can join the ends of the prismatic strand with almost no apparent twisting (Fig.9c). However, where one lobe transitions into the next one, the Frenet frame that defines the osculating plane at each curve point exhibits a 90° torsional twist. Thus when we follow one of the prism edges, we find that it will jog to an adjacent position as we travel once around the whole knot, and we only return to the starting point after four passes around the knot. Splitting the 4-sided prismatic strand into four square fibers will thus lead to a single knotted loop of four times the length of the original strand.

Figure 9b explores the result of splitting the original strand that forms the trefoil knot into three fibers. In this case I have chosen a hexagonal cross section for the individual fibers and have used a minimal twist of 120° in the original strand to force the three fibers to connect into a single fiber traveling three times around the whole trefoil knot. Inspection of Figure 9b reveals that we have lost the original 3-fold symmetry of the knot. Maintaining that symmetry would force us to chose a twist value that then results in a linked configuration of three separate trefoil knots.

Figure 10: *Bronze sculpture "Infinite Duality" based on split trefoil (in two different positions).*

8. Snow Sculpture

In 2005 the theme of a split knot was used in the design of the entry of Team Minnesota to the annual snow sculpting competition in Breckenridge, Colorado. The design started from "Infinite Duality" (Fig.10b). However, the 3-fold symmetry was abandoned in order to obtain a more dramatic looking sculpture and to make the best possible use of the given snow blocks, measuring 10ft x 10ft x 12ft tall. The three lobes were raised to different heights to make a more artistic sculpture, with the tallest lobe spanning the full 12-foot height of the block (Fig.11). The whole curve was represented with a cubic B-spline, and the 15 control points were carefully adjusted so that the swept profile would just touch all sides of the block.

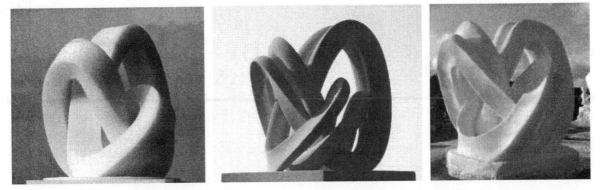

Figure 11: *Maquettes for a Snow Sculpture: "Knot Divided" (a), (b), and final result (c).*

In the first two days of snow sculpting we carved a rough representation of a triply twisted Moebius band wound up into a trefoil knot resting on three of its lobes (Fig.11a). Then we carefully split the upward lobes lengthwise, giving the resulting strands a more dramatic, crescent-like cross section. Since the original ribbon has an odd number of half-twists and thus is single sided, the splitting operation will not actually divide the knot into two parts, but will just produce a single strand of twice the length of the original ribbon

hence the name of the sculpture: "Knot Divided." During the first three days of the competition, the weather was unseasonably warm, with a strong sun and temperatures climbing up into the 40° range. Our major concern was the structural stability of the large leaning arched lobes. To reduce the weight of the lobes, the cross section was lightly tapered down towards the top. For better support, we let the lower sections of the lobes touch each other, and we did not split the original band into two strands all the way down to the platform on which the sculpture rested. This compromise solution is hardly visible in the photos taken from a few feet away and does not affect the beauty of the final result (Fig.11c). Fortunately on the last day of the competition, the temperature dropped considerably, and our sculpture stood for several days.

For the mathematically inclined, this sculpture also presents an interesting puzzle. While the original ribbon forms the simplest possible knot, the 3-crossing trefoil knot, the final structure forms a much more complicated knot. Can you figure out its crossing number? So far nobody has come up yet with the right answer on their first guess.

9. Splitting Graphs

All the objects we have split so far have been topologically equivalent to a simple loop, even though this loop may have been twisted and even knotted. In this final section we briefly consider what may happen if we split branching structures. Now the starting configuration may form a more complicated graph, and we

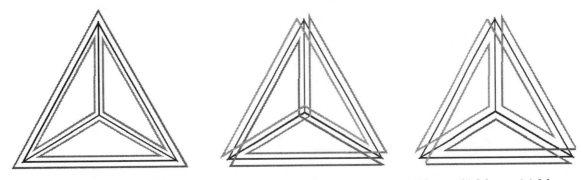

Figure 12: *Three ways of splitting the edge graph of the tetrahedron: (a) 4 loops, (b) 3 loops, (c) 1 loop.*

now attempt to split/double each edge of this graph. To reduce the bewildering number of possible graphs that can be produced in this process, we limit ourselves to pairwise connections of the new edges, so that the final graph simply consists of one or more loops. As an example, if we start with the edge graph of a tetrahedron, we may then end up with just 4 triangular loops, one for each face of the tetrahedron (Fig.12a). Alternatively, we may construct three loops of four edges, each forming a Hamiltonian cycle on this graph (Fig.12b). Finally we can even connect all 12 edges into a single cycle (Fig.12c), which now allows to make this into a sculpture that holds together without any additional supports or connectors.

A couple of sculptures by Bathsheba Grossman [1], such as "FourWays" (Fig.13a) and "Alterknot" (Fig.13b) explore similar ideas. However, "FourWays" does not really separate the different strands, so it does not clearly reflect this paradigm. "Alterknot" maintains 3-way junctions at the inner tetrahedral shell. When I tried to re-design this structure so as to get rid of any junctions, I first obtained four separate clover leaves, one each on every face of the tetrahedron. I then tried to connect them into a single loop by rotating the split links through 180°. However, I have not found a way to obtain just a single loop while maintaining the full symmetry of the oriented tetrahedron. The best I could do is to maintain C_3-symmetry, i.e., making one face (and one corner) somewhat different from the other three. One of the single-loop path solutions is shown in Figure 13c.

Figure 13: *(a)"FourWays" and (b)"Alterknot" by Grossman; (c) split graph derived from "Alterknot."*

10. Conclusions

Many artists are fascinated by knots and tangles. Splitting the strands of such configurations lenghtwise is a simple structured way to obtain objects of the same kind but of higher complexity. Thus, in principle, the process could then be repeated. For sculptures that have to be created by manual labor, this recursion very quickly reaches a practical limit. On the other hand, objects designed procedurally on a computer can go much further, and the results may even be fabricated with a layered manufacturing technology.

Acknowledgements

I would like to thank Keizo Ushio for giving me permission to use his pictures of his work in this presentation. John Sullivan deserves credit for his constructive contributions and thorough review of the manuscript. I would like to express my gratitude to Stan Wagon, Dan Schwalbe, John Sullivan, and Richard Seeley for doing such a great job with the sculpting of "KNOT DIVIDED" and for providing a wonderful week of hospitality and friendship in Breckenridge, Colorado.

References

[1] Bathsheba Grossman's website: -- http://www.bathsheba.com/ (2005).
[2] ISAMA 99, Conf. of Intnl. Soc. of The Arts, Mathematics and Architecture, San Sebastian, Spain, June 1999.
[3] C. H. Séquin, "- *To Build a Twisted Bridge -*" BRIDGES Conf. Proc., Winfield KS, July 2000, pp 23-34.
[4] Stratasys, FDM machine: -- http://www.stratasys.com/NA/ (2005).
[5] Keizo Ushio's website: -- http://www2.memenet.or.jp/~keizo/ (2005).
[6] Conrad Valett's website: *Valett Design:* -- http://www.valett.de/ (2005).

Symmetry and Symmetry-Breaking
An Approach to Understanding Beauty

Carol Bier
Research Associate
The Textile Museum
2320 S Street, NW
Washington, DC 2008
cbier@textilemuseum.org

Abstract

Considering the relationship of symmetry and beauty, the author examines three textiles from the collection of Doris Duke at Shangri La in Honolulu. Referring to abstract expressionism of the 20th century as antithetical to symmetry, and the Arts & Crafts Movement of the 19th century as countering the insistency of industrial mass production, Bier explores the relative roles of symmetry and symmetry-breaking in the construction of three embroideries (called *suzani*, after the Persian and Tajik word for "needlework"), using as her point of departure a recent research initiative, the Shangri La Suzani Project. The study of colors, motifs, stitches, designs and patterns suggests the identification of a local aesthetic preference for local symmetries without global symmetry, and global symmetries without local symmetry. These embroideries typify styles associated with Bukhara in the 19th century. The results of this research lead to more general consideration of symmetry and symmetry-breaking in the construction of beauty.

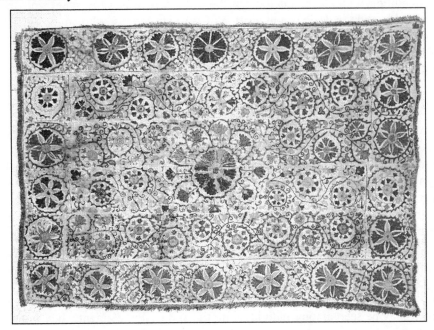

Figure 1 *Suzani* I (embroidery), from the Collection of Doris Duke at Shangri La, Honolulu (85.29).

1. Introduction: The Approximation of Symmetry in Nature and Art

Symmetry, whether in art or in nature, is only ever approximate [2]. The human body, a tree, the gait of an animal, seasonal cycles, all offer examples from nature of approximate symmetries that appear to be regular in their periodicity, but which, in fact, are slightly irregular in the repetition of forms through time and space. This natural irregularity in seashells may be seen in the patterns generated along the leading edge, described as algorithmic beauty [18]. This term, combining concepts of mathematics and aesthetics, is also apt for the description of the arts of traditional cultures, which although algorithmic in their construction, are often perceived as being imperfect with respect to the resulting symmetries. Whether in the cutting and piecing of strips of wood or bone for inlays, or the stamping of leather or the printing of cloth, or the juxtaposition of individual segments of color in a carpet [3], or the journeys of the needle to embroider a fabric, the mechanisms used to create designs and manipulate them to form patterns often relies upon algorithms of process as developed within individual craft traditions. Symmetry, whether wittingly or not, is most often the organizing principle that structures the patterns [11].

The arts of traditional cultures, generally, express a playfulness that is dependent on symmetrical constructions for designs as well as for patterns [24; 25]. But abstract expressionism in the 20th century sought to avoid symmetry all together. In contrast, the works of M. C. Escher [19] countered this trend, playing extensively with symmetries and tilings, drawing much of his inspiration from Islamic designs he sketched while visiting the Alhambra in Spain. Narrative representation and pictorial depictions, as developed since the Renaissance in Western arts tend to be asymmetrical, while relying nonetheless upon the assumed external symmetry of the human body. One respected art theorist, the late Meyer Shapiro, takes a highly skeptical approach to the notions of "perfection, coherence, and unity of form and content" in the arts [1:3-13]. And recent assessments of abstraction argue for a relationship between abstraction and ornament that is highly structured and dependent upon underlying mathematical principles [7].

In studying the arts of Islamic cultures, I have often pondered the nature of beauty, sometimes in relation to the beauty of nature. What has struck me on more than one occasion is that beauty seems to lie in symmetry-breaking, rather than in symmetry. The truest approximation of symmetry came only with the Industrial Revolution, quickly countered by the Arts & Crafts Movement and the philosophical writings of John Ruskin and the designs and writing of William Morris, who advocated and promoted the values of hand-made objects and craft traditions, with their natural and organic standards of beauty. One contemporary fiber artist, Katherine Westphal, specifically sought in her art to overcome what she called "the tyranny of the repeat" that so characterized industrial mass production [20].

2. *Suzani* from the Region of Bukhara: The Artistic Appropriation of Symmetry

In the case of embroideries from the region of Bukhara (**fig. 1**), called *suzani* ("needlework" in Persian and Tajik languages), a particular style emerged in the 19th century in which there is a preponderance of intentional symmetry-breaking. At first glance, these embroideries appear to be symmetrical. But what appears to be symmetry, is really only the implication of symmetry. More careful observation reveals the visual dominance of asymmetry within a symmetrical layout. The implication of symmetry seems to seduce us into thinking there is symmetry where there is none. This paradox may be more clearly expressed in terms of global symmetries and local symmetries. Global symmetries are present in the overall layout of the composition in which there is a rectangular central field surrounded by a main border defined by narrow inner and outer borders. The horizontal and vertical axes of reflection that structure the global symmetry, however, do not structure the layout of individual motifs and design elements. It does not break down to evince symmetry at the local level. Paradoxically, there are numerous local symmetries, which may be seen among individual motifs and design elements, but these do not repeat to form global symmetries.

A richly diverse collection of these embroideries was acquired by Doris Duke in the middle of the 20th century, which she displayed at Shangri La, her home in Honolulu [17]. She used the suzanis in a manner much in the way they were intended, as hangings and covers. The strength and importance of this early collection has inspired a recent initiative, the Shangri La Suzani Research Project [5], undertaken to support the development of an exhibition scheduled for Fall 2005 at the East-West Center in Honolulu, to be organized by Sharon Littlefield and Michael Schuster.

3. Doris Duke's Collection of Suzani at Shangri La

Doris Duke married James Cromwell in 1935 and together they embarked on a year-long honeymoon that took them around the world. The last stop was Honolulu, where they stayed longer than anticipated; eventually they purchased a spot of land and proceeded to construct a house at Black Point, which would ultimately house many of the acquisitions of their honeymoon [17]. Among the purchases made in Bombay, India, was a selection of embroideries identified as "sujnee," today known as suzanis after the Persian and Tajik word for needlework [15]. Duke's purchases of these materials long preceded the acquisition of suzanis by European and American collectors and museums, which did not occur for the most part until the late 20th century. George Hewitt Myers, founder of The Textile Museum, purchased his first suzani as early as 1916, but increased demand for suzanis among collectors in Europe and America did not grow strong until the promotion by rug dealers in the early 1980s [6]. Duke continued to acquire suzanis over the years; at the time of her death in 1993, she had fifteen examples with numerous additional textiles and other objects related by style, techniques, and design. Examination of three examples here will suffice to demonstrate the attention given to symmetry and symmetry-breaking by the embroiderers and seamstresses who worked on these objects. To judge by the range of published work concerning these embroideries, which draws from ethnographic research, museum records, collection catalogues, and exhibitions [15; 21; 22; 27], these textiles were embroidered by groups of women who were engaged in preparing dowry items for a bride's marriage ceremony and wedding celebration.

3.1 *Suzani* I (85.29): Variations upon a Theme

The first suzani to be illustrated (**fig. 1**) is composed of six strips of cloth basted together to create a ground fabric. Each strip is 10.5 inches wide. The designs would have been drawn on the six strips, which were separated and then joined again after having been embroidered. As a result, typically, there is a slight disjuncture in the embroidered patterns at the seam joins. All of the embroidery is executed in chain stitch. Thirteen colors have been identified (dark red, purple, reddish brown, orange, yellow, light green, light blue, light violet, light pink, medium green, dark blue, yellow green, and black). The four colors described as light are variegated. In spite of some fading on the front face of the object, initial visual inspection suggests an even wider range of colors, not only because of the variegated yarns, but also because of the many combinations of colors juxtaposed with one another. The colors on the back face retain more vibrancy; the applied looped fringe shows fading and considerable damage and loss.

Figure 1a. Large central rosette in field of *Suzani* I (**fig. 1**, detail).

With a central field surrounded by a main border, the layout of the composition is also typical of suzanis produced in and around Bukhara. At the center a large floral rosette (**fig. 1a**), divided unequally into eight scalloped sections, has nine radial extensions each of which supports a composite blossom in profile, offering a hint of the variations in local symmetries. Each blossom is different, offering further evidence for the magnitude of these variations in radial symmetries with the use of reflection.

Throughout the field smaller rosettes are set within undulating vines that comprise rows, each row corresponding to a strip of cloth (**fig. 1b**).

Figure 1b. Uppermost strip of central field of *Suzani* I (**fig. 1**, detail).

A single row of larger rosettes constitutes the main border (**fig. 1c**), which surrounds the central field on all four sides. Most but not all of the rosettes in the border are segmented into sixths with a radial arrangement of petals. Although similar, none of these rosettes are identical, and their orientations are all slightly different. In the top border, shown below, the central rosette is divided into eighths with a scalloped arrangement roughly parallel to that of the central rosette in the field, which is larger.

Figure 1c. Upper horizontal border of *Suzani* I (**fig. 1**, detail).

Although the rosettes of the border (**fig. 1c**) and the rosettes of the central field (**fig. 1b**) are each set within a scalloped outline, the rosettes in the border are somewhat more dominant. There are several factors that contribute to this perception. The border rosettes are larger, and they have higher proportions of dark or vibrant colors, and they are surrounded by undulating vines with more leaves. In contrast, the rosettes of the central field (**fig. 1a**) are relatively smaller, are divided variously into six or seven or eight segments, and are surrounded by vines with fewer leaves and scrolls with curling tendrils.

There seems to be a harmonious play between the abstraction of the approximately symmetrical rosettes, removed from any identifiable floral form, and the somewhat more naturalistic leafy vines and scrolls with curling tendrils. What characterizes this suzani is a dynamic balance between uniformity and lack of uniformity, a tension between sameness and difference. It is the combination of symmetry and symmetry-breaking that seems to keep the eye wandering and the mind engaged.

3.2 *Suzani* II (85.39): Global Symmetries and Local Symmetries

3.2.1 Global Symmetries, No Local Symmetry

The layout of the composition in the second example of a suzani (**fig. 2**) is carefully articulated by the prominent use of leafy vines composed of green leaves and stems all outlined in black. The layout implies a strong central vertical axis and two secondary side axes which define the surrounding side borders. In addition, there is a main horizontal axis dividing the central field, approximately at the middle and extending into the main borders right and left, and two secondary axes which, again, define the surrounding border at top and bottom. In addition, in the central field there are two secondary horizontal axes, which divide the upper and lower sections in half, with reflectional symmetry above and below each horizontal axis and to the right and left of each vertical axis. In the border, two subsidiary axes divide each of the main border segments horizontally (top and bottom) or vertically (sides). This division roughly corresponds to the layout of most Oriental carpets, made in a broad geographic region stretching from Turkey across Central Asia to Western China, a significant visual relationship described and assessed in the recent documentation of a private collection of suzanis in New York [16].

3.2.2 Local Symmetries, No Global Symmetry

Analysis of the borders of this suzanis as line symmetries reveals the use of glide reflection as described by the zig-zag vine with opposite leaves (**fig. 2a**). Working in visual opposition to this vine is a second vine, also with opposite leaves. The course of this second vine, however, is curvilinear, but it is regularly interrupted. At the local level, these symmetries of form are at best approximate.

Figure 2 *Suzani* II, from the collection of Doris Duke at Shangri La, Honolulu (85.39).

Defining the main border, the narrow inner and outer borders (**fig. 2a**) show glide reflection in a linear pattern of two leaves with color alternation.

Figure 2a. Left vertical border of *Suzani* II (**fig. 2**, detail), viewed sideways.

When one examines the individual motifs of floral rosettes and blossoms in profile (**figs. 2b-c**), leafy vines, and other design elements of this suzani, there is local symmetry only. For any given form, locally symmetrical by rotation (**fig. 2b**) or reflection (**fig. 2c**), it is not repeated even approximately in a symmetrical location within the composition of what appears to be a symmetrical composition.

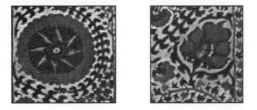

Figures 2b-c. Rosette (left) and blossom in profile (right) from main border of *Suzani* II (**fig. 2**, detail).

The global symmetry evident in the layout may be identified is a symmetry of space, but not of form. The local symmetries evident in the floral rosettes exhibit symmetries of form, and symmetries of color, but these are not replicated within the global symmetry of space.

3.3 *Suzani* III (85.30): Two Suzanis in One

The third suzani to be studied here (**fig. 3a**) presents a different set of issues. The textile is actually composed of twenty-six pieces, pieced together as an assemblage (**fig. 3b**).On inspection, the central field may be recognized as having a different ground fabric than that of the main border (**fig. 3d**). The main border seems to be integral with the inner and outer borders. Closer inspection of the entire object in its present condition reveals many seams, which are hand-stitched or machine-sewn. Detailed examination of seams, selvedges, and cut edges folded back, leads to the recognition that this suzani is composed of parts of two suzanis, plus a couple of in-fill pieces. The border of this textile exhibits a series of diagonal seams that led us to recognize the lines and angles of a niched suzani (**fig. 3c**), the spandrels of which were flipped and repositioned to form the horizontal border at the top. The fragments that comprise the central field show selvedges in a horizontal orientation, whereas the norm for a suzani's construction shows a sequence of narrow loom-widths, with a selvedge on each side, oriented in warp direction.

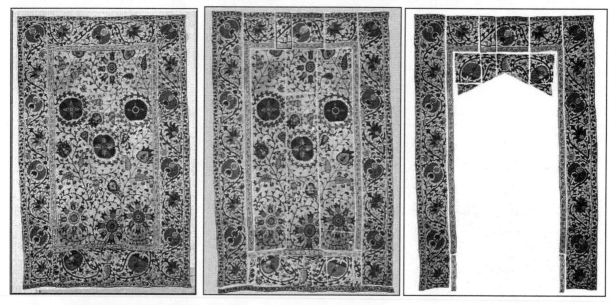

Figure 3a (left) *Suzani* III, from the collection of Doris Duke at Shangri La, Honolulu (85.30).
Figure 3b (center) *Suzani* III is assembled from twenty-six fragments, sewn together (85.30).
Figure 3c (right) Reconstruction of niched suzani from main borders of *Suzani* III (**fig. 3a**).

3.3.1 A Niched Suzani with Symmetry and Asymmetry

The niched suzani (**fig. 3c**) shows an asymmetrical element – a tear-drop shaped leaf – at the top of the niche, flanked by floral designs. Disposed symmetrically on either side of the central element, an almost circular blossom is shown in profile and set within a larger tear-drop shaped form defined by leafy vines. The symmetrical disposition betrays the asymmetry of the tear-drop shape, the design of this suzani displaying both symmetry and asymmetry in the playful use of this form. The main border shows flower blossoms in alternate alignment within an undulating vine composed with glide reflection. The inner border is composed of a vine with an arrangement of small tripartite leaves with glide reflection (**fig. 3d**).

3.3.2 An Older Suzani with Balance and Harmony

The central field of *Suzani* III (**fig. 3a**) in its present configuration shows no symmetry of space or form. The large rosettes each exhibit a radial symmetry with four-fold reflection or rotation; smaller rosettes with radial extensions show reflection in the treatment of each tulip-like flower. They are displayed

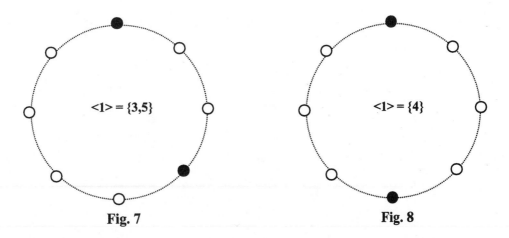

Fig. 7   **Fig. 8**

2.2 Spectra Width: We define the width of the spectrum of a **d**-out-of-**c** circular distribution, written as $\Delta^d_c(I)$, as the difference between the largest and smallest member of the spectrum I; that is:

$$\Delta^d_c(I) = \max <I> - \min <I> \qquad (1)$$

The spectra widths for Figures 5-8 are: 6, 4, 2, and 0 respectively.

If we consider the spectrum widths of our 3-out-of-8 example, the possibilities up to rotation and inversion are shown in Figures 9 through 13:

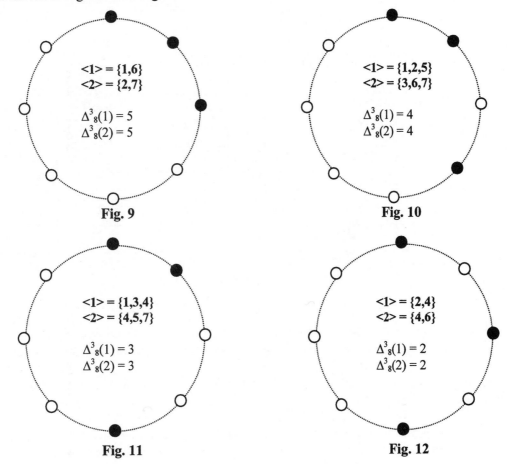

Fig. 9   **Fig. 10**

Fig. 11   **Fig. 12**

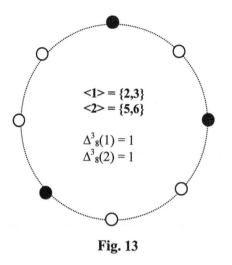

$$<1> = \{2,3\}$$
$$<2> = \{5,6\}$$

$$\Delta^3_8(1) = 1$$
$$\Delta^3_8(2) = 1$$

Fig. 13

Superimposed on these figures are the spectrum widths associated with each distribution.

2.3 Spectra Variation: We define the *spectra variation* for each distribution as the average of the spectra widths with respect to the number of filled dots:

$$V^d_c = \frac{1}{d} \sum_I \Delta^d_c(I) \tag{2}$$

The spectra variations for Figures 9-13 are shown in Table 1.

Figure	<1>	<2>	$\Delta^3_8(1)$	$\Delta^3_8(2)$	V^3_8
9	{1,6}	{2,7}	5	5	3.33 (10/3)
10	{1,2,5}	{3,6,7}	4	4	2.33 (8/3)
11	{1,3,4}	{4,5,7}	3	3	2.00 (6/3)
12	{2,4}	{4,6}	2	2	1.33 (4/3)
13	{2,3}	{5,6}	1	1	0.667 (2/3)

Table 1.

We see that the larger the spectra variation the less even the distribution. Moreover, the most even distribution, the maximally even distribution, has the smallest spectra variation and is less than one.

If we consider any exactly equal distribution, such as the one shown in Figure 4 or Figure 8, the spectra variation is exactly zero.

2.4 Another Example: The spectra variation allows us to compare the evenness of circular distributions with different numbers of filled dots. For example, consider the distributions shown in Figures 14 through

19. For brevity we consider only maximally even sets as these have variations less than one compared to all other distributions.

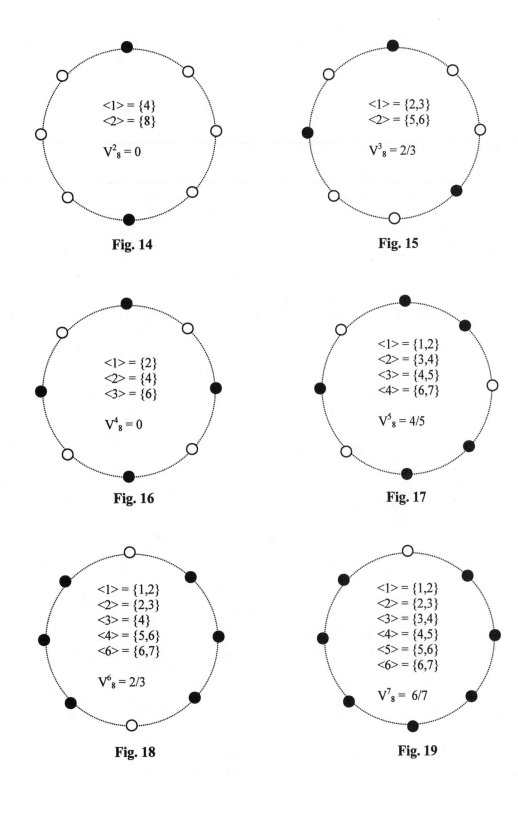

$\langle 1 \rangle = \{4\}$
$\langle 2 \rangle = \{8\}$

$V^2_8 = 0$

Fig. 14

$\langle 1 \rangle = \{2,3\}$
$\langle 2 \rangle = \{5,6\}$

$V^3_8 = 2/3$

Fig. 15

$\langle 1 \rangle = \{2\}$
$\langle 2 \rangle = \{4\}$
$\langle 3 \rangle = \{6\}$

$V^4_8 = 0$

Fig. 16

$\langle 1 \rangle = \{1,2\}$
$\langle 2 \rangle = \{3,4\}$
$\langle 3 \rangle = \{4,5\}$
$\langle 4 \rangle = \{6,7\}$

$V^5_8 = 4/5$

Fig. 17

$\langle 1 \rangle = \{1,2\}$
$\langle 2 \rangle = \{2,3\}$
$\langle 3 \rangle = \{4\}$
$\langle 4 \rangle = \{5,6\}$
$\langle 6 \rangle = \{6,7\}$

$V^6_8 = 2/3$

Fig. 18

$\langle 1 \rangle = \{1,2\}$
$\langle 2 \rangle = \{2,3\}$
$\langle 3 \rangle = \{3,4\}$
$\langle 4 \rangle = \{4,5\}$
$\langle 5 \rangle = \{5,6\}$
$\langle 6 \rangle = \{6,7\}$

$V^7_8 = 6/7$

Fig. 19

Superimposed on each of these figures are the interval spectra and associated spectra variation. Shown in Table 2 are the distributions shown in Figures 14 through 19 ranked according to their spectra variations.

2-out-of-8	4-out-of-8	3-out-of-8	6-out-of-8	5-out-of-8	7-out-of-8
0	0	0.667 (2/3)	0.667 (2/3)	0.800 (4/5)	0.857 (6/7)

Table 2.

3   A Musical Example

We turn, now, to a musical example. Most people are familiar with the scale of the white keys on the piano, the so-called diatonic, or major, scale. Shown in Figure 20 is the diatonic scale as a circular distribution. The diatonic set is a maximally even set of 7-out-of-12 with a spectra variation of 6/7. Superimposed on Figure 20 are the spectra widths, spectra variation, and the usual notes of the diatonic scale.

Two other common scales are the natural minor and the descending melodic minor both of which are rotations of the diatonic scale. Each is a rotation of diatonic scale three half-steps clockwise, as shown in Figure 21.

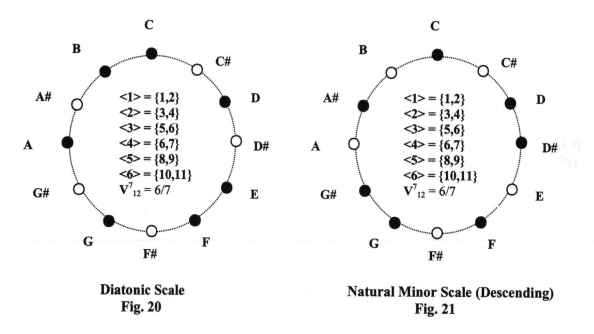

Diatonic Scale
Fig. 20

Natural Minor Scale (Descending)
Fig. 21

As each of these scales is a maximally even set, they all have spectra variations less than one and are the most even 7-out-of-12 scales.

Shown in Figure 22 is the next most even 7-out-of-12 scale, the ascending melodic minor with a spectra variation of 8/7. It is only one half-step away from being maximally even (D# => E).

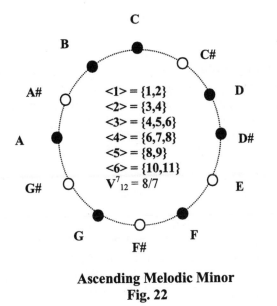

$$\langle 1 \rangle = \{1,2\}$$
$$\langle 2 \rangle = \{3,4\}$$
$$\langle 3 \rangle = \{4,5,6\}$$
$$\langle 4 \rangle = \{6,7,8\}$$
$$\langle 5 \rangle = \{8,9\}$$
$$\langle 6 \rangle = \{10,11\}$$
$$V^7_{12} = 8/7$$

Ascending Melodic Minor
Fig. 22

The two next most even 7-out-of-12 scales are the harmonic minor and whole-tone-plus-one scale, shown in Figures 23 and 24 respectively. Each has a spectra variation of 10/7.

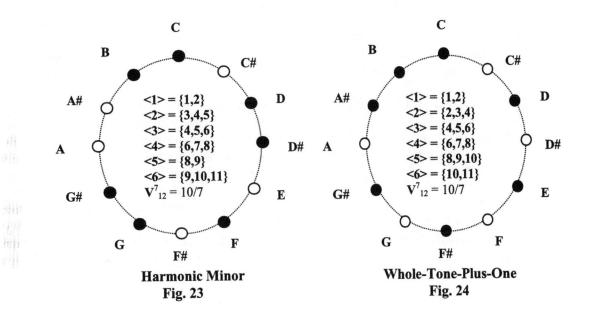

Harmonic Minor figure:
$$\langle 1 \rangle = \{1,2\}$$
$$\langle 2 \rangle = \{3,4,5\}$$
$$\langle 3 \rangle = \{4,5,6\}$$
$$\langle 4 \rangle = \{6,7,8\}$$
$$\langle 5 \rangle = \{8,9\}$$
$$\langle 6 \rangle = \{9,10,11\}$$
$$V^7_{12} = 10/7$$

Harmonic Minor
Fig. 23

Whole-Tone-Plus-One figure:
$$\langle 1 \rangle = \{1,2\}$$
$$\langle 2 \rangle = \{2,3,4\}$$
$$\langle 3 \rangle = \{4,5,6\}$$
$$\langle 4 \rangle = \{6,7,8\}$$
$$\langle 5 \rangle = \{8,9,10\}$$
$$\langle 6 \rangle = \{10,11\}$$
$$V^7_{12} = 10/7$$

Whole-Tone-Plus-One
Fig. 24

Comparisons of the six most familiar 7-note scales are those that are most even as measured by the spectra variation. It is left to the reader to show that all other 7-out-of-12 circular distributions have larger spectra variations than those shown above, some 2 or 3 times larger.

4 Summary

We have developed the spectra variation method based on the, well-known, spectra of circular distributions, which allows comparison of the evenness of different circular distributions. The method is developed using a simple n-out-of-8 example and then applied to the 7-out-of-12 distribution common in Western music. We show that the smaller the spectra variation the more even the distribution. Ranking the 7-out-of-12 scales according to the smallest spectra variations shows that the most common 7-note scales in use are also those that are the most even.

5 Discussion

Clough and Myerson's work [2,3] dealt with the mathematical formalization of several musical properties. One of these properties is known as Myhill Property (MP): A set has MP if every interval spectrum is a doubleton (consists of two numbers). In particular, they focused on sets in which the members of the spectra were integers. Although their investigation was not related to evenness, they established the ground work for Clough and Douthett's [5] investigation on maximally even sets.

One class of maximally even sets consists of sets with MP in which each spectrum consists of two <u>consecutive</u> integers Musical scales in this class include the (black key) pentatonic and diatonic scales. In addition, Clough and Douthett's definition of maximally even sets allowed for sets in which some or all spectra are singletons (consists of a single integer). Musical sets with single integer spectra are the augmented triad, the fully-diminished seventh chord, and the whole-tone scale. The octatonic scale (also known as the diminished scale) is an example of a set in which some spectra are singletons and others consist of two consecutive integers. While the musical examples given above are in the usual chromatic universe of cardinality 12, Clough and Douthett's work extended these properties to musical universes of any size. Measures that justify the term "maximally even" can be found in Block and Douthett [4], Krantz, Douthett, and Clough [1]; and Douthett [6].

For any given chromatic and set cardinalities, Clough and Douthett identified a class of sets that were maximally even. They did not, however, discuss the comparative evenness of maximally even sets with differing cardinalities. For example, while both the diatonic scale and whole-tone scales are maximally even, intuition suggests that the whole-tone scale is "more even" that the diatonic scale. Indeed, the pitches in a whole-tone scale are distributed totally evenly around the octave (an equal-tempered system). We build on Clough's work with both Myerson and Douthett and construct a measure that compares the evenness of maximally even sets with differing cardinalities. For maximally sets, our measure varies between 0 and 1, including 0 but not 1. The value of this measure for equal-tempered sets is 0, while maximally even sets with MP measure closer to 1. Sets which are not maximally even always measure greater than or equal to 1.

References

[1] R.J. Krantz, J. Douthett, and J. Clough, *Bridges 2000 Conference Proceedings,* 193 (2000).
[2] J. Clough and G. Myerson, Am. Math. Mon. **93**(9), 695, (1986).
[3] J. Clough and G. Myerson, J. Music Theory, **29**, 249, (1985).
[4] S. Block and J. Douthett, J. Music Theory, **38**(1), 21, (1994).
[5] J. Clough and J. Douthett, J. Music Theory, **35**, 93, (1991).
[6] J. Douthett, Ph.D. dissertation (University of New Mexico, Albuquerque, NM; May 1999).

Illustrating Number Sequences

L. Kerry Mitchell
3783 West Park Avenue
Chandler, AZ 85226 USA
lkmitch@att.net

Abstract

While critically important mathematically, number sequences can also be foundational artistically. This work presents several techniques for illustrating number sequences using geometric shapes and image processing technology. The resulting images can reveal characteristics of the sequences that are of interest to both the mathematician and the visual artist.

Introduction

Number sequences are a foundational part of mathematics, from a child's first look at arithmetic, to a number theorist's research. One of the best compendia of number sequences is the Online Encyclopedia of Integer Sequences, compiled by Neil Sloane [1]. A few of the sequences filed there and known to many others have been used in the present work to demonstrate techniques by which images can be created that are both visually pleasing and mathematically substantive.

The images herein rely extensively on image processing technology for combining several independent images (each representing a term of a sequence) into a final image. The goal was to find images that in some respect were "stationary," that is, either they include all terms of a finite sequence, or the image did not change significantly with the incorporation of additional elements. Although not necessarily fractal in nature, all the images were created using the Ultra Fractal program [2].

All Diagonals

A natural number larger than 2 can be considered to be the number of sides of a polygon for which all of the diagonals have been drawn. For example, the multiples of 5 can be considered to be polygons with 5, 10, 15, etc. sides, and their diagonals. The entirety of a sequence of natural numbers is visualized by stacking these polygons and forming the arithmetic mean of the images. This is shown in Figure 1 for the multiples of 5. The last panel shows an approximation of what I claim is in some sense the unique limiting value of that sequence.

This technique affords a great deal of flexibility to the artist, particularly with regard to the locations of the vertices of the polygons. In Figure 1, each polygon is regular and its vertices lie on a circle. Other bounding shapes can be used, such as rectangles, regular polygons, and spirals. In addition, the orientations of the elemental polygons can be varied. In Figure 1, each polygon has a vertex at the top of the circle. Instead, the polygons can be rotated, so what appear as straight dark lines in the composite image become curved. Figure 2 shows two completed works by the author, along with schematics of two of the generating polygons. In each case, the composite images were created by overlaying polygons whose numbers of sides were multiples of 3, from 6 to 63. The vertices of the polygons were spaced at equal angular increments along an equilateral triangle. In the image "Master" (second panel), the polygons were aligned such that they all had vertices at the corners of the bounding triangle. An example dodecagon is shown in the first panel. For the image "Student" (fourth panel), the polygons were rotated such that their vertices straddled the corners of the bounding triangle. These effects caused the triangle vertices to be highlighted in "Master" and in the shadows in "Student."

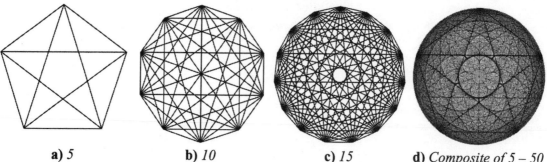

a) *5*   **b)** *10*   **c)** *15*   **d)** *Composite of 5 – 50*

Figure 1: *Polygons with multiples of 5 sides, with all diagonals*

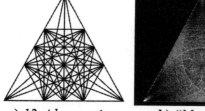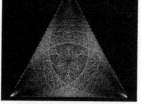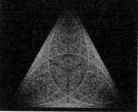

a) *12 sides, vertices in corners*   **b)** *"Master" by the author (2004)*   **c)** *12 sides, vertices straddling corners*   **d)** *"Student" by the author (2004)*

Figure 2: *Polygons with multiples of 3 sides and vertices along the sides of an equilateral triangle*

Circle Cutting

The "pancake" numbers are those numbers that represent the maximum number of sections into which a circle can be cut with a given number of lines. Four of the smaller pancake numbers are shown in Figure 3. In the first and second panels, the circle and the cutting lines are shown. In the third and fourth panels, the regions are alternately dark and light and the cutting lines are the boundaries.

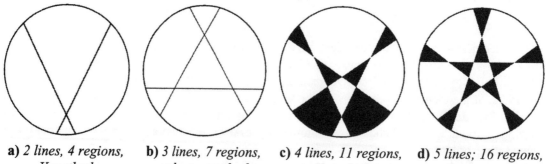

a) *2 lines, 4 regions, V method*   **b)** *3 lines, 7 regions, polygon method*   **c)** *4 lines, 11 regions, V method*   **d)** *5 lines; 16 regions, polygon method*

Figure 3: *Circles cut into the maximum number of regions by 2 –5 lines*

The four panels illustrate two different techniques for drawing such figures. For an odd number of lines, a regular polygon with that number of sides can be drawn concurrent with the circle and its sides extended until they have all intersected inside the circle. This was done with the 3-line and 5-line cases above. For any number of lines, a V can be used as the first two (shown in Figure 2a). Each subsequent line is then drawn from a point on one leg of the V to a point on the other leg, in a manner reminiscent of string art [3]. Figure 3c shows the V with two additional lines, which cross at the center of the circle.

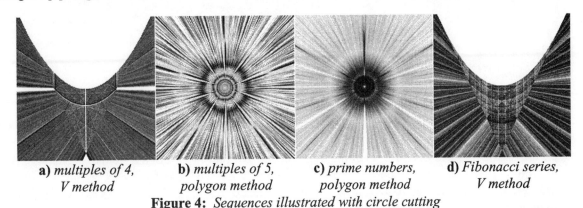

a) *multiples of 4,*
V method

b) *multiples of 5,*
polygon method

c) *prime numbers,*
polygon method

d) *Fibonacci series,*
V method

Figure 4: *Sequences illustrated with circle cutting*

These methods can be extended to sequences of numbers by combining the images for individual terms, as before. In Figure 4, four sequence images are shown (without the circles). The first is the multiples of 4, rendered using the V method and showing the regions as dark or light, as in Figure3c. Note the white areas of the image, which indicate that the images for each term share some of the same white areas. In Figure 4b, the multiples of 5 are illustrated in the manner of Figure 3b: using a central regular polygon and only drawing the lines. The fivefold symmetry reflects the use of polygons with numbers of sides that are multiples of 5. In contrast, the next panel shows the same method used with the prime numbers. While there is still some structure apparent, the only symmetry is due to the fact that all the polygons had vertical lines of symmetry. The last panel of Figure 4 shows the Fibonacci series, using the same method as in the first panel. Again, the only symmetry is along the vertical axis, but there is extensive structure in the image, particularly inside the V.

Polylines

A polyline is a curve consisting of line segments, and can be thought of as "connecting the dots" with a sequence of discrete points. This technique is ideally suited for sequences that have two components. One candidate is the signature sequence for an irrational number [4]. For a particular number x, form the terms $y = i + jx$, where i and j are nonnegative integers. If x is irrational, then every y will be different and the set of y values can be ordered from least to greatest. Within this ordering, the set of i integers is the signature sequence for that x. For the golden ratio F (~1.618034), the signature sequence begins 0, 1, 0, 2, 1, 3, 0, 2 and is a fractal sequence in the manner of Kimberling [5, 6].

To draw a figure with this sequence, both the i and the j values were used, as the x- and y-coordinates of the vertices of the polyline. Mathematically, the sequence extends to infinity, but operationally, i and j were both limited to some maximum value. In Figure 5, the data for the first few terms of the sequence are shown, along with polylines for maximal i and j values of 4, 8, and 16. The zigzag line extends continuously from (0,0) to (*maximum, maximum*). For larger maximum values, the figures begin to show gradations of shading and suggest rectangles of varying dimensions. This is how the image, "Signature of Phi," [7] was created by the author, with i and j both ranging from 0 to 64.

i	j	$y = i + \Phi j$
0	0	0
1	0	1
0	1	1.618034
2	0	2
1	1	2.618034
3	0	3
0	2	3.236068
2	1	3.618034

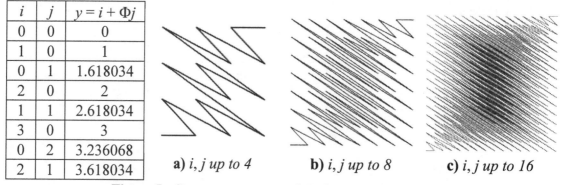

a) *i, j up to 4*   **b)** *i, j up to 8*   **c)** *i, j up to 16*

Figure 5: *Signature sequence of Φ, drawn on a square grid*

Alternatively, only the *i* or *j* sequence can be used. Imagine starting at the point (1, 0). Subsequent points lie on the unit circle, at angle increments determined by the sequence. For example, if the maximum value of *i* and *j* were 8, then the angle increments could be $2\pi i/8$ radians, or one-eighth of the circle, times *i*. This idea was incorporated into the image "Eleven," created by the author and shown in the last panel of Figure 6. The base of the signature sequence was 11; an integer was chosen so that the segments would naturally cluster around the circle. In the first three panels of Figure 6, various maximal values were used, and the voids left by the clustering are apparent. The maximal value used in "Eleven" was chosen so that there would be eleven voids (the smallest two are too small to be seen in at this scale).

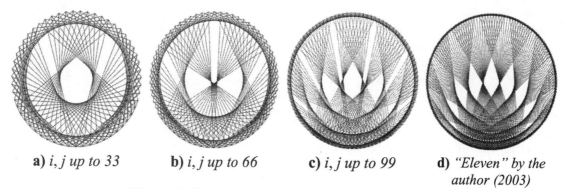

a) *i, j up to 33*   **b)** *i, j up to 66*   **c)** *i, j up to 99*   **d)** *"Eleven" by the author (2003)*

.**Figure 6:** *Signature sequence of 11, drawn on a circle*

Another idea is to draw the trajectory of a billiard ball rolling on a perfect table without friction. [8] The ball begins at one corner and bounces off the rails, stopping only if it reaches a corner. For a rectangular table, this problem is ruled by fractions. Specifically, if the table has a rational ratio of length to width, and the tangle of the initial angle of the ball is a rational number, then the ball will eventually find a pocket. Several examples are shown in Figure 7, where the trajectories are shown on a table with proportions of 2:1. In each case, the ball begins in the lower left corner. Its trajectory has an angle (with respect to the bottom rail) whose tangent is a fraction. In the first case, the angle's tangent is 1/1 (45°) and the ball bounces off of the top rail before stopping in the bottom right pocket. In the second case, two trajectories are shown, for angles whose tangents are 1/2 and 2/1 (approximately 26.6° and 63.4°, respectively). The third case shows the trajectories for the five fractions 1/5, 2/5, 3/5, 4/5, and 5/5.

In Figure 7c, a pattern is beginning to develop, with regards to the points where the trajectories intersect. This pattern is shown more clearly in Figure 8a, where the 16 trajectories with tangents 1/17, 2/17, etc., up to 16/17 are shown. The image is imbued with artifacts of 17, such as the 8.5 points on either end of the table and the 17 diamond voids in the center. If the table is viewed as a number line with 0 at the left end and 1 at the right end, then at fractions *m/n* (in lowest terms), the number of voids is 34/*n*,

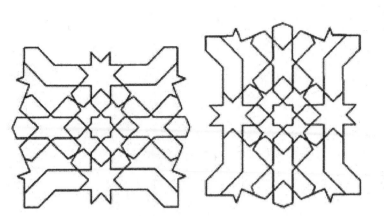

Figure 6: *The two diamond shapes; the second one is offset from the first one by 90 degrees*

Figure 7: *The 16-pointed star polygon design (Star 2)*

By recreating and connecting the diamond shapes and the 16-pointed star design, a grid for the *Seven Heavens* ceiling starts to take shape, as in Figure 8. shown below. Counting from the bottom up, Levels 1, 3 and 5 contain only these two motifs, which alternate from left to right, starting with all or part of the diamond shape. It is interesting to note that the diamond shapes in Levels 1, 3, 5, 7 and 8 are of the first form in Figure 6. and of the second form (that is, rotated 90 degrees with respect to the first form) in Levels 2, 4 and 6.

Figure 8: *Grid consisting of only two of the design elements, a diamond shape and a 16-pointed star*

With the formation of a grid of diamond shapes and 16-pointed star polygons, the remaining star polygon designs (shown in Figures 9. – 13.) may now be constructed within each of the apparent regular octagons, or on either side of the diamond shape on Level 7 for Star 8, (see Figure 14.). The star surrounding the cupola (on Level 8.) consists only of an outer band containing eight-pointed stars, which may be created in a manner similar to any of the star polygon designs shown in Figures 9. – 13.

Figure 9: *Star 4 motif found in Levels 2 and 4 (in the center)*   **Figure 10**: *Star 6 motif found in Level 2*   **Figure 11**: *Star 3 motif found in Level 4*

Figure 12: *Star 1 motif found in the center of Level 6*   **Figure 13:** *Star 5 motif found in Level 6*   **Figure 14**: *Star 8 motif found in Level 7*

All of the star designs discussed so far (and shown above) were relatively straightforward to construct from either squares inscribed in circles or line segments joined to points of a regular octagon. The stars within the regular octagons (Stars 1, 3, 4, 5 and 6) were all surrounded by equally-spaced congruent eight-pointed star polygons. The stars contained within square shapes (Stars 2 and 8) also contained the same eight-pointed star polygon at the vertices of each square. The star motifs 4 and 6 (given in Figures 9. and 10., respectively) are found in Level 2, symmetrically arranged on either side of the middle star (Star 7), with Star 4 found on the far extreme ends. The star motifs 4 and 3 (in Figures 9. and 11., respectively) are found in Level 4, with Star 4 found between two copies of Star 3. The star motifs 1 and 5 (given in Figures 12. and 13., respectively) are found in Level 6, with Star 1 sandwiched between two copies of Star 5. Lastly, Star 8 (given in Figure 14.) is found in Level 7. Actually, two halves of Star 8 motif flank a diamond shape, which is itself adjacent to an octagonal ring of eight-pointed stars surrounding the cupola. For the placement of the star polygon designs, please refer to Figure 8. on the preceding page.

The last star to be discussed, designated as Star 7, is the most elaborate one of the entire ceiling and may be found in the center of Level 2. It is quite different from all of the others, and, in fact, the grid in Figure 8. had to be altered to accommodate it (see Figure 15. below). Star 7 does not share any common eight-pointed stars or any other common design motifs with its neighboring star polygons. Even parts of the surrounding diamond shapes were replaced with other shapes in the construction of Star 7.

Figure 15: *Grid structure modified to accommodate Star 7 in the middle of Level 2.*

To recreate Star 7, four copies of Star 2, the 16-pointed star motif (see Figure 7. on a preceding page), were created with their centers on the vertices of a square. The four inner eight-pointed stars of Star 2 were removed, and then lines parallel to line segments that already existed were drawn. Connecting the points of intersection generated by these new lines, this process was continued, until all of the design of Star 7 (shown in Figure 16.) eventually emerged.

Figure 16: *Star 7 design, found in the middle of Level 2*

Discussion

All of the individual, Islamic star polygon designs discussed here (and recreated in an idealized skeletal form) have either eight or sixteen points and are highly symmetric, with four-fold rotational symmetry (about a central point interior to the eight-pointed star polygon) and four mirror reflections at 45 degrees to one another through that point. As a result, they are all classified as belonging to the *p4m* symmetry group, one of the most common classifications for Islamic patterns [13]. The diamond shape has two-fold rotational symmetry and mirror reflections, and so may be classified as belonging to the *pmm* symmetry group. The overall pattern of the *Seven Heavens* ceiling may not be classified using the 2-dimensional symmetry groups, since it is not all contained in a single plane. None of the three individual planes comprising each of the four sides exhibits any overall symmetry. However, all four sides are identical, and in that regard, the *Seven Heavens* may be considered highly symmetric.

Small eight-pointed star polygons may be found at the centers of the diamond shapes and the seven of the star polygon designs, as well as at the four vertices of the square designs (see Figures 3. and 14.) and the eight vertices of the regular octagon designs (see Figures 9. – 13.). Sixteen-pointed star polygons may be found at the center of Stars 1 and 2. All of the star polygons designs were straightforward compass and straightedge constructions, except for Star 7, whose construction required a surrounding square grid of 16-pointed star polygon designs (centered on the vertices of a square) from which to start.

The medieval Islamic artists and woodworkers conceived and created an extraordinary stepped pyramidal ceiling in the throne-room of the Alhambra. The *Seven Heavens* is very unusual and unique; no other ceiling like this exists in Islamic Spain. Consisting of 8017 pieces of wood, the ceiling is a masterpiece of marquetry, serving as the prototype for all subsequent *artesonado* ceilings. Finding a way to recreate the design was a great and rewarding challenge for the author.

References

[1]   O. Grabar. *The Alhambra*. Harvard University Press, 1978.

[2]   G. dePrangey. *Impressions of Granada and the Alhambra*. Garnet Publishing, 1996.

[3]   I. El-Said and A. Parman. *Geometric Concepts in Islamic Art*. Dale Seymour Publications, 1976.

[4]   B. L. Bodner. *La Mezquita's Geometric Window Grilles,* presented at and abstract published in the Proceedings of the Art + Math = X conference, 2005.

[5]   B. L. Bodner. *Unique Moroccan Designs: Reconstructed and Classified,* presented at the Mathematical Association of America (MAA), New Jersey Section conference, 2005.

[6]   B. L. Bodner. *Star Polygon Designs of La Alhambra's Wooden Ceiling,* presented at and abstract published in the Proceedings of the Bridges conference, 2004.

[7]   B. L. Bodner. *An Unusual Nine-Pointed Star Polygon Design of La Alhambra,* presented at and abstract published in the Proceedings of the ISAMA conference, 2004.

[8]   B. L. Bodner. *Constructing and Classifying Designs of al-Andalus,* presented at and abstract published in the Proceedings of the Joint ISAMA-Bridges conference, 2003.

[9]   B. L. Bodner. *Mathematics of Islamic Art,* 45-minute invited talk and 1-hour invited workshop at the Mathematical Association of America (MAA), New Jersey Section conference, 2002.

[10]   B. L. Bodner. *Islamic Art,* 2-hour Special Invited Session presented at the Mathematical Association of America (MAA) Mathfest conference, 2001.

[11]   The *Geometer's Sketchpad* software (version 4), distributed by Key Curriculum Press, 2001.

[12]   J. B. Lopez and P. G. Andrew. *Official Guide: The Alhambra and Generalife*. Patronato de la Alhambra y Generalife, 1999.

[13]   S. J. Abas and A. S. Salman. *Symmetries of Islamic Geometrical Patterns*. World Scientific, 1998.

On Parsimonious Sequences as Scales in Western Music

Richard Hermann
MSC04 25701
University of New Mexico
Albuquerque, NM 87131
harhar@unm.edu

Jack Douthett
Department of Music
State University of New York
Buffalo, New York 14020
douthett@comcast.net

Abstract

Musicians have narrowed the continuous range of frequency into discrete sequences of frequencies, interpreted as pitches, of various types called scales from the earliest writings on music onwards. This study provides some answers as to scope and relationships between modes and scales in areas where, surprisingly, little systematic study has been done. The approach reveals that the Fibonacci sequence provides the key to unlocking the question of scope. Techniques from post-tonal and modal music theory provide answers to relational questions.

1. Preliminaries

Musicians have narrowed the continuous range of frequency into discrete sequences of frequencies, interpreted as pitches, of various types called scales from the earliest writings about music onwards.[1] We pass over other topics deeply intertwined with scales such as tuning and temperament as well as referential pitch level in order to focus on an enumeration technique for stepwise sequences. These partition the space between terminal pitches formed by boundary intervals of less than or equal to the octave. Each of these sequences may be thought of as a scale with a distinct structure selecting the pitches for an instance of that scale type.

Thinking of a scale as a sequence of intervals rather than of pitches has the natural advantage of abstraction. These sequences form equivalence-classes induced by transposition (translation in mathematical terms); the pitches change while the intervallic sequence remains invariant. Usually, the first and last notes of a scale mark a 2:1 frequency ratio between them called the octave, and this acts as a modulus that maps the octave related frequencies into the type representative within the scale. Parsimonious for this study means that the interval between any two adjacent notes of the scale must be either a semitone or a whole tone (two semitones), and given historical musical practice, this is a reasonable limit for adjacent-note intervals, parsimonious intervals.[2] For example, the C major scale or Ionian mode is represented as follows where the letter names of the pitches are listed and aligned beneath are distances given in semitones that constitute the parsimonious sequence:[3]

---

[1] The earliest theoretical writings on music are Asian and predate Western theories by about a thousand years. For a recent study of such thought, see Clough, Douthett, Ramanathan, and Rowell [1].

[2] While there are from a parsimonious point of view, "gapped" scales such as the harmonic minor, these play a lesser role in actual musical practice.

Richard Cohn [2a] first emphasized the idea of parsimony with respect to voice-leading as a direct outgrowth from work by Hugo Riemann. We have The further developed this idea in Hermann and Douthett [2b], Douthett and Hermann [2c], and here.

[3] Renaissance church modes differ from the modern church modes as used by composers such as Debussy and Ravel as well as by jazz musicians to this date. Because the tuning systems of the Renaissance did not result in closed systems, very few transpositions were available, and several of the

```
        C     D     E     F     G     A     B     C
           <2     2     1     2     2     2     1>
```

As has been long well known, using this parsimonious sequence starting on any other pitch generates another member of the major scale equivalence-class induced by transposition. Here the two Cs form the boundary pitches and the boundary interval between them is the octave. Naturally, the intervals of these parsimonious sequences sum to the boundary interval, 12, and that intervallic distance is another definition for the octave.

   Other well known parsimonious sequences that have the boundary interval of the octave include the octatonic, <12121212>, and whole tone scales, <222222>; however, there are many other less well known as well as the ubiquitous modern church modes that we will specifically revisit later. As we can see from the parsimonious sequences above, there is more than one cardinality of parsimonious intervals that generates a scale between the boundary intervals of an octave: the major scale has 7, the octatonic 8, and the whole tone has 6 parsimonious intervals partitioning the octave. We q be the number of intervals in the parsimonious sequence.

   Musicians also find it useful to study scales with other boundary intervals. For instance in the Medieval and Renaissance eras, tetrachords, pentachords, and hexachords (four, five, and six note sequences) figured prominently in music theory; these have boundary intervals of 5, 7, and 9 semitones respectively.[4] Thus, we study parsimonious sequences for all sizes of boundary intervals between 1 and 12. The enumeration technique presented here is general for parsimonious sequences of any sized boundary interval.[5] While there are historical and current uses for parsimonious sequences where n is less than 12, the octave modulus remains in effect for all sequences in this study.

2. An Enumeration Technique for Parsimonious Sequences

An insight that some of the resulting intervallic distances in a scale sum to Fibonacci numbers led us to investigating its relevance. Taking the C major scale above, we have <2212221> where the parsimonious interval values of 1 and 2 themselves, the sum of the second two digits, and the sum of the first three digits are Fibonacci numbers.[6]

   In tackling this problem, there are two questions to be answered initially.

   Question 1: Given a boundary interval of length n and parsimonious sequences with m whole-steps, how many distinct sequences are there?

   Question 2: Given a boundary interval of length n, what is the total number of distinct

---

intervals had two different sizes. Today's equal temperament system is closed allowing intervallic patterns to be transposed to start from any pitch in the system and each interval is of only one size. It is ironic that the Renaissance church modes are named for locations in the ancient Hellenic world predating Christianity and that the Italian scholars of the middle ages mistranslated the ancient texts and associated the wrong place names with these scalar patterns. See David E. Cohn [3a] for more on this historical mistake and Cristle Collins Judd [3b] for information on the modes during the Renaissance. The Locrian mode is of modern invention predating World War II. It is used today in jazz pedagogy and is helpful for our purposes as it provides a name for that rotation-class member.

[4]These music theoretical works were frequently pedagogical. For a brief study on music theory pedagogy from Antiquity to the present that touches on these intervals and their role in context, see Wason [4]. intervals 5, 7, and 9 are know as the perfect fourth, perfect fifth, and major sixth in music of those eras.

[5]For more on these mappings and the operation of transposition (translation), see Morris [5].

[6]See Kramer [6a] for more on the Fibonacci series in 20th-century music and Huntley [6b] for other applications of the series.

parsimonious sequences?

To address the first question, we need the formula that determines the number of ways to choose m objects from a set of n distinct objects (n choose m):

$$C(n,m) = \frac{n!}{m!(n-m)!} .$$

The numbers generated by this formula are also called *binomial coefficients*. This relates to the question in the following way: Suppose our boundary length is $n = 5$. If there are 5 intervals in the sequence, then all 5 are half-steps and there are 0 whole-steps. One can think of this sequence as having 5 distinct positions and that 0 of them will be whole-steps. Whence, there are 5 choose 0 sequences with 5 half-steps and no whole-steps:

$$C(5,0) = \frac{5!}{0!5!} = 1 .$$

On the other hand, with 4 intervals and a boundary length of 5, 1 of the intervals must be a whole-step. Whence, of the 4 distinct positions, 1 must be chosen to be whole-step. It follows that there are 4 choose 1 sequences with 3 half-steps and 1 whole-step:

$$C(4,1) = \frac{4!}{1!4!} = 4 .$$

The sequences are

<2111>, <1211>, <1121>, and <1112>.

Finally, with 3 intervals and a boundary interval of length 5, there are 2 whole-steps. So, there are 3 choose 2 ways of placing the whole-steps in the sequence:

$$C(3,2) = \frac{3!}{2!1!} = 3 .$$

These sequences are

<221>, <212>, and <122>.

Any fewer than 3 intervals in our sequence with boundary length 5 and our sequence could not be parsimonious. So, we stop. For a boundary interval of length n and m whole-steps in the sequence, there are $C(n-m,m)$, $0 \le m \le \lfloor n/2 \rfloor$, distinct parsimonious sequences (if $m > \lfloor n/2 \rfloor$, then the sequence cannot be parsimonious).

On the second question, we need the Fibonacci numbers: $F_1 = 1$, $F_2 = 1$, $F_3 = 2$, $F_4 = 3$, $F_5 = 5$, $F_6 = 8$, $F_7 = 13$, and so forth ($F_1 = 1$, $F_2 = 1$, and $F_n = F_{n-1} + F_{n-2}$). Note that the total number of parsimonious sequences with boundary length 5 in the example above is a Fibonacci number:

$$\text{Total} = C(5,0) + (4,1) + (3,2) = 8 = F_6.$$

This is not a coincidence! In general, to get the total number of parsimonious sequences for a boundary interval of length n, all the cases above must be added together:

$$\text{Total} = C(n,0) + C(n-1,1) + C(n-2,2) + L + C(n-\lfloor n/2 \rfloor, \lfloor n/2 \rfloor).$$

It is known in mathematics that this sum is the Fibonacci number F_{n+1}; that is,

$$F_{n+1} = C(n,0) + C(n-1,1) + C(n-2,2) + \text{L} + C(n-\lfloor n/2 \rfloor, \lfloor n/2 \rfloor).$$

For $n = 1$ through 12, Table 1 below shows the number of parsimonious sequences in which m whole-steps appear (Column 3) and the total number of parsimonious sequences (Column 2). For each boundary interval length n in Column 1, the sum of the values in Column 3 yields the corresponding Fibonacci number shown in Column 2.

$\underline{n}$	$\underline{F_{n+1}}$	Values of $C(n–m,m)$ where n is the interval boundary length
1	1	C(1,0) = 1
2	2	C(2,0) = 1 C(1,1) = 1
3	3	C(3,0) = 1 C(2,1) = 2
4	5	C(4,0) = 1 C(3,1) = 3 C(2,2) = 1
5	8	C(5,0) = 1 C(4,1) = 4 C(3,2) = 3
6	13	C(6,0) = 1 C(5,1) = 5 C(4,2) = 6 C(3,3) = 1
7	21	C(7,0) = 1 C(6,1) = 6 C(5,2) = 10 C(4,3) = 4
8	34	C(8,0) = 1 C(7,1) = 7 C(6,2) = 15 C(5,3) = 10 C(4,4) = 1
9	55	C(9,0) = 1 C(8,1) = 8 C(7,2) = 21 C(6,3) = 20 C(5,4) = 5
10	89	C(10,0) =1 C(9,1) = 9 C(8,2) = 28 C(7,3) = 35 C(6,4) = 15 C(5,5) = 1
11	144	C(11,0) = 1 C(10,1) = 10 C(9,2) = 36 C(8,3) = 56 C(7,4) = 35 C(6,5) = 6
12	233	C(12,0) = 1 C(11,1) = 11 C(10,2) = 45 C(9,3) = 84 C(8,4) = 70 C(7,5) = 21 C(6,6) = 1

Table 1: *The Number of Parsimonious Sequences for n = 1 to 12.*

These sums to Fibonacci numbers can also be seen in the Pascal triangle in Table 2. Each arrow goes through the binomial coefficients that sum to the Fibonacci number at the head of the arrow. The coefficients that sum to the Fibonacci number F_{n+1} are the number of parsimonious sequences with m whole-steps and boundary length n. For example, the arrow that points to F_6 goes through the numbers 1, 4, and 3, which are the number of parsimonious sequences with boundary length 5 that contain 0, 1, and 2 whole-steps, respectively.

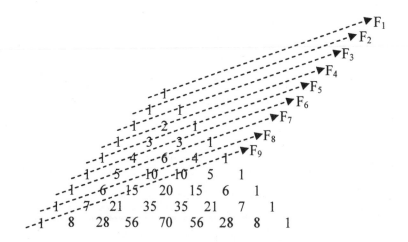

Table 2: *The Pascal Triangle with Diagonal Sums to Fibonacci Numbers.*

While it is easy to generate the specific parsimonious sequences when the value of n is low, it becomes progressively less so as the F_{n+1} values make their rapid climb. So a third question emerges.

<u>Question 3</u>: What are efficient methods for generating all specific parsimonious sequences with a boundary interval of *n*?

Before we answer this question directly, it is convenient to return to the modern church modes. Recall the major scale—Ionian mode presented above. Clearly, rotating the notes so the last note becomes the first preserves its parsimonious structure. Since there are 7 distinct notes, there are 7 different rotations, and it is these rotations that define the modern church modes. Table 3 lists these rotations, and each mode's name is given to the write of the sequence. These modes form a *rotation-class* of parsimonious sequences with a boundary interval of length *n* = 12. The rotations of the octatonic scale, discussed above form another rotation class of parsimonious sequences with a boundary length of 12. In this case, there are only 2 sequences in this class; <12121212> and <21212121>. The whole-tone scale rotation-class has only 1 member: <222222>. Whence, every parsimonious sequence with boundary length 12 belongs to some rotation-class.[7] This observation will be useful in answering the question posed above.

C		D		E		F		G		A		B		C		Ionian
	<2		2		1		2		2		2		1>		

B		C		D		E		F		G		A		B		Locrian
	<1		2		2		1		2		2		2>		

A		B		C		D		E		F		G		A		Aeolian
	<2		1		2		2		1		2		2>		

G		A		B		C		D		E		F		G		Mixolydian
	<2		2		1		2		2		1		2>		

F		G		A		B		C		D		E		F		Lydian
	<2		2		2		1		2		2		1>		

E		F		G		A		B		C		D		E		Phrygian
	<1		2		2		2		1		2		2>		

D		E		F		G		A		B		C		D		Dorian
	<2		1		2		2		2		1		2>		

Table 3: *The Rotation-Class of the Modern Church Modes.*

For our purposes here, we may informally describe a method for obtaining all specific parsimonious sequences. We start with the sequence of all parsimonious interval 1s summing to *n* and then successively adding a parsimonious interval 2 (subtracting the requisite number of 1s), which generates all of the members of each rotation-class that sum to *n*. As we know how many parsimonious sequences are in a rotation-class of length *n*, we can divide each $C(n,m)$ within some specific F_{n+1} situation by the appropriate *q* to remind us of how many rotation-classes are needed. The process ends when the rotation-class of all parsimonious interval 2s in the case of even values for *n* or all 2s plus one 1 in the case of odd values for *n* is recorded. Table 4 uses this method to generate all parsimonious sequences for *n* = 9, F_{10} = 55. The rotation-classes are separated by rows of asterisks.

---

[7]See Rahn [7] for more on this operation in post-tonal (atonal) music theory, but it is not limited to parsimonious sequences.

\<111111111\>

* * * * * * * * * *

\<11111112\>, \<21111111\>, \<12111111\>, \<11211111\>, \<11121111\>, \<11112111\>, \<11111211\>, \<11111121\>

* * * * * * * * * *

\<1111122\>, **\<2111112\>**, \<2211111\>, \<1221111\>, \<1122111\>, \<1112211\>, \<1111221\>

* * * * * * * * * *

\<1111212\>, \<2111121\>, \<1211112\>, \<2121111\>, \<1212111\>, **\<1121211\>**, \<1112121\>

* * * * * * * * * *

\<1112112\>, \<2111211\>, **\<1211121\>**, \<1121112\>, \<2112111\>, \<1211211\>, \<1121121\>

* * * * * * * * * *

\<111222\>, \<211122\>, \<221112\>, \<222111\>, \<122211\>, \<112221\>

* * * * * * * * * *

\<112122\>, \<211212\>, \<221121\>, \<122112\>, \<212211\>, \<121221\>   &

* * * * * * * * * *

\<121212\>, \<212121\>

* * * * * * * * * *

\<121122\>, \<212112\>, \<221211\>, \<122121\>, \<112212\>, \<211221\>   &

* * * * * * * * * *

\<12222\>, \<21222\>, **\<22122\>**, \<22212\>, \<22221\>

Table 4: *The Parsimonious Sequences of n = 9, F_{10}.*

3. Observations on Parsimonious Sequences

Just as today's musicians may think of the modern church modes as a set of scales preserving intervals under rotation that is based on the traditional diatonic collection, any of the rotation-classes of parsimonious sequences may be thought of as a unique collection of "parsimonious modes." In the diatonic collection, the choice of the mode Ionian—major scale as the type representative of this rotation-class is arbitrary from this point of view as it would be for any such class.[8]

Many composers from Debussy onwards have been intensely interested in the effects of mirror symmetry (reflection) in musical materials including scales as demonstrated by actual passages of music.[9] Returning to Table 3, we may see reflection within or between the modern church modes. Note that the Dorian mode's sequence of parsimonious intervals are the same whether read from left to right or the reverse. This mode's intervallic structure and any other with this feature are invariant under reflection. This operation is called inversion by musicians. Modes that are *not* their own reflection, not invariant, are paired with another that holds the same sequence of intervals when read in the opposite direction. These inversionally equivalent pairs in the modern church modes are Ionian/Phyrgian, Locrian/Lydian, and Aeolian/Mixolydian as can be confirmed in Table 3. When the value of *n* is less than or equal to 8, the inversionally equivalent pairs are found within the same rotation-class. For values of *n* greater than 8, this is usually but not always the case. Returning to Table 4, note that two of the rotation-classes have ampersands, "&," after the last member of the class. In these cases, one member of each inversionally equivalent pair is found within one ampersand marked rotation-class and the other of the pair is found in the other ampersand marked rotation-class. As *n* increases, so does the number of inversionally paired rotation-classes. As a last point made here on Table 4, those parsimonious sequences that are

---

[8]For a recent study on transformations between modes in a similar sense of the same value for n, see Santa [8].

[9]For well known examples, see Bartók [9a], Debussy [9b], and Webern [9c].

inversionally invariant (self reflections) are presented in boldface type.

4. Concluding Thoughts

With this enumeration technique, musicians can quickly generate all parsimonious sequences ("scales") and recognize their rotational ("modes") and inversional equivalences for any value of n of interest. Jazz musicians in particular may find this of interest as their pedagogy is today centered on the application of a wide variety of scales and modes.[10] While some post-tonal composers and theorists have studied pitch-class sets and their various transformational groups quite extensively, they have not given the same kind of attention to modes and scales much less to parsimonious sequences.[11] Given this intense interest in pitch structures and scales/modes during the last century or so, it is odd that we know of no previous study that provides a map of the terrain and a means for traversing it.[12] For our musician friends, here is that map and vehicle; enjoy the trip!

References

[1] J. Clough, J. Douthett, N. Ramanathan, and L. Rowell. "Early Indian Heptatonic Scales and Recent Diatonic Theory." *Music Theory Spectrum* Vol. 15 No. 1, pp. 36-58. Spring 1993.

[2a] R. Cohn. "Maximally Smooth Cycles, Hexatonic Systems, and the Analysis of Late-Romantic Triadic Progressions." *Music Analysis* Vol. 15 No. 1. pp. 9-40, March 1996.

[2b] R. Hermann and J. Douthett. "Steps Towards a Generalized Theory of Parsimonious Voice-leading," *Society for Music Theory annual meeting*, Madison, Wisconsin, Nov. 2003, unpub. mss.

[2c] J. Douthett and R. Hermann. "Wreath Products, n-Cubes, and Musical Voice-Leading" Special Session, "Mathematical Techniques in Musical Analysis," *Central Section meeting of the American Mathematical Society*, Evanston, Illinois, Northwestern University, in preparation. 23-24 October, 2004.

[3a] D. Cohen. "Notes, scales, and modes in the earlier Middle Ages." in *The Cambridge History of Western Music Theory*. ed. Thomas Christensen. Cambridge: Cambridge University Press, pp. 307-63.

[3b] C. Judd. "Renaissance modal theory: theoretical, compositional, and editorial perspectives." in *The Cambridge History of Western Music Theory*. ed. Thomas Christensen. Cambridge: Cambridge University Press, pp. 364-406. 2002.

[4] R. Wason. "Musica practica: music theory as pedagogy." in *The Cambridge History of Western Music Theory*. ed. Thomas Christensen. Cambridge: Cambridge University Press, pp. 46-77. 2002.

---

[10]Slonimsky [10a], initially published in 1947, provided the first influential source on scales for jazz musicians. Later Russell [10b], circulated in manuscript in 1955, became and remains in its following editions the most respected source on scales in jazz theory. Reeves [10c] is a typical pedagogical text used in American universities for jazz studies.

[11]See Morris [4] and Morris [11] for important summaries of this work.

[12]Nonetheless, much valuable work has been done on the topic. For some recent work that may be of interest to mathematicians, see Carey and Clampitt [12a], Clough, Engebretsen, and Kochavi [12b] and Vieru [12c].

[5] R. Morris. *Composition with Pitch-Classes*. New Haven, Connecticut: Yale University Press, 1987.

[6a] J. Kramer. "The Fibonacci Series in Twentieth-Century Music." *Journal of Music Theory* Vol. 17 No. 1, pp. 110-148. Spring, 1973.

[6b] H. Huntley. *The Divine Proportion: A Study in Mathematical Beauty*. New York: Dover, 1970.

[7] J. Rahn, *Basic Atonal Theory*. New York: Longman, 1980.

[8] M. Santa. "Defining Modular Transformations." *Music Theory Spectrum* Vol. 21 No. 2, pp. 200-229. Autumn, 1999.

[9a] B. Bartók, "From the Isle of Bali," no. 109 in *Mikrokosmos for piano solo*. 4 np: Boosey & Hawkes, pp. 24-25. nd.

[9b] C. Debussy, "Voiles," no. 2 from *Preludes, Book 1 for piano solo*. Miami: Kalmus, pp. 7-10. nd.

[9c] A. Webern. *Variationen für Klavier, Op. 27*. Vienna: Universal Edition, 1937.

[10a] N. Slonimsky. *Thesaurus of Scales and Melodic Patterns*. 4th ed. New York: Amsco, 1975.

[10b] G. Russell. *Lydian Chromatic Concept of Tonal Organization*. Brookline, Massachusetts, Concept, 2001.

[10c] S. Reeves. *Creative Jazz Improvisation*. 2nd ed. Englewood Cliffs, New Jersey: Prentice Hall, 1995.

[11] R. Morris. *Class Notes for Advanced Atonal Theory*. 2 vols. Lebanon, New Hampshire: Frogpeak, 2001.

[12a] N. Carey and D. Clampitt. "Aspects of Well-Formed Scales." *Music Theory Spectrum*. Vol. 11 No. 2 pp. 187-206. Autumn, 1989.

[12b] J. Clough, N. Engebretsen, and J. Kochavi. "Scales, Sets, and Interval Cycles: A Taxonomy." *Music Theory Spectrum* Vol. 21 No. 1, pp. 74-104. Spring, 1999.

[12c] A. Vieru. "Modalism-A 'Third World.'" *Perspectives of New Music*. Vol. 24 No. 1, pp. 62-71. Autumn-Winter, 1985.

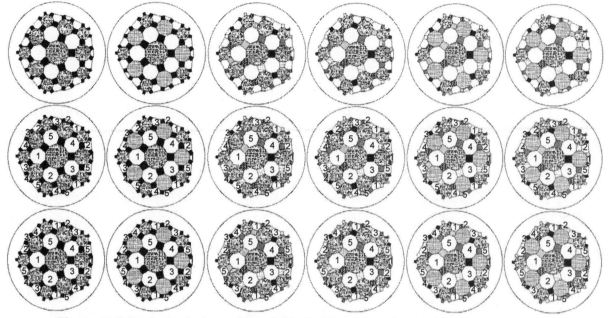

Figure: (25) Perfect colorings of the $4 \cdot 10 \cdot 8$ tiling where the orbits do not share colors

Observe that if J_i is used to color one orbit of tiles, it can also be used to color a second orbit of tiles as long as J_i contains the stabilizer of a tile in the second orbit of tiles. Moreover, if a color used to color tile t in the first orbit of tiles is to be used to color tiles in the second orbit, then the tile t' that will be assigned the same color as tile t should have a stabilizer contained in J_i.

In coloring the $4 \cdot 10 \cdot 8$ tiling, the orbit of 4-gons and the orbit of 8-gons can share the same color. These colorings appear in Figure 26. The colorings A and B are obtained using $J_1 = G$ to color both orbits of 4-gons and 8-gons. The colorings in C and D are obtained using $J_2 = \langle Q, P, RPR, RQRPRQR \rangle$ while the colorings in E and F are obtained using $J_3 = \langle Q, P, RPQR \rangle$.

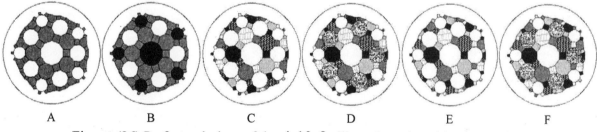

| A | B | C | D | E | F |

Figure: (26) Perfect colorings of the $4 \cdot 10 \cdot 8$ tiling where the orbits share colors

5. Conclusion

In this note, we give an approach to color semi-regular tilings on the hyperbolic plane. We use the general framework for coloring planar patterns where an orbit of tiles in the given tiling is colored using a subgroup of the symmetry group G of the tiling containing the stabilizer of the tile. We use the GAP program to generate the subgroups of G while a helpful tool in studying more closely the subgroup structure of G is the CHP program.

We intend that the approach provided here in obtaining perfect colorings of semi-regular tilings will provide a springboard in the construction of colorings (both perfect and non-perfect) of tilings in general on the hyperbolic plane.

References

[1] Aziz, Shahid. *A Computer Algorithm for Coloring A Hyperbolic Tessellation*. A Masteral Thesis, The University of the Philippines – Diliman, 1996.

[2] Coxeter, H.S.M., and W.O. Moser. *Generators and Relations for Discrete Groups*. 2nd ed. New York: Springer-Verlag, 1965.

[3] De Las Peñas, Ma. Louise Antonette N., René P. Felix, and M. V. P. Quilinguin. *A Framework for Coloring Symmetrical Patterns* in Algebras and Combinatorics: An International Congress, ICAC '97 Hong Kong. Singapore: Springer-Verlag. 1999.

[4] Felix, René P. *A General Framework for Coloring Planar Patterns*, a paper presented in National Research Council of the Philippines (NRCP) Conference. Philippines. February, 2004.

[5] Grünbaum, B., and G.C. Shephard. *Tilings and Patterns*. New York: W.H. Freeman and Company, 1987.

[6] Hernandez, Nestine Hope Sevilla. *On Colorings Induced by Low Index Subgroups of Some Hyperbolic Triangle Groups*. A Masteral Thesis, The University of the Philippines – Diliman. 2003.

[7] Mitchell, Kevin J. *Constructing Semi-Regular Tilings*, a paper presented in The Spring 1995 Meeting of the Seaway Section of the Mathematical Association of America. 1995. http://people.hws.edu/mitchell/tilings/Part1.html.

[8] The GAP Group. *GAP – Groups, Algorithms, and Programming*, Version 4.3, 2002, http://www.gap-system.org.

Two and Three-Dimensional Art Inspired by Polynomiography

Bahman Kalantari
Department of Computer Science
Rutgers University
Hill Canter
New Brunswick, NJ, 08903, USA
E-mail: kalantari@cs.rutgers.edu

Abstract

In several previous articles I have described polynomiography as the art and science of visualization in approximation of zeros of complex polynomials. Polynomiography amounts to a colorful two-dimensional image, called a polynomiograph, created via a prototype polynomiography software that could typically allow a great deal of human creativity and control. In this article I describe several types of 2D and 3D artwork that could be inspired by polynomiography. These include work of art as paintings, tapestry designs, carpet designs, animations, sculptures, neon light-like polynomiographs, and more. The realization of some of these applications as serious work of art takes coordinated effort, collaborations, and support. I will report on progress in the realization of some of the above-mentioned artwork.

1. Basic 2D Polynomiography

1.1. Introduction.

Polynomiography has been defined to be "the art and science of visualization in approximation of zeros of complex polynomials." An individual image is a "polynomiograph." These images are obtained using a variety of algorithms for root-finding, based on the application of iteration functions. The creation of a single polynomiograph is based either on the individual use of an iteration function, or the collective use of a family of iteration function and its point-wise convergence properties. It is not the intention of this article to give any detailed mathematical description of these techniques here. For the mathematical description of polynomiography, see [3], [5], [7]-[9], [11], and [12]. To be able to carry out serious polynomiography one ideally needs to have a good software implementation of the techniques as well as a manual or a book that would describe some rendering techniques. The preparation of these are among the list of projects currently being undertaken. But I would like to make it clear to the reader that just as in photography a great deal of creation lies on the part of the individual polynomiographer. And that is what makes polynomiography a new medium for art, as well as a medium for education and for scientific explorations.

Polynomiography can give many images of the same polynomial. This is analogous to photography where one can shoot many pictures of the same subject. As an example the images in Figure 1 are all polynomiographs of the polynomial equation describing the cube-roots of unity, viewed within a particular square. The only image possibly familiar to the reader is the very first which has appeared quite frequently in the literature describing fractals. A polynomiograph however may or may not turn out to be a fractal image. Here I have limited the number of different polynomiographs of this equation to five, but it is possible to give many many more fractal and non-fractal polynomiographs of this single polynomial equation having very different shapes or colors.

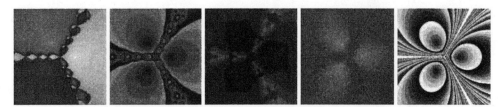

Figure 1: *Five different polynomiographs of roots of unity*

Polynomiography applies to a general complex polynomial. A polynomial equation can be described via its coefficients:

$$p(z) = a_n z^n + a_{n-1} z^{n-1} + \mathrm{K} + a_1 z + a_0 = 0,$$

or its complete set of roots as:

$$p(z) = (z - \theta_1) \times \cdots \times (z - \theta_n) = 0.$$

There are advantages in each of these two modes of description. Traditionally a polynomial is described through its coefficient set. But the intention of polynomiography is not just the computation of the roots, rather how the roots are being computed and the effect of this computation in the coloring of the points within a certain domain of the complex plane. This coloring is determined via the use of iteration functions, see [8], and [12]. One of the features of polynomiography is the reversal of the root-finding problem altogether, i.e. given the roots of the polynomial we may ask what iteration function to employ in order to create a pleasing or desired image. This in particular allows the artist or designer working with a polynomiography software the ability to select the location of the roots as he/she wishes.

In the subsequent section I will consider several different applications of polynomiography.

2. Artwork Inspired by Polynomiography

In this section I will describe several applications of polynomiography in creating 2D and 3D artwork. These include, creating paintings, carpet designs, tapestry designs, animations, polynomiography of two or more variables, neon light-like polynomiography, and more. The section also provides some images of the realization of these artwork. These merely show the wide scope of polynomiography and is not intended to be exhaustive.

2.1. Paintings Inspired by Polynomiography

One of the great aspects of polynomiography images and in contrast to most computer-generated art, is in producing images that could resemble a hand-painted artwork. As an example one of my images that has been repeatedly exhibited is the piece I call "Summer," see [6]. This and its variations have inspired me to experiment with real paint and canvas. But I mention that this aspect of polynomiography, i.e. creating actual paintings based on the images is what a number of professional artists have suggested. Thus it is a worthy effort to pursue further. For example the polynomiograph in Figure 2 is an image that inspires hand-painted artwork. I have numerous images like this and in fact one of the features of polynomiography software is that the polynomiographer can experiment with such images before he/she begins to paint one.

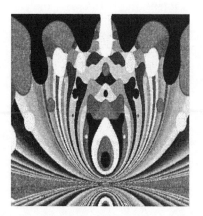

Figure 2: *A polynomiograph that could be turned into a painting*

2.2. Carpet Designs Inspired by Polynomiography

It is possible to create patterns based on polynomiography lending themselves to elegant carpet designs. For instance by using 36 points selected as the roots of a polynomial on three concentric circles I made a polynomiograph which was in fact inspired by an actual Persian carpet design. In turn I had this design turned into an intricate hand-woven carpet having about 1,400,000 knots which took more than 6 months to make. The carpet was produced by one of the finest carpet makers in Iran, Alinasab, whose workshop for carpet making is well-known in the country. Figures 3 shows the carpet in the making and the final artwork, an exact replica of the polynomiograph.

Figure 3: *A hand-woven carpet based on a polynomiograph*

A second carpet-maker produced the carpet in Figure 4. The design corresponds to a polynomiograph of the same underlying polynomial that gave the first carpet. The difference in coloring and design is due to different use of iteration functions done intentionally to create the contrast between the two designs.

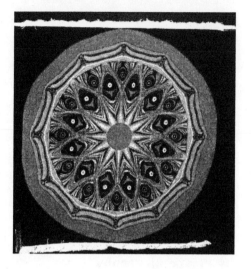

Figure 4: *A carpet based on the same polynomial for carpet in Fig 3*

2.3. Tapestry Inspired by Polynomiography

Polynomiography could also provide a great source for producing tapestry. As an example a polynomiograph I call "Acrobats," Figure 5, was the basis for the tapestry of Figure 6 made by an artist, Mrs. Azam Barakhshan.

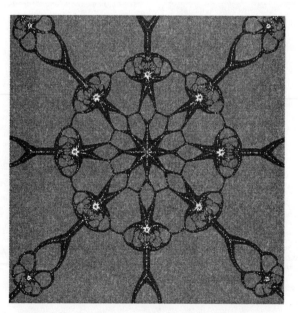

Figure 5: *A polynomiograph called "Acrobats."*

Figure 6: *Realization of Acrobats as tapestry*

2.4. Sculptures Inspired by Polynomiography

Lillian Schwartz, one of the pioneers of digital art made it evident to me that viewing polynomiographs under 3D chromatic glasses could often reveal an interesting three-dimensional structure. She thus proposed that some polynomiographs could give rise to 3D sculptures. As an example the image that inspired the carpet of Figure 3 could conceivably be turned into a three-dimensional intricate sculpture. In this sense polynomiography provides an alternative means for mathematically inspired sculptors. Traditionally the field of topology has provided a major source for these sculptors, see e.g. [1], [2], [13]. For instance, Möbius bands have been turned into sculptures numerous times. But there is good reason to believe that polynomiography could result in another rich and alternative source for serious mathematically inspired sculptors.

2.5. Animations Inspired by Polynomiography

Animation with polynomiography is a useful technique both in the context of education and art. For instance in [10] we generated some animations that use visualization through polynomiography as a means for conveying certain mathematical concepts. This application could be quite wide in its scope. This is in the sense that polynomiography animations could be helpful to students of various level as well as for highly advanced visualizations that may attempt to capture or discover a deep mathematical property. As an example the following gives a visualization of in the phenomenon known as *sensitivity*. It is well known that the roots of polynomials could be sensitive to small changes in their coefficients. Classical example is the polynomial

$$p(z) = (z-1) \times (z-2) \times \cdots \times (z-7).$$

The coefficient of the sixth power of z is –28. Even if we change this to –28.002 the roots will change drastically and in fact some of them become complex. The following sequence of images can show the gradual change of roots. For the animation of this as well as other animations see [10] and my web site www.polynomiography.com

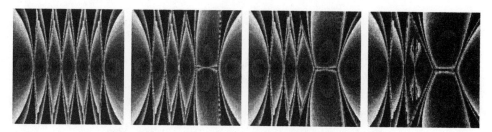

Figure 7: *Animation of sensitivity effect.*

2.6. Polynomiography of Polynomials in two or more variables.

Polynomiography deals with the visualization of complex polynomials in one variable. But we can still carry out polynomiography on polynomials in two or more variables. Consider for instance a polynomial in two complex variables x and y. For each fixed value of y we get a polynomial in one variable and we can generate a polynomiograph. This in a sense amounts to a cross-sectional polynomiography. By repeating this for a range of values of y, we get more and more cross sections. These cross sections then can be viewed in the form of animation or as a discrete set of images. This too can be a source of for creating animations as art. Figure 8 gives such a cross-sectional polynomiography for the polynomial

$$p(x, y) = x^3 + xy + y^2$$

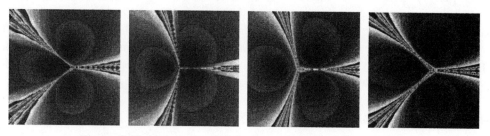

Figure 8: *Polynomiography of cross section for y=1,1/2,-1/2,-1*

2.7. Neon Light-Like Images Inspired by Polynomiography

Artistically speaking, polynomiography has much to offer. Here I will exhibit a few polynomiographs first produced via a prototype polynomiography software, subsequently subjected to various filters available on existing commercial software to produce new neon-like effects. These filters could have directly been implemented within a polynomiography software itself. These images, see Figures 9, accentuate certain paths that get colored by the polynomiography software based on the degree of proximity of points to polynomial roots, as dictated by the family of iteration functions used in the software. These images suggest neon light-like designs. If actually realized as such they could be quite appealing.

Figure 9: *Neon Light-Like Polynomiographs*

3. Concluding Remarks and Future Work

In this article I have described several different 2D and 3D applications of polynomiography. These support the proposition that polynomiography represents an excellent medium with diverse applications in art, science and education. The successful implementation and realization of some of the projects into serious work of art or science will however depend upon coordinated effort, collaboration, and support. But probably as evident some of these artwork are already worthy of exhibition.

A referee of this article considered the list of polynomiography-inspired artwork as a "wish list." Moreover, he appeared to object to the fabrication of the two carpets by someone else. These are both very ironic coming from an art-math referee. Firstly, I do not see anything wrong with someone else using my designs in order to produce a beautiful carpet or tapestry. I did not intend to take credit for their artistry. Secondly, it is absolutely true that it is my wish and desire that others will be inspired by polynomiography. Indeed it has already inspired many and I see nothing wrong with that either! The referee also objected that no new mathematics was offered in the article. I did not think it was necessary to discuss the detailed mathematics of the subject here. On the one hand, it really takes a whole book and a software to describe all the details. On the other hand, I do already have several articles on the general mathematical aspects of polynomiography, containing new mathematics that I am very much proud of. Polynomiography is indeed an innovative work that embodies both art and science. As the referee noted I have already used some of the same polynomiographs in published articles. I see nothing wrong with this either. The point of this article is to convey new ideas, rather than new polynomiography artwork of which I have hundreds. There is no need to bombard the reader with variety of images, rather with variety of ideas. In particular the animation, which the referee feel out of place, is yet a new application of polynomiography offering new possibilities as art or as science, although some animation may have been witnessed before, say in chaos (as mentioned by the referee). There are literally hundreds of mathematical ideas that can be conveyed through polynomiography of which the article mentions a couple. And that application, inspired by polynomiography, is a new idea in itself.

This article also serves as an invitation to other artists to create new artwork inspired by polynomiography. It is "my wishful desire" that my polynomiography artwork are transformed into new art forms. Clearly this particular referee and I have very different views. In my opinion art-math societies must strive to make the practice well-defined among their participants, and also try to be inviting, not just to those who practice art-math themselves, but possibly to all who may exclusively practice art or math, students and otherwise.

Acknowledgements. I would like to thank a friend, Mr. Edward Greenblat, an excellent photographer who kindly took the photographs of the two carpets given in this article.

References

[1] C.P. Bruter, *Mathematics and Art: Mathematical Visualization in Art and Education,* Springer-Verlag, 2002.

[2] M. Emmer, *The Visual Mind: Art and Mathematics,* MIT Press, 1993.

[3] B. Kalantari, *Polynomiography: The art and mathematics in visualization of polynomials,* in Proceedings of ISAMA (International Society of Art, Mathematics, and Architecture), 2002.

[4] B. Kalantari, *Can Polynomiography be Useful in Computational Geometry?,* DIMACS Workshop on Computational Geometry, New Brunswick, NJ, November, 2002. (http//dimacs.rutgers.edu/Workshop/CompGeom/abstracts/005.pdf).

[5] B. Kalantari, *Polynomiography and Applications in Art, Education, and Science,* in Proceedings of SIGGRAPH 2003 on Education.

[6] B. Kalantari, *Summer,* artwork and its description in Electronic Art and Animation Catalog, pp. 87, SIGGRAPH 2003.

[7] B. Kalantari, *The Art in Polynomiography of Special Polynomials,* in Proceedings of ISAMA/BRIDGES Conference, pp. 173-180, 2003.

[8] B. Kalantari , *Polynomiography and application in art, education, and science,* Computers & Graphics, 28, pp. 417-430. 2004.

[9] B. Kalantari, *A new medium for visual art: Polynomiography,* Computer Graphics Quarterly, 38, pp. 22-24. 2004.

[10] B. Kalantari, I. Kalantari, F. Andreev, *Animation of mathematical concepts using polynomiography,* Proceedings of SIGGRAPH 2004 on Education.

[11] B. Kalantari, *Polynomiography in art and design,* Mathematics & Design, Vol. 4, pp. 305-311. 2004. Proceedings of Fourth International Conference of Mathematics & Design.

[12] B. Kalantari, *Polynomiography: From the Fundamental Theorem of Algebra to Art,* to appear in LEONARDO, Volume 38. 2005.

[13] I. Peterson, *Fragments of Infinity, A Kaleidoscope of Math and Art ,* Wiley, 2001.

Tessellations from Group Actions and the Mystery of Escher's Solid

Ioana Mihaila
Department of Mathematics and Statistics
California State Polytechnic Univ., Pomona
3801 W. Temple Ave.
Pomona, CA 91768, USA
e-mail: imihaila@csupomona.edu

Abstract

In the paper [1], Joyce Frost and Peg Cagle show how to construct a tessellation with squares of the plane from another one of smaller squares, and how this process can be generalized in three dimensions to construct a tessellation of the space with rhombic dodecahedra from a tessellation with cubes. The authors then proceed and explain how to construct a stellated rhombic dodecahedron (Escher's solid), and why this solid is space-filling as well. Interestingly, the procedure of constructing a tessellation from a given one by conveniently cutting some of the tiles can be iterated in all these cases, and the tessellations obtained can be associated to group action in the plane, or three-dimensional space, respectively.

1. Plane Tesselations and Group Actions

Let's start with an easy tessellation: consider the plane covered by unit squares. If we consider the group $G_1 = \langle f, g \rangle$ of plane transformations generated by the transformations $f(\mathbf{x}) = \mathbf{x} + \mathbf{i}$ and $g(\mathbf{x}) = \mathbf{x} + \mathbf{j}$, where $\mathbf{x}$ denotes a point in the plane, and $\mathbf{i}$, and $\mathbf{j}$ are the unit vector on the axes, then all the squares of the tessellation are equivalent under the group action of G_1.

Now imagine the squares colored in a checkerboard pattern, mark the centers of the white squares, and join them with the sides (figure 1). This procedure will divide each white square into four triangles. Add the triangles to the adjacent black squares to which they share a full edge. The plane now becomes tiled by squares with vertical and horizontal diagonals of length 2 (figure 2). This tessellation can be viewed as the result of the action of the group $G_2 = \langle h, k \rangle$ on the plane, where $h(\mathbf{x}) = \mathbf{x} + \mathbf{i} + \mathbf{j}$ and $k(\mathbf{x}) = \mathbf{x} + \mathbf{i} - \mathbf{j}$. It is not too hard to show directly that G_2 is a subgroup of G_1, and that $[G_1 : G_2] = 2$. However, this is even easier if we repeat the procedure of coloring the squares and attaching the resulting triangles one more time. By doing this, we obtain a new square tessellation, in which the tiles have the edges parallel to the axes again, and the length of the edges is 2. So a group whose action generates this

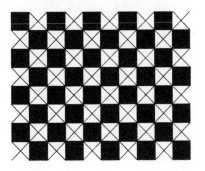

Figure 1.

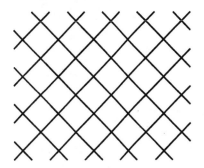

Figure 2.

tessellation is $G_3 = \langle l, m \rangle$, with $l(\mathbf{x}) = \mathbf{x} + 2\mathbf{i}$ and $m(\mathbf{x}) = \mathbf{x} + 2\mathbf{j}$. It is now obvious that $G_3 \le G_2 \le G_1$, and since $[G_1 : G_3] = [G_1 : G_2][G_2 : G_3] = 4$ and all subgroups are proper, then $[G_1 : G_2] = [G_2 : G_3] = 2$. Of course, this can be continued indefinitely.

2. Space-Filling Polyhedra

Now let's apply the same procedure in three dimensions, starting with a tessellation of the space into cubes. Imagine the cubes colored alternating in black and white. Cut the white cubes into six pyramids each, by joining the centers to the vertices. Attach the pyramids to the adjacent cubes, thus obtaining a tessellation of the space with rhombic dodecahedra. The cubic tessellation is obtained by considering the action of the group $G_1 = \langle f, g, h \rangle$, where $f(\mathbf{x}) = \mathbf{x} + \mathbf{i}$, $g(\mathbf{x}) = \mathbf{x} + \mathbf{j}$, $h(\mathbf{x}) = \mathbf{x} + \mathbf{k}$, while the rhombic dodecahedron tessellation is generated by $G_2 = \langle \mathbf{x} + \mathbf{i} + \mathbf{j}, \mathbf{x} + \mathbf{j} + \mathbf{k}, \mathbf{x} + \mathbf{k} + \mathbf{i} \rangle$.

What happens if we continue? The next step is to dissect some of the rhombic dodecahedra. Since each has 12 faces, this produces 12 pyramids with rhombic bases. Attaching these pyramids to the adjacent dodecahedra produces three-dimensional tiles, which are stellated rhombic docecahedra. The figures below show the rhombic dodecahedron and the stellated rhombic dodecahedron. The latter is also known as Escher's solid, because it was represented by Escher in his woodcut "Waterfall". The space tessellation with Escher solids, accompanied by a good illustration of how the solids fit together can be found in [2].

What is interesting is that repeating the dissecting and attaching procedure one more time gets us back to a cubic tessellation. This is easier to see with real models and it is due to the fact that each stellated rhombic dodecahedron breaks into 48 tetrahedra, out of each groups of 6 get attached together to the adjacent solid. Finally, let's denote by G_3 the group of space transformations generating the tessellation by Escher solids, and G_4 the group generating the subsequent cubic tessellation. The cubes have sides of length 2, and hence $G_4 = \langle \mathbf{x} + 2\mathbf{i}, \mathbf{x} + 2\mathbf{j}, \mathbf{x} + 2\mathbf{k} \rangle$. Thus $[G_1 : G_4] = [G_1 : G_2][G_2 : G_3][G_3 : G_4] = 8$, and each group has index 2 in the next one.

As a final observation, the fact that in this type of construction the index of each subgroup in the next group is equal to 2 is in agreement with the fact that the area or volume of the tiles used in the tessellation doubles at each iteration.

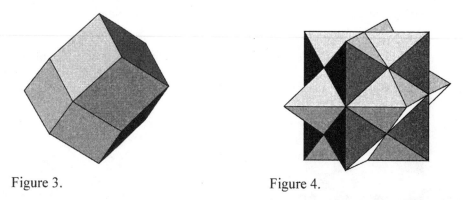

Figure 3.   Figure 4.

References

[1] Joyce Frost, Peg Cagle, *An Amazing, Space-Filling, Non-regular Tetrahedron*,
    http://mathforum.org/pcmi/hstp/resources/dodeca/paper.html
[2] Alan Holden, Shapes, Space and Symmetry, Columbia University Press, NY, 1971.

Wisdom in Art: Mathematics in Islamic Architecture in Iran

Hourieh Mashayekh
906-257 Lisgar St.
Ottawa, Ontario K2P 0C7
CANADA
Email: hourimashayekh@yahoo.ca

Abstract

Architecture through the ages, has embraced a wide variety of arts and sciences. By using mathematics, Iranian architecture has achieved a high level of beauty and perfection. It is evident that advanced geometry was used by the prominent architects at that time. Geometry was used not only to solve structural problems, but also in the details of the designs of various structures. These range from the immense high entrances of Friday Mosques in important cities, to entrances of ordinary homes. By reviewing examples of medieval Iranian architecture, one becomes aware of its close relationship to scientific fields such as mathematics, geometry, cosmology, and astrology. This Relationship made it possible to achieve perfection, monumentality and poetic beauty. **It is wisdom within art.**

"This high dome is simple, yet complexly designed,
No sage ever knows the secrets behind the gate"- Hafiz (14th century)

Architecture through the ages, has embraced a wide variety of arts and sciences. By using mathematics, Iranian architecture has achieved a high level of beauty and perfection. This is especially evident in the Islamic Iranian architecture of the Middle Ages (10th to 14th century). During this period there were astonishing and glorious achievements of this endeavor – that is – the application of mathematics in architecture.

Many researches show the close relationship between mathematics and Islamic Iranian architecture. "The Study of mathematics had long been an area of original and fruitful research in Islam. Arabic translations of Euclid were of course already available in the Abbasid (early Islamic) period. While the scientists of Saljuq and Mongol Iran (early 10th century) were the best of their age, it has been estimated that it was the Timurid (14th century) period which saw the apogee of Islamic work in computational mathematics."[1]

The transition of a square into a circle by using triangles is one of the characteristics of Iranian architecture from the pre-Islamic period. Later, Iranian architects used this process to create more complicated and elaborate forms in the design of their buildings. The center point of the square, marked by the intersection of two diagonals, is the most important point in the transition to a circle process. This called for a further geometrical solution in the corners in order to create the desired forms and volumes. In order to create the vast varieties of forms which were achieved by the turning, rotating, and twisting of a simple square, the usage of circles and triangles was common and widely used in much of the medieval Islamic Iranian architecture.

It is evident that advanced Geometry was used by the prominent architects at that time. "The techniques of tower construction established in earlier centuries continued and spread under the Saljuq Sultan, their governors, and their neighbors. The cylindrical brick shaft of a variable taper was decorated with brick patterns and inscriptions of varied quality and complexity." [2]

Usage of advanced mathematics continued into the Il Khanids period. "Its apparent feature was a more immense scale. The structural load-bearing components of monuments were concentrated. A large ratio of height to the interior width of the chamber was displayed." For example: " the weight of the double shelled dome of the mausoleum of Uljayto in Sultanieya central Iran (45 meter high with a diameter of 24.5 meter) is concentrated on a small number of supporters, without the use of any shoulder or buttress."[3] So it needed to be calculated prior to its construction.

Geometry was used not only to solve structural problems, but also in the details of the designs of various structures. These range from the immense high entrances of Friday Mosques in important cities, to entrances of ordinary homes. The more modest residential architecture conceals private and common-use areas of the houses. The layout of such houses varied according climate, culture, tradition, and aesthetic tastes. In order to satisfy these demands, and the placement of these structures within an urban setting, the architects had to rely on mathematics in order to achieve the best results.

The mastery of advanced mathematics among the architects, and the application of this knowledge in the various aspects of design led to the creation of amazing and admirable architecture[1]. There is no doubt that only those architects who were acquainted with an advanced knowledge of geometry, algebra and astrology, as well as, poetry and philosophy, could design such architectural elements that protected the structural stability while achieving perfection of beauty -- characteristic of medieval Iranian architecture in Iran. This level of balance and elegance would not have been attained without the mastery of mathematics by the creators of the work[2].

The ratio of height to the diameter of the towers or minarets in medieval Iranian architecture shows another aspect of the use of mathematics in architecture. The Tower of Gonbad-I-Qabus near Gorgan (in northern Iran), is a unique example of such a case. While this tower "reaches the amazing height of sixty-one meters, its diameter is only seventeen meters." [5] This mathematical relationship helped the architect to create the sense of "the ascension from earth toward heaven." This effect is achieved by narrowing the diameter of the tower where the entrance is placed, in comparison to the height of the structure.[*Ibid.*]

An additional example is the Gonbad-i- Ali Tower at Abarquh, in central Iran. This octagonal tomb consists of a tower of rubble masonry, rather than the traditional brick, and features a "bold three-tiered muqarnas[3] cornice, also of rubble, [that] once probably supported a pyramid roof."[6]

Further use of advanced mathematics is evident in medieval Islamic architecture of Iran, especially the period between the Seljuk and the Timur dynasties, in the height of the towers and entrances, and the two shelled domes, used in the mosques of various cities. The "lofty minarets, with their ambitious construction and rich geometric and epigraphic decorations were designed and constructed with immense skill."[7] "Construction techniques have not been studied thoroughly, but the continued ability of these slender towers to resist earthquakes suggests that their builders employed some sophisticated method, perhaps wooden tie beams, to give tensile strength to the structure." [8]

---

[1] "The astronomical tables of Ulugh Beg represent an advance on previous work, and the most important mathematician of his court, Ghiyath sl-Din Kashi, included in one of his many treatises, the Miftah al hisab, a table for the setting up of arches, domes and stalactite systems of different profiles" [1].

[2] "The poet Nezami, writing in the twelfth century, describes the talent of mythical architect, Shida, who designed and erected a fabulous seven-domed palace for Bahram Gur. Shida was of honorable birth, a master in drawing, a famed geometer in surveying, a finished worker in the building art and artist skilled in sculpture and painting" [4].

[3] "In Iran stalactite systems have been designated by Arabic word muqarnas or "joined" which also has the broader meaning of vaulted and by the Persian word "khonj whose basic meaning is " corner" or " solid angle" [4].

Other examples are the Masjid-i-Jameh at Tabriz and Masjid-i-Jameh at Varamine. The first one "consisted of a single immense Iwan[4] of brick 99 feet wide, about 213 feet deep, to the springing of now collapsed vault, about 82 feet tall, shows an immense sahn[5] with centre pool and single-aisled porticoes," [6] while the latter had "a small dome behind the main portal completes the portal iwan, … the dome chamber is articulated, as is all else, by squinch filled with muqarnas in brick, which signal the transition from the square to the octagon" [Ibid.]

Among the large number of examples of the close relationship between Iranian medieval architecture and geometry, I would like to review a magnificent example – which is worth researching more thoroughly in the future – that is the entrance of the Friday mosque, Masjid-I-Jame, at Yazd, situated near the centre of this large city.

This Friday Mosque (Figures 1, 2, & 3) is notable for "its exceptionally narrow pishtaq[6] surmounted [by] twin minarets. The interior of the dome has an almost complete tile revetment, and the elimination of the rear wall of the iwan in the qibla[7] side ensured, for first time, that congregation in the court yard could see it. The upper galleries produce a considerable lightening of the dome chamber, both visually and structurally, and more complex succession of solids and voids. The same considerations are found in the transverse vaulting of the prayer hall." [10]

Figure 1: *View from central courtyard (Hayedeh Mashayekh, 2004)*

Figure 2: *Floor Plan (Reproduced from documents published by the Iranian cultural Heritage Organization, n.d.)*

---

[4] "Iranian architecture developed an interpretation of enclosed exterior space; indeed, the essence of the Iranian aesthetic can be said to lie in the organization of the courtyard. Here the simple motifs of iwan and the arcaded courtyard are combined, with the added emphasis of the sanctuary domed and sometimes of the minarets above the sanctuary iwan, all organized in relation to the overarching sky, their volumes immaterialized by the attenuation of their masses and by a pervasive ceramic vesture basically the color of the sky. Iranian architecture also initiated the expression of the aesthetic of the façade in its portal." [9]

[5] Sahn is the main salon where worshippers stand to the Ghiblea in the direction of Mecca and is the biggest and main parish salon.

[6] Main iwan or pishtagh (the first arch of iwan) gives access to the Principle part of mosque especially to the mihrab. Meanwhile regular iwan is the covered area for worshippers facing the main court. There could be one two or four iwan courts or iwan domed as well.

[7] Ghebla is the Mecca direction towards which worshippers face.

Figure 3: *detail of entrance (Hayedeh Mashayekh, 2004)*

The principal entrance to the mosque, which is composed of an iwan and the minarets from the 14th century, is exceptional in that it is the tallest entrance in Islamic architecture of Iran. The height achieved in this part of the structure would not have been possible without structural mathematical analyses. The height is stressed further by the ascending line molding of the minarets. (Figures 4, 5, and 6.)

Figure 4: *Entrance (Reproduced from documents published by the Iranian Cultural Heritage Organization, n. d.)*

Figure 5: *Entrance (Hayedeh Mashayekh, 2004)*

Figure 6: *Entrance (Hayedeh Mashayekh, 2004)*

As mentioned before the purpose of the tall towers or minarets was to create the sense of reaching to God. This sense could be embodied in the structure by narrowing the entrance as much as possible, and by making it as tall as possible, with the help of mathematical calculations. (Sketches 1 and 2)

Sketch 1   **Sketch 2**

Masjid-I-Jame, Yazd, Iran
(Sketches were created by the author.)

By reviewing examples of medieval Iranian architecture, one becomes aware of its close relationship to scientific fields such as mathematics, geometry, cosmology, and astrology. This relationship made it possible to achieve perfection, monumentality and poetic beauty. **It is wisdom within art**[8, 9].

Acknowledgment

I wish to thank Mehdi Nasrin and Hagit Hadaya for their comment and assistance.

References

[1] O,Kane, B. *Studies in Persian Art and Architecture*, Cairo, pp.33-34, 1995.

[2] J.Bloom, *Minaret Symbol of Islam*, Oxford p. 157, 1989.

[3] M. M. Hejazi, *Historical Buildings of Iran: Their Architecture and Structure*, Southampton, pp. 30-157,1997.

[4] D. N. Wilber, *The Architecture of Islamic Iran: Ilkhanid period,* Princeton, p.47, 1969.

[5] A. Daneshvari, *Medieval Tomb Towers of Iran,* Lexington, p. 14, 1986.

[6] J. D. Hoag, 1977. *Islamic Architecture,* New York, pp. 257, 330-338, 1977.

[7] H.Laleh, *The Splendour of Iran*, London, p. 114, 2001.

[8] J. Bloom, *The Splendour of Iran*, London, p. 181, 2001.

[9] J. Pereira. 1994. *Islamic Sacred Architecture a Stylist History*: New Delhi, p. 110,1994.

[10] A. Hutt, & L. Harrow, *Islamic Architecture*. London, color plate 6 and 7, 1978.

[11] R. Hillerbrand, R. *Islamic Art and Architecture*, London, pp. 105-108, 1999.

---

[8]"The distinctive Saljuq contribution lies rather in the final establishment of several of the classic forms of Iranian architecture and in the capacity of Saljuq architects to draw out the utmost variety from these types. Mosques with one, two, three or four iwans are known, and the 4 iwan plan receives its classic formulation in association with an open courtyard and a monumental domed chamber: a hierarchy of size distinguished major iwans from minor ones...The pishtagh was developed from a simple salient porch to a great screen which conferred a grandiose façade on the building behind it" [11].

[9] "The double-shell dome of the mausoleum of Uljaitu in Sultaniya (1350-13 A.D.) 54 m. high with a diameter of 24.5 m. is the largest existing dome in Iran ... Its section is a void. The thickness of the dome shell is respectively 0.6 m. and 0.4 m. thick near the base "structurally the building is a masterpiece". In a detailed study of the building in 1883, Dieulafoy found the use of geometry in the design on the interior and exterior elevation" [3].

NAMAN
Dream Altars, Vietnam
A Search for use of the Golden Mean and its Affect on Design and Content

Michael McConnell, Mathematics
Jim Rose, Art
Clarion University
Clarion, PA 16214
E-mail jrose@Clarion.edu
E-mail MmcConnell@Clarion.edu

Abstract

My recently completed installation "Dream Altar, Vietnam" deals with my memory of my experiences in Viet Nam. Since memory tends to be amorphous, I began to utilize the Golden Ratio as a means of imposing order on the project. I found that incorporating Golden Rectangles in the design enhanced the impact of the artwork. To further this enhancement, Dr. McConnell and I will experiment with other uses of the Golden Ratio in the actual arrangement of the installation, especially its relationship to the three dimensional space that it will be contained within.

I will install a Memory Altar at the Bridges Conference and discuss the discoveries we have made and how we used the golden section and other mathematics in the overall construction of the piece.

Memory Altar, Vietnam, by Jim Rose, exhibited at Clarion University Gallery 2005

Introduction

NAMAN is a compound of the words NAM and MAN. NAM is a slang word for Vietnam and MAN stands for man. . My goal is to create an installation called a "Dream Altar", that consists of photographic montages and objects that I acquired in Saigon. These thoughts and photographic montages, combined with objects I acquired in 1970, are accumulated and presented thirty-four years later, allowing me to explore how my memories have changed over time.

Dream Altars are a combination of objects, photographs, plants and projected slides. The goal is to share my thoughts and memories with the observer, since memories are a dream after the fact. The past is a limited database in one's mind that slowly dissolves with time giving glimpses of life, sometimes subliminal and sometimes conscious. This Dream Altar is a work in progress. The installation at Bridges will be a further step in seeing how the geometric structure of the golden rectangle affects the visual or emotional impact of the artwork.

Vietnam Memory Scrolls are a montage of my photographs of Vietnam. The format, which is like a Chinese scroll, symbolizes the admiration and agreement I have for art and culture of the orient. They also represent the first introduction of the golden ratio into this artwork. The dimensions of the photographs and the cloth portions of the scrolls are in Golden Rectangle proportion. After changing the dimensions to represent the Golden Ratio, I noticed this enhanced the visual impact of the scrolls. My next step is to find further ways to incorporate the Golden Ratio and see if this enhances the piece by adding geometric structure to unstructured memories. The harmony of the Golden Section may introduce peace into unharmonious memories of war.

Background Information The introduction of classical mathematics into my art started with my collaboration with Dr. Steve Gendler from Clarion University. We presented a Making Connections class called Art in Perspective, which showed the relationship between art and mathematics. Although I was aware of the Golden Ratio, until then I never really used or understood it.

Optimization. Working with my memories and random thoughts I use geometry to construct my images from random experimentation. What is the correct amount of structure? Optimization of impact is my goal using art and mathematics. I have used the golden section in some pieces of my art consciously and unconsciously. I will team up with Mike McConnell and study various ways I can use mathematics to help with not only the production of my scrolls but also the arrangement of all elements included in my installation. This will expand my understanding of the Golden Section and allow me to formalize the process using mathematics. We will then view our experiments and decide which composition works best according to our own personal experience, which includes some mathematical analysis.

Dr. McConnell will work with me to explore as many mathematical variants of these objects in three dimension and present our findings at Bridges.

Aesthetic Aspects of Venn Diagrams

Barry Cipra
305 Oxford St.
Northfield, MN 55057
bcipra@rconnect.com

Peter Hamburger
Department of Mathematical Sciences
Indiana-Purdue University
Fort Wayne, IN 46805
hamburge@ipfw.edu

Edit Hepp
Windswept Drive Studio
Fort Wayne, IN 46815
hamburger1@comcast.net

Introduction

Venn diagrams are familiar to anyone who has taken high school algebra. The standard two- and three-circle Venn diagrams have a pleasing look. This stems partly from their symmetries. As customarily drawn, each has a horizontal mirror symmetry. The two-circle diagram also has a second, vertical mirror symmetry. In addition to these, each diagram also has rotational symmetry: The two-circle diagram is invariant under rotation by 180 degrees around a point inside the lens-shaped intersection of the circles, while the three-circle diagram is invariant under rotation by 120 degrees around a point inside its triple-intersection region.

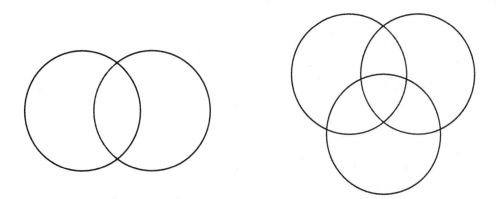

Figure 1: *The familiar 2- and 3-set Venn diagrams.*

In 1963, David Henderson at Swarthmore College raised, and partly answered, the question whether Venn diagrams with more sets could have analogous rotational symmetry [8]. To be precise, is it possible to draw a simple closed curve, rotate it by multiples of 360/*n* around some point in its interior to produce *n* congruent copies of the curve so that the result is a Venn diagram for *n* sets (each set being the interior of one of the curves)?

Henderson showed that this cannot be done if *n* is not a prime number. The basic reason is illustrated by the simplest case, *n*=4. If a Venn diagram were symmetric under rotation by 90 degrees, then each region corresponding to a pairwise intersection of sets would belong to a group of 4 such regions. This means that the number of pairwise intersections must be a multiple of 4. But with four sets, there are 6 pairwise intersections, which is not a multiple of 4. In general, n must divide each binomial coefficient $C(n,k)=n!/k!(n-k)!$ for k equal 1 to n-1, but a classic theorem, attributed to Leibniz, says this only happens if n is prime.

This negative result leaves open the question of the existence of symmetric Venn diagrams when n is prime. Henderson gave two examples of symmetric diagrams for n=5. One uses (irregular) pentagons, the other uses quadrilaterals. Branko Grünbaum at the University of Washington later gave a lovely construction with equilateral triangles [3]. He also produced a striking example with five ellipses [2].

Seven, Eleven, Etc.

It took nearly 30 years from the publication of Henderson's paper to the discovery of rotationally symmetric Venn diagrams for n=7. Grünbaum published the first in 1992 [4]. Anthony Edwards at Cambridge University subsequently found a total of six different examples. (Two Venn diagrams are "different" if it is not possible to continuously deform each to match the other or its mirror image.) Images of various symmetric Venn diagrams for n=5 and 7 are available online in a dynamic survey of Venn diagrams by Frank Ruskey at the University of Victoria [9].

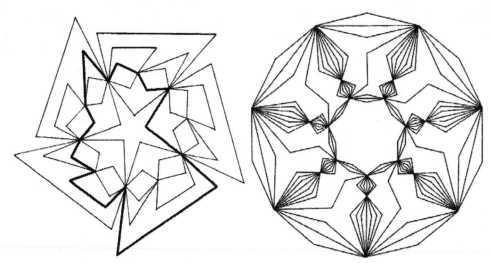

Figure 2: *Symmetric Venn diagrams with 5 and 7 sets. These diagrams have the minimum number of vertices (10 and 21, respectively) for their size. The (polygonal) curve whose rotations create the 5-set diagram is highlighted. For details, especially on the 7-set diagram, see [6] and [7].*

The answer for n=11 took nearly another decade. Peter Hamburger at Indiana-Purdue University at Fort Wayne found an approach that produced a symmetric Venn diagram with 11 sets [5]. He titled his paper "Doodles and Doilies," because the approach involves doodle-like drawings that lead to Venn diagrams with a lacy, doilie-like appearance, as least as Hamburger draws them.

Hamburger's wife, Edit Hepp, has turned his 11-set "doilies" into works of art, using color to highlight regions corresponding to different types of intersections. Hepp's originals are large (approximately 32 inches in diameter). She creates the Venn diagram by hand drawing one "wedge" of it, pasting together xerox copies of the wedge and xeroxing the result. (She also drew the diagrams in Figure 2, above.) Hepp uses colored pencils, she says, "to obtain the richest possible textures."

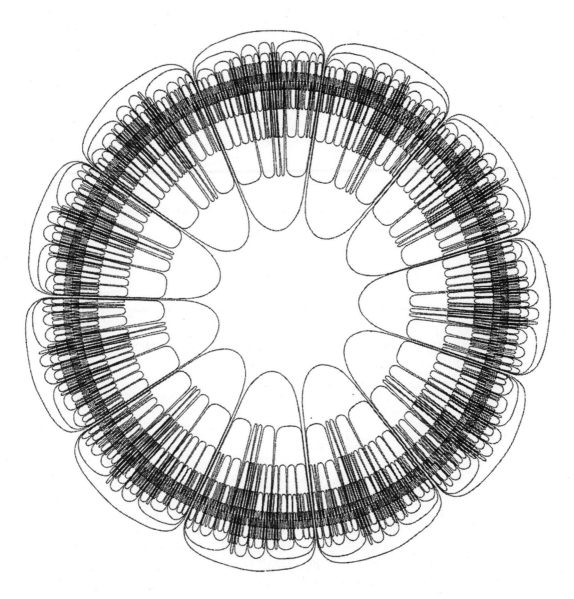

Figure 3: *Peter Hamburger's rotationally symmetric 11-set Venn diagram "doilie" [5].*

Rotationally symmetric Venn diagrams allow for innumerable artistic choices. Within each wedge, for example, the arcs can circular, sinusoidal, or even polygonal. It is also possible to disrupt the symmetry by emphasizing just one of the diagram's curves. (With the exception of Grünbaum's ellipses and equilateral triangles for $n=5$, all of the rotationally symmetric Venn diagrams with more than three sets are based on curves with little if any symmetry.) As Hepp puts it, "Symmetry creates beauty, but the most stunning images are those where the symmetries are intentionally destroyed by the artist in order to dive deep into a mathematical principle." In one picture, Hepp deletes everything outside of one curve, which removes half of the regions of the Venn diagram, and then colors the remaining regions. The result is wonderfully abstract.

What about rotational symmetry for $n=13$ or other primes? The approach Hamburger took for n=11 was expanded on by Jerry Griggs at the University of South Carolina and Charles Killian (an undergraduate) and Carla Savage at North Carolina State University, who proved that rotational symmetry can be achieved for all primes (thereby cutting short a potentially infinite sequence of papers) [1]. So far there have been no pictures–a good opportunity for an artistically oriented triskaidekaphilic.

References

[1] Griggs, J., Savage, C., and Killian, C., Venn diagrams and symmetric chain decompositions in the Boolean Lattice, *Electronic Journal of Combinatorics* 11 (2004), Research Paper 2 (available online at www.combinatorics.org).

[2] Grünbaum, B., Venn diagrams and Independent Families of Sets, *Mathematics Magazine*, 48 (Jan-Feb 1975) 12-23.

[3] Grünbaum, B., The Construction of Venn Diagrams, *College Mathematics Journal*, 15 (1984) 238-247.

[4] Grünbaum, B., Venn Diagrams II, *Geombinatorics*, Volume II, Issue 2, (1992) 25-32.

[5] Hamburger, P., Doodles and doilies, non-simple symmetric Venn diagrams, *Discrete Mathematics*, 257 (2002), 423-439

[6] Hamburger, P., Pretty drawings. More doodles and doilies, symmetric Venn diagrams, *Utilitas Mathematica*, to appear.

[7] Hamburger, P., and Pippert, R. A symmetrical beauty. A non-simple 7-Venn diagram with a minimum vertex set, *Ars Combinatoria*, 66 (2003) 129-137.

[8], Henderson, D., Venn diagrams for more than four classes, *American Mathematical Monthly*, 70 (1963) 424-426.

[9] Ruskey, F., A Survey of Venn Diagrams, *Electronic Journal of Combinatorics*, Dynamic Survey DS5, 1997, www.combinatorics.org/Surveys/ds5/VennEJC.html. (Note: The dynamic survey was first posted in 1997. It has been updated to include more recent work.)

Dynamics on Discrete Structures: A Dialog between Squares and Circles

Tiziana Giorgi and Robert Smits
Department of Mathematics
New Mexico State University
Las Cruces, New Mexico 88003
tgiorgi@nmsu.edu & rsmits@nmsu.edu

Discretized versions of continuous structures can be used to great effect to increase the amount of information conveyed in mathematics, art and science. As an example, we will examine a model for a confined polymer in a solution, Figure 1, as imagined by Pierre-Gilles de Gennes [1], and an analogous mathematical model of the same decomposition of space, rotated counterclockwise through 90 degrees as in Figure 2, [3].

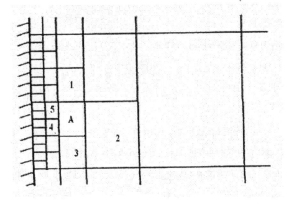

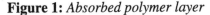

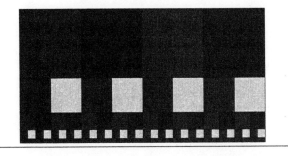

Figure 1: *Absorbed polymer layer*   **Figure 2:** *Hyperbolic tiling of half-space*

To visualize the theory of Stochastic Schramm-Loewner Evolutions [5] in the upper-half space, where a continuous set of conformal maps is generated by applying at the boundary a random process, traditionally one looks at the trace of the set of points that are eliminated in time. Unfortunately, this visualization conveys very little information regarding the family of maps. The hyperbolic tiling in Figures 1 and 2 can be taken as a discrete approximation of the upper-half space on which to apply the dynamics just described. While these rectangular models serve the purpose of performing a hyperbolic tiling of the upper-half plane, the fundamental rectangular blocks are interlocked and this rigidity does not allow for natural dynamics to occur.

To move things about, we notice that the essential component in the tiling of both Figure 1 and Figure 2 is their combinatorial structures, among other things the fact that every square has exactly five neighbors, thirteen square which are two away and so on. One can transfer this structure to the unit circle by using the theory of circle packing, recently developed in complex analysis [4]. A basic result of the theory is that any finite, connected planer graph gives rise to a unique packing, modulo some basic transformations [2].

To build a circle packing isomorphic to the hyperbolic tiling of Figure 2, we could construct a graph by connecting the centers of adjacent rectangles in the composition. The associated circle packing is a moveable configuration where every circle has five neighbors, thirteen away and so forth, that is the combinatorics of the original tiling is preserved. A portion of this packing with circles away from the boundary is shown in Figure 3, which we generated using the computer algebra system Maple. Each circle and its neighbors represents a rectangle of the planar decomposition of Figure 2 and its adjacent rectangles. The radius of the circle is proportional to the distance from the boundary.

A dynamical system modeling the effect of applying a random variable on the boundary can be introduced on the circle packing by randomly deleting circles on the boundary, which corresponds to deleting vertices from the original graph, and then repacking the unit circle with the new graph. One can then visually retrace the entire history of the random walk on the boundary by examining the fractal like set of circles from the original packing, which have been deleted in time. The construction gives a clear visualization of Schramm-Loewner Evolutions.

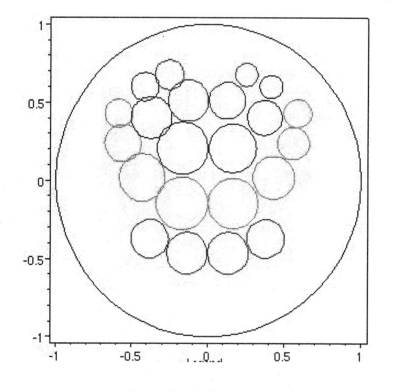

Figure 3: *Circle packing*

References

[1] P.-G. de Gennes, *Simple Views on Condensed Matter*, World Scientific Publishing Co., 1998.

[2] Z.-X. He; O. Schramm, *On the Convergence of Circle Packings to the Riemann Map*, Invent. Math., 125 (1996), no. 2, 285-305.

[3] R. G. Smits, *Square Decompositions with Hyperbolic Consequences in Art, Chemical Physics and Mathematics*, Meeting Alhambra, ISAMA-Bridges 2003 Conference Proceedings.

[4] K. Stephenson, *Circle Packing: A Mathematical Tale*, Notices of the AMS, 50 (2003), no. 11, 1376-1388.

[5] W. Werner, *Random Planar Curves and Schramm-Loewner Evolutions*, Lecture Notes, Saint-Flour, 2002.

Strange Physical Motion of Balls in a Cylinder

Akihiro Matsuura

College of Science and Engineering

Tokyo Denki University

Hatoyama-cho, Hiki-gun, 350-0394, Japan

E-mail: matsu@k.dendai.ac.jp

Abstract

We report on the strange physical motion of balls rolled inside a cylinder, which at a glance seems to contradict physical laws. Based on this motion, we develop a new type of juggling in which several balls are manipulated in a cylinder to draw a variety of spatio-temporal patterns. In the presentation, we will demonstrate some manipulation□

1. Introduction

The Feat of manipulating several objects skillfully in the air is generally known as juggling. Nowadays, it is not only enjoyed physically but also explored artistically and scientifically. For example, performing artist M. Moschen has created performances in which geometric objects are manipulated in innovative ways, e.g., he bounces balls in a huge triangle in various rhythms and patterns. From a scientific standpoint, C. E. Shannon showed a theorem on the timing of catching and throwing of objects and made a juggling robot [2]. In the mid 1980's, a mathematical notation for expressing juggling patterns was discovered [4]. With the notation, a pattern is expressed with a sequence of non-negative integers (see [1] for details). The author presented a new type of juggling called *spherical juggling* [3] in which we insert several balls in a clear globe and roll them inside. This juggling is closely related to spherical geometry.

In this paper, we make a new connection among mathematics, physics, and performing arts. Namely, we first introduce the strange physical motion of a ball rolled inside a cylinder. At a glance, the phenomenon seems to contradict physical laws (though it does not). Based on this motion, we develop a new kind of juggling in which several balls are manipulated inside a cylinder. We also report on the implementation of a cylinder and the performance we produced.

2. Motion of a Ball Rolled in a Cylinder

We suppose that a long and clear cylinder is laid horizontally to the ground as shown in Fig. 1. We roll a ball inside the cylinder and observe its movement. The ball is assumed to be elastic like a rubber ball and there is some friction between the ball and the cylinder. If the ball is released on the vertical section as shown in Fig. 1, it apparently rolls around the vertical circle. What if the ball is released to the *non-vertical* direction? It might be imagined that the ball proceeds in a spiral motion while declining by friction. But this is not always true. The ball can *roll back* almost to the place it is released as shown in Fig. 2. The returned ball continues to move to the opposite direction and rolls back again. Namely, the trace forms the shape of infinity (∞). If the ball is rigid, it can not happen. So it must be caused by friction and elasticity of a ball, though we have not succeeded in the complete physical analysis yet.

Figure 1: *A ball which rolls vertically in the cylinder.*

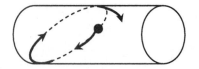

Figure 2: *A ball which rolls back.*

3. Juggling in a Cylinder

3.1. Basic Patterns. We use the ball motion in Section 2 to define a new type of juggling. Figure 3 shows one way of manipulating three (or an odd number of) balls in a cylinder. The balls are inserted from the center hole and rolled on the inner surface. Balls are released to the left and the right orbits using both hands alternately. Similarly, Figure 4 shows one way of manipulating four (or an even number of) balls. Note that two sets of balls are manipulated independently on the two orbits. Besides these patterns, an infinite number of patterns are possible using the mathematical notation introduced in Section 1.

   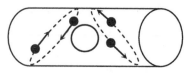

Figure 3: *A basic pattern with three balls.*   **Figure 4**: *A basic pattern with four balls.*

3.2. Implementation and Performance. We implemented clear acrylic cylinders (Fig. 5) and checked if the basic patterns of balls are actually possible. Based on the juggling, we created a performance with a theme of encounter of a performer with the unknown cylinder. Having some play, the performer happens to find the strange motion of a rolling ball. He starts to make a variety of beautiful patterns in the cylinder, which would also be the encounter of the audience with the new visual world. The performance was presented in several performing events including the international performance festival in Shizuoka, Japan (Fig. 6). Many of the audience seemed to get interested in the cylinder and enjoy the performance.

Figure 5: *The acrylic cylinder.*   **Figure 6**: *The cylinder performance.*

4. Concluding Remarks

We reported on the strange physical motion of balls in a cylinder and on the new juggling performance. Through the exploration, we have seen that simple mathematical objects and the physical movement contribute to creating a new performance. Such an idea will be further pursued to build a new connection among mathematics, science, and performing arts. The remaining future work includes the complete physical analysis of the ball motion and the refinement of the performance.

This work is supported in part by Hayao Nakayama Foundation for Science, Technology and Culture.

References

[1] B. Polster, The Mathematics of Juggling, Springer-Verlag New York, 2002.

[2] C. E. Shannon, *Scientific Aspects of Juggling,* Claude Elwood Shannon: Collected Papers, edited by N. J. A. Sloane and A. D. Wyner, IEEE Press, 1993.

[3] A. Matsuura, *Spherical Juggling,* Proc. of Interdisciplinary Conference of the International Society of the Art, Mathematics and Architecture (ISAMA/CTI2004), pp. 89-94, 2004.

[4] B. Tiemann, and B. Magnusson, *The Physics of Juggling,* The Physics Teacher, Vol. 27, pp. 584-589, 1989.

Space from Nonspace: Emergent Spatiality in Dynamic Graphs

Tim Boykett
Time's Up Research Department
and
Dept. Algebra, Johannes–Kepler University Linz
tim@timesup.org

Abstract

We are attempting to construct immersive dynamic realtime visualisations of some modern theories of quantum foam. Physicists claim that graph structures underlie our physical universe, and that the dynamics of these graphs give rise to such phenomena as matter and interaction. The first part of this project has revolved around making embeddings of these graphs into higher dimensional space in order to obtain a locally (nearly)three dimensional form. The next stages will involve finding ways to represent these forms in an immersive and dynamic way in order to make the effects of the dynamics clear.

Roots

There are many streams of thought that lead to the idea that our three dimensional physical world is but an illusion. That we perceive three dimensions and that objects act in that three dimensionality is clear: we have, on the level of our actions and perceptions, something that we call geometry. There are many ways of thinking about space and spatiality, whether analytically or perceptually. Many directions of thought tell us that this is illusion, from ancient traditions through to modern quantum theory. There is a need to explain what it is that lies under our usual perceptions that leads to this geometry. As mathematicians and artists we are unable to deal with the more spiritual directions in our work, however there are several fragments of ideas that try to begin to talk about this idea in a more formal sense. Fifty years ago Wheeler coined the term pregeometry for such ideas.

For out purposes here, let us take the term pregeometry to apply to some system which: 1) has no geometrical terms in its formalism, and 2) shows geometry–like properties in its results. We say that the geometry is emergent or that it is an epiphenomenon of the formalism. In particular we are interested in ways that a metric pregeometry can arise from weighted graphs.

The Project

A series of physicists from Wheeler onwards, have claimed that there is a combinatorial (i.e. graph theoretical) pregeometric structure underlying our universe. Cahill has suggested, based upon the paradigms of particle physics, one possible model[1]. His claim that this structure is pregeometric is based upon Nagel's analysis [2]. The graphs used by Cahill and his collaborators have certain properties which should enhance their pregeometric attributes.

We would like to develop some representation of these models. The main tool that we use is embedding. Technically, an embedding is a one–to–one homomorphism of one structure into another. This means that we map objects in one structure into objects into the second in order that some properties are preserved. A fuzzy embedding is an embedding with a tolerated level of inexactness in the structural mapping(Note that this does not necessarily correspond to ideas of "fuzzy logic."). In our case we embed the nodes of the graph into Euclidean n–dimensional space with the structure of the graph node-to-node distance mapping to Euclidean distance. We attempt to lower the summed errors (i.e. the fuzziness) in this mapping, weighted by the graph-distance closeness (nodes that are closer together are required to have their Euclidean distance more exactly closer to their graph theoretical distance). Closeness is more important that distant-ness. This is known as a relaxation technique in graph visualisation.

The central claim is that the structure of the resulting embedding carries across the structure of the original graph structure. In particular the global distance topology of the graph is represented in the Euclidean space.

Two analyses were then made of the resulting embeddings. The first analysis investigates the distribution of embedded points and their resulting distances from the center of mass. The second investigates the relationship between graph theoretical shortest distance and Euclidean distance between nodes.

The first analysis demonstrates a strong shell structure. In any fuzzy n–sphere, the distribution of the radii from the center of mass, i.e. the center of the sphere, is strongly peaked at the radius of the sphere. Precisely this was observed in the 4– and higher–dimensional embeddings (Figure 1 a)), indicating that we have a structure that is globally a fuzzy 3–sphere. The second analysis (Figure 1 b)) shows a strong and well–structured relationship between the graph shortest path (geodesic) and Euclidean (straight line) distances. The curves follow closely those expected of a 3–sphere.

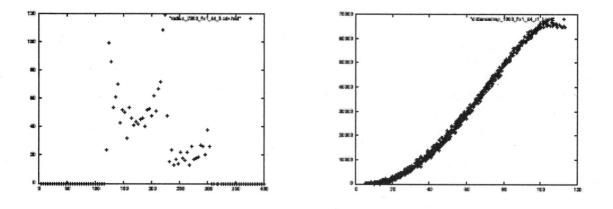

Figure 1: a) *Radius distribution* b) *Euclidean versus geodesic distance*

It remains to find suitable representations of these structures, able to best show the emergent local three dimensionality. Preliminary attempts indicated that this is somewhat problematic, however the above analysis indicates that it must be possible; there is a pregeometry in the graph structures. Once this has been obtained, in a somewhat efficient manner, we anticipate that the representation of the process suggested by Cahill will lead to a relatively intuitive picture of what is happening in this model of physical space.

References

[1] Reg Cahill and Christopher Klinger. Self-referential noise and the synthesis of three-dimensional space. General Relativity and Gravitation, 32(3):529 – 540, 2000.
[2] G. Nagels. Space as a 'bucket of dust'. General Relativity and Gravitation, 17:545–557, 1985.

The author gratefully acknowledges support from the City of Linz as part of the LinzExport grant. Conversations with Kirsty Kitto, Chris Klinger and Reg Cahill have been very important in formulating these ideas. An extended version of this note and related texts are available at the author's website at http://algebra.uni-linz.ac.at/~tim.

Satellite Ballet by Flower Constellations

Daniele Mortari
Aerospace Department
Texas A&M University
College Station, TX 77843-3137, USA
E-mail: mortari@aeromail.tamu.edu

1.   Extended Abstract

In recent years, satellite constellations and constellations around planets received a great deal of attention. However, to date, only simple string-of-pearl type simple constellations have been flown in Earth observing missions. The challenge lies in the difficult and high cost of maintaining non-trivial constellations that have prevented this technology from blossoming. The *Flower Constellations* solutions not only solve the constellation maintenance problem, but also provide a new capability for global 3D spatial observations around the planets. In other words, they create space art as shown in Figures 1 and 2.

Figure 1: (C) The *Lone-Star* Flower Constellation [2]

The satellites do not only form interesting shapes in space but also keep their relative position constant by creating an illusion of satellite ballet in space. The reason behind this phenomena is that with the introduction of the *Flower Constellations* theory [1], the resulting constellation can be seen as a new *object* characterized by an axis of symmetry about which the constellation is rotating, as a rigid body, with a prescribed angular velocity. The dynamics of a *Flower Constellation* can be seen as made of two distinct parts: 1) an *internal part*, that describes the dynamics of the satellites within the "object-constellation", and 2) an *external part*, where the "object" has an assigned shape which rotates in the inertial space about a spin axis and with an angular velocity that can be positive or negative. Some of these objects are shown in Figure 2, showing both the versatility and the infinite variety of possible shapes which we call "*choreographies*".

The *Flower Constellations* open a new frontier on complex satellite constellations for two main reasons. Firstly, the *Flower Constellations* can be seen as constituted of two distinct parts: an "internal part", associated with the motion of all the satellites along a prescribed identical relative space track, and an "external

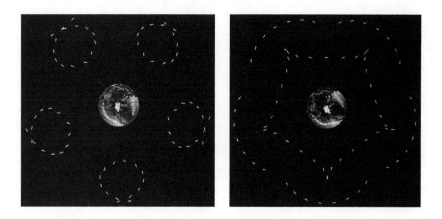

Figure 2: An example of morphing Flower Constellation [2].

part", associated with the dynamic of the whole constellation, as a rigid *object*, that spins about an axis with a prescribed angular velocity. Secondly, these new constellation-objects are used, as *building blocks*, to construct more complex configurations that allow to accomplish more complex tasks.

Flower Constellations are elegant, majestic, beautiful, and are characterized by order and symmetry! By using different object-constellations as building blocks enabling embedded objects into one another, we are achieving the same level of shift as the one that occurred in programming. We believe that our suite of embeddable objects with their own functionalities makes it easy to think of building constellations in the same manner as "Object Oriented Programming" (OOP). OOP was a paradigm shift for traditional programming, the *Flower Constellation* will provide a similar paradigm shift in thinking of constructing constellations. *Flower Constellations* will provide a means to think of constellations as an ensemble of modular functionalities in space.

The *Flower Constellations* are revolutionary, new and not duplicative of concepts previously studied by NASA. They are the building blocks of a very large space architecture that has functionalities. The *Flower Constellations* can be very easily thought of as viable concepts within NASA's present and future mission. The *Flower Constellation* concept is revolutionary because current approaches to satellites constellation are a simple by-product of the functionality they are designed for. By enabling the general population and the research community to think of constellation as *objects*, with morphing capabilities show two snapshots of a morphing *Flower Constellation*), we want to enable new functionalities of satellites that have not been devised, except maybe in science fiction books. In effect, objects defined by these constellations could then be used as building blocks to construct more complex and large objects for which functionalities have yet to be found.

This architecture not only provides space art but also presents a new means of enabling different functionalities such as a near-term better communication throughout the solar system. It also provides a means to establish a basis for a significantly large observation platform to study extra-solar planets and it has the potentiality to replace very large one-piece structures.

References

[1] D. Mortari, M. P. Wilkins and C. Bruccoleri, Journal of the Astronautical Sciences, Special Issue: The John L. Junkins Astrodynamics Symposium, Vol. 52, No. 1-2, pp. 107-127, January-June, 2004.

[2] http://flowerconstellations.tamu.edu/

Anamorphosis.com: Computers, Mathematics and Art

Phillip Kent
London Knowledge Lab – Institute of Education
University of London
United Kingdom
E-mail: p.kent@ioe.ac.uk

Abstract

This paper will comment on the development over a period of several years of an exhibition, website and software application based on the ideas and history of anamorphosis – the technique of creating distorted images according to the mathematical rules of perspective and mirror reflection. I will review some of the goals of the project in developing connections between mathematics and art through the use of computers.

My interest in exploring the connections between art and mathematics stems mainly from an educational point of view. I'm basically interested in the idea of making mathematics a more accessible subject for "ordinary people". Since ancient times, mathematics has sustained a reputation for being "unreachable". I believe this situation is now changing; my own interests in mathematics have always been expressed through computer software, and I think that this can be a means of access for everyone.

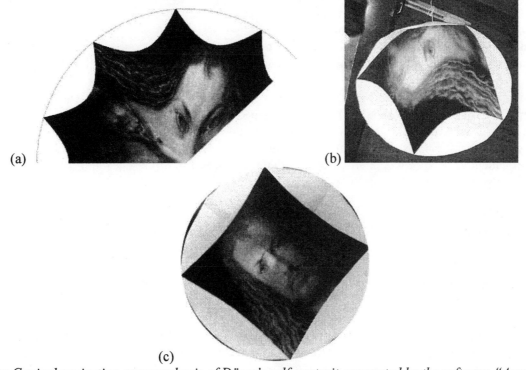

Figure: *Conical projection anamorphosis of Dürer's self-portrait, generated by the software "Anamorph Me!". (a) a print-out of the anamorphosis ready to be rolled into a cone; (b) viewing the image inside the cone from a wrong position; (c) viewing the image from the right position to "decode" it.*

I enjoy mathematical art, including computer-generated pieces, but let me emphasize that my intention with this anamorphosis project is not on the side of producing "art" for consumption by others. Rather I would like to stimulate as many people as possible to be producers themselves, and thus create at the very least a spark of interest in the underlying mathematics – whilst accepting that only a fraction of people will wish to pursue that interest in mathematics.

Anamorphosis is concerned with the creation of distorted images according to the mathematical rules of perspective and mirror reflection. The distinctive thing about an anamorphosis (that is, the distorted image), which contrasts it with *trompe l'oeil*, is that the undistorted form of the image must be recovered by looking at the image from an unusual or surprising location, or using an unusual shape of mirror (cylindrical, conical). For example, in the figure above are three views of one of Dürer's self-portraits, "anamorphosed" by a software package that I wrote, *Anamorph Me!*

I have used anamorphosis as the basis for an ongoing project, "Art of Anamorphosis", which took physical form as an exhibition held in the United Kingdom in 2001, and since then it has continued in virtual form as a website [www.anamorphosis.com] and software application.

The idea for an exhibition was particularly inspired by the delightful engravings of Jean Du Breuil created in the 1640s (*see example on right*), showing "cabinets of anamorphoses" in which curious viewers inspect the contents of rooms filled with anamorphic objects. I particularly tried to imitate the use of *large* objects suspended from walls and ceilings (the Dürer cone illustrated above was about 80cm tall) since these allow the viewer to truly walk around them and experience different perceptions of the objects.

A guiding design principle was that the exhibition should not force attention on the mathematics of anamorphosis, but rather that should be one of the aspects that a visitor might wish to pursue. Then the website, along with printed materials, should open up some of the various directions for further investigation. Anamorphosis is a particular rich topic for this because its mathematical history, as part of the development of perspective, intertwines with the development of art, science and society between the Renaissance period and the nineteenth century.

It is remarkable to reflect how the internet has revolutionized the possibility of access to information. Previously scholarly knowledge, lurking in the confines of academic institutions is increasingly available directly on the internet or via a rapid e-mail exchange with an author. Yet mathematics is not essentially knowledge of this kind, since it must be used and worked on to be meaningful. Symbolic manipulation with algebra is central to the traditional mathematical approach, and it has for long been the major stumbling block for most people's access to mathematical ideas.

The computer opens up new possibilities for the manipulation of symbols. *Anamorph Me!* takes only the first step, in making algorithms for anamorphosis more usable for manipulating images; it does not try to open up the mathematical ideas, to deal with the manipulation of symbols (this idea is still to be developed). But the first step is powerful – it allowed people visiting the exhibition, and later on visitors to the website, to *make* anamorphic art for themselves, and thus progress from consumption to creation, and hopefully, a certain amount of mathematical thinking for themselves.

References: for readings and further information, please visit www.anamorphosis.com

Mathematical Models of Gothic Structures

Javier Barrallo[*] & Santiago Sanchez-Beitia[**]
Applied Mathematics Department[*] & Applied Physic Department[**]
School of Architecture
The University of the Basque Country
Plaza Onati, 2
20018 San Sebastian. SPAIN

Abstract

The constructive characteristics of the Gothic style are unique in the history of Architecture. Gothic cathedrals pushed structure to the limit associating their structural elements to a linear frame that supports forces in a delicate balance. In order to understand this fragile equilibrium we must create a precise geometric model of the building, simple conceptually but substantially representative of the structural and constructive system. Each part of the building has specific constructive and structural characteristics that must be represented in the model. The mathematical model of the building will be the result of combining a geometric model with a mechanical model containing the physical properties obtained from experimental measurements.

1. Introduction

Showing the visitor a range of geometrical models, Spanish Architect Antonio Gaudi once remarked, with, with excitement in his eyes: *Wouldn't it be beautiful to learn geometry in this way?* Without any doubt, mathematical education for architecture students will be more effective and pleasant if all the theoretical knowledge were explained with the help of real architectural examples. The relationship between classic architecture and mathematics is well known. Architecture, unlike other scientific disciplines, can be used as a never ending source of numerical, algebraic, geometric, analytic and topologic problems, to name just a few fields of mathematics. A modern concept of architecture should necessarily include mathematics for its comprehension. Reciprocally, the teaching of mathematics in architecture should be based on the constructive event to be effective.

Interdisciplinary education provides a positive stimulus for both teachers and students, resulting in a much more persistent and interesting training. It is obvious that mathematical knowledge acquired inside an architectural environment is more likely to be applied by future architects after their university studies. As an example of this way of learning mathematics, in this paper we will show some ideas and mathematical concepts related to one of the more complex branches of architecture: restoration, repair and maintenance of Gothic buildings.

2. Why such interest in the Gothic Style?

The constructive characteristics of the Gothic style are unique in the history of Architecture. Gothic cathedrals pushed structure to the limit —soaring cross-vaulting, pointed arches, hollow walls and piers covered with tracery— and used the arch as an external brace, the flying buttress, to form one of the most beautiful stylistic elements of the gothic style.

shown in Figure 3.1, we obtain the sculpture shown in Figure 3.2. This sculpture shows an irregular hexagon, starting from the midpoints, morph into a planar affine regular hexagon. If we continue sliding these balls to the midpoints of the diagonals, we would fold the hexagon into a triangle.

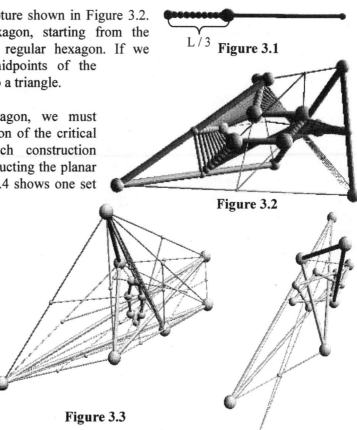

L / 3   **Figure 3.1**

Figure 3.2

Heptagon Constructions. For a heptagon, we must construct four lines to identify the location of the critical red ball. Figure 3.3 shows one such construction containing all 28 lines required for constructing the planar convex affine regular heptagon. Figure 3.4 shows one set of four lines necessary for constructing one of the red balls for a different construction. This constructs a stellar affine regular heptagon. (For those curious, to construct the lines shown in Figure 3.4, begin by constructing the midpoint m_{24} between points p_2 and p_4 and the midpoint m_{15} between points p_1 and p_5. Then connect p_3 to m_{24} and place a yellow ball at a ratio of 1.29 from p_3 towards and past m$_{24}$. Connect this ball to m_{15} and place the red ball at a point .70 of the ratio from the yellow ball.)

Figure 3.3

Figure 3.4

Weighted Averages. The easiest method to identify the desired location of the final position of the red balls is to calculate them as a weighted average of the initial balls. For example, the formula $(1/6)p_1+(1/3)p_2+(1/3)p_3+(1/6)p_4$ is a weighted average of four points, p_1, p_2, p_3, and p_4. To the computer, weighted averages are trivial to construct. For brass and wood, it is necessary to change weighed averages into symmetric linear constructions since locating a new ball along a line segment defined by two existing balls is constructible in brass. Algebraically, weighted averages can always be turned into symmetric linear constructions if desired. For example, the weighted average $(1/6)p_1+(1/3)$ $p_2+(1/3)$ $p_3+(1/6)$ p_4 is equivalent to the hexagon construction stated above. And, in fact, weighted averages were used as a tool in determining the procedures described above [1]. The following sculptures were created using weighed averages, and therefore, the final polygons "hang in midair."

The Critical Weights and Type. One way to calculate a set of critical weights for an n-gon is the following. Let t be a positive integer less than $n/2$ and let $d_i = \cos(\pi / n) - \cos(t (2i+1) \pi / n)$ for each $i=1,2,..., n$. Letting s be the sum of these distances and the critical weights are $w_i = d_i / s$. That is, for any random points $p_1, p_2, ..., p_n$ the points $q_k = w_1p_k + w_2p_{k+1} + ... + w_np_{k+n-1}$, with subscripts modulo n, will form a planar affine regular polygon when connected sequentially [1]. Moreover, the variable t describes the "type" of the polygon. If $t = 1$, then the resulting polygon will always be convex – each vertex will be connected to adjacent vertices. When $t = 2$, there will be a vertex between successively numbered vertices. The stellar pentagon is type 2 and so is the heptagon in Figure 3.4. In general, when $t = m$, the resulting polygon will have $m-1$ vertices between successively number vertices. Figure 3.7, below, shows the type 1, type 2, and type 3 heptagon. While it is most interesting when t is relatively prime to n, it need not be the case. When $t = 2$, for the hexagon, the resulting symmetric linear construction wraps the hexagon around the triangle formed by the midpoints of the diagonal twice. We see this in Figure 3.2 if we continue sliding the six balls up to the three diagonal lines.

Morphing Type. Once we fix the order of the polygon, the only variable in our formula for weighted averaged is the type t. Thus we now morph one image into the next by letting the t change. Only when type is a whole numbers will the polygon be planar. We can not let $t=0$, and so we let t slide from one natural number to another.

Figure 3.5 shows an irregular pentagon with the convex pentagon morphing into the stellar pentagon by morphing type. Within this sculpture are

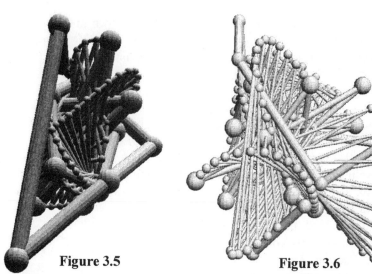

Figure 3.5

five beads of string connecting each vertex of the stellar affine regular pentagon to its corresponding vertex on the convex affine regular pentagon. Although nothing connects to the original polygon, the sculpture is completely defined by the location of the initial random pentagon. Figure 3.6 consist of an irregular heptagon and the type 2 planar heptagon morphing into a type 3 planar heptagon.

Figure 3.6

Morphing Type with Translational Motion. Adding in translations to stretch out this motion – and by removing the irregular n-gon we get the Figure 3.7 which morphs an affine regular convex heptagon into a type 2 stellar affine regular heptagon and then into a type 3 affine regular stellar heptagon.

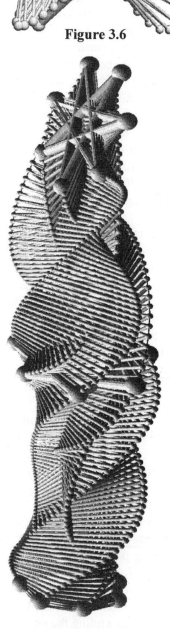

Summary

Symmetric linear constructions and the weighted averages provide a method for creating a variety of predictable and pleasing sculptures which begin from irregular polygons. By morphing these images from either the random polygon to a planar affine regular, or by morphing these images from one planar type to one or more other types, one produces unexpected curves which fold and unfold the polygon.

References

[1] Douglas G. Burkholder, *Parallelogons and Weighted Averages*, Revista de Física y Matemática (FISMAT) de la Facultad de Ciencias, Escuela Poltécnica Nacional (Quito-Ecuador), XII, to Appear.

[2] Jesse Douglas, *A Theorem on Skew Pentagons,* Scripta Mathematica, Vol. 25, 1960.

Figure 3.7

Coxetering Crystals

Marjorie Senechal
Mathematics Department
Smith College
Northampton, MA 01063 U.S.A.
senechal@smith.edu

A reader whose standpoint is more severely practical may take comfort in Lobatschewsky's assertion that 'there is no branch of mathematics, however abstract, which may not some day be applied to phenomena of the real world.' [*Regular Polytopes*, p. *vi*]

Donald Coxeter, 1993,
photograph by Stan Sherer

"Applied mathematics" is not a phrase "Coxeter" evokes in anyone's mind, and probably never in his own. But H.S.M. Coxeter appreciated -- indeed, delighted in -- the symbiotic relation between polytopes and crystals. His classic *Regular Polytopes* is indispensable for the mathematical study of crystals, never more than now.[1]

Coxeter also appreciated and delighted in the symbiotic relation between models – the kind you can pick up, turn over, study from different perspectives – and their abstract descriptions. (Or do the models describe the abstractions?) Eggs and chickens aside, crystallography is a mathematical gold mine in any dimension, and Coxeter delighted in this too.

Regular polytopes and tessellations in four, five, *n* dimensions: *we can never fully comprehend them by direct observation,* Coxeter wrote. *In attempting to do so, however, we seem to peep through a chink in the wall of our physical limitations, into a new world of dazzling beauty.* A beauty so dazzling we must study its shadows, and he taught us how.

I hope, in these eight pages, to justify these statements. That's why I've written this paper in the form of a picture booklet. Look before you read. The pictures come first. All the rest – quotations from *Regular Polytopes* and Coxeter's world-wide correspondence, my supplementary remarks – is commentary.

---

[1] H.S.M. Coxeter, *Regular Polytopes*, Dover Publications, 3rd edition, 1973.

Crystals and Polyhedra

The foundations for our subject were laid by the Greeks . . . but all the more elaborate developments are less than a century old. This revival of interest was partly due to the discovery that many polyhedra occur in nature as crystals. [*Regular Polytopes*, p. vi]

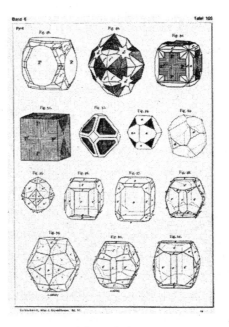

from Goldschmidt's
Atlas der Krystallformen

Many polyhedra do occur in nature as crystals, and many crystals have polyhedral forms. A century ago, mineralogists pored over drawings like those you see here, 14 of the 23,606 crystal forms in Viktor Goldschmidt's nine-volume *Atlas der Krystallformen*.[2]

Why all this painstaking labor, this manic detail? Not for art's sake, nor for geometry's sake, but for science's. Long before recorded history, people marveled at crystals and their striking geometric shapes and wondered how and why. Even fragments of shattered crystals have smooth flat faces, unlike glass. Early in the 19th century, René Just Haüy, a French mineralogist, proposed a how and why: crystals are stacks of sub-visible bricks.[3] The crystallographer's job, then, was to deduce, for each polyhedral crystal, the shape of its brick – its height, width, depth, and interfacial angles. Hence the study of form.

Goldschmidt's labor of love was obsolete before the first volume appeared. The discovery, in 1912, that X-rays are diffracted by crystals unlocked the mysteries of the solid state.[4] The positions of atoms in any crystal, polyhedral or otherwise, could be deduced from the scattered rays. Haüy's hypothesis became history, but diffraction's overnight success rested squarely on his notion that a crystal's building blocks – atoms, molecules, whatever – line up in rows and columns. Tilings, polyhedra and symmetry groups remained in the crystallographer's toolbox.

---

[2] V. Goldschmidt, *Atlas der Krystallformen*, Munich, 9 volumes, 1913 - 1923.

[3] R. J. Haüy, *Traite de Mineralogie*, Paris, 1822.

[4] Max von Laue received the Nobel Prize in Physics for this discovery in 1914.

The Crystallographic Restriction

There is a law of symmetry which prohibits the inanimate occurrence of any pentagonal figure, such as the regular dodecahedron. The two more complicated regular solids cannot form crystals, but need the spark of life for their natural occurrence. [*Regular Polytopes*, p. 13]

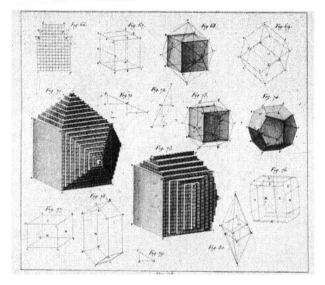

from R. J. Haüy's
Traité de Mineralogie

In this drawing, from *Traité de Mineralogie*, Haüy shows how two different polyhedral crystal forms can be approximated by stacking bricks of the same size and shape. Both forms display the symmetries of the stacking pattern. The difference in the exterior forms is literally superficial.

Look closely at the polyhedron in the middle on the right, a common form of the mineral pyrite. Although the "pyritohedron" has twelve pentagonal faces, it's not a *regular* pentagonal dodecahedron (see *Regular Polytopes*): one edge in each of its pentagons is longer than the other four. According to Haüy, crystal faces *can't* be regular pentagons. Haüy's brick theory implies that the vertices of every crystal are rational triples in the coordinate system defined by its brick. A pyritohedral stack is shown in lower center.

Mineralogists call this the "Law of Rational Indices." Regular pentagons, and hence regular pentagonal dodecahedra, don't have rational vertices in *any* coordinate system. Nor do regular *n*-gons for any *n* greater than 6. In symmetry group language, Haüy's law becomes The Crystallographic Restriction:[5]

If a discrete group of displacements in the plane has more than one centre of rotation, then the only rotations that can occur are 2-fold, 3-fold, 4-fold, and 6-fold.

The regular dodecahedron and icosahedron are outlaws in the crystal kingdom.

---

[5] *Regular Polytopes*, p. 63

Kaleidoscopes and honeycombs

A three-dimensional honeycomb (or solid tessellation) is an infinite set of polyhedra fitting together to fill all space just once, so that every face of each polyhedron belongs to one other polyhedron. . .Three dimensional honeycombs help us to understand the arrangement of atoms in a crystal. [*Regular Polytopes*, p. 74.]

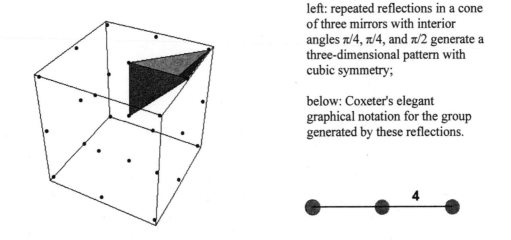

left: repeated reflections in a cone of three mirrors with interior angles $\pi/4$, $\pi/4$, and $\pi/2$ generate a three-dimensional pattern with cubic symmetry;

below: Coxeter's elegant graphical notation for the group generated by these reflections.

The kaleidoscope, introduced in 1818, "very quickly became popular . . . no fewer than two hundred thousand instruments were sold in London and Paris in three months."[6] This grieved its inventor, the Scottish physicist David Brewster, for most of these "instruments" were patent-infringements and – just as sadly – "out of this immense number there were perhaps not one thousand constructed on scientific principles." Brewster expected the kaleidoscope would be, first and foremost, a tool for industrial design, and only secondarily an "instrument of rational amusement." But a toy it remained for 116 years, until Coxeter gave it gravitas.[7]

While crystallographers argued over Haüy's bricks (are they solid? or fictional containers for possibly fictional molecules?), mathematicians analyzed the arrangements, not the arranged.[8] In *Regular Polytopes*, Coxeter described highly symmetrical tessellations in the plane and in three-space, and in the beyond. He's best known for his study of groups generated by reflections: the analysis, classification, and systematization of tessellations generated by reflections in any dimension. Brewster himself had constructed a 3-D kaleidoscope (the mirrors above generate a cubic pattern), but Coxeter generalized the kaleidoscope beyond Brewster's fondest dreams.

In Coxeter's famous graphical notation for these groups, the generating mirrors are represented by dots which are joined by line segments unless the mirrors are perpendicular. Since adjacent mirrors generate a circular pattern with a whole number of mirror-symmetric images, the angles must be π/p, where p is an integer greater than one. In Coxeter graphs, a line is labeled by that integer if $p > 3$. Hence the 4 in the graph above. If we added a fourth mirror to complete the tetrahedron, the pattern would be crystallographic: infinite in all directions.

---

[6] Quoted by David Brewster in *The Kaleidoscope, its history, theory, and construction*, reprinted by Van Cort Publications, Holyoke, MA, 1987.

[7] H.S.M. Coxeter, "Discrete groups generated by reflections," Annals of Mathematics, 35, 1934, 588-621.

[8] As Arthur Schonflies put it, "within the fundamental domain the crystallographer may do as he likes."

Color Symmetry

The problem of systematically coloring periodic patterns has interested textile designers, artists, and crystallographers since 1935. The classification of possible procedures has been seen to depend on space groups and their subgroups and factor groups. Crystallographers naturally worked in Euclidean 3-space before generalizing to two, and then four, dimensions.[9]

All M. C. Escher works © 2005. The M. C. Escher Company – The Netherlands. All rights reserved. Used by permission. www.mcescher.com

Crystallographers and mathematicians discovered the mathematical drawings and prints of M. C. Escher in the 1950s. His tessellations soon appeared in their monographs and texts, giving life to group theory and to the tedious study of crystalline arrangements. In Escher's kaleidoscopic tessellation above, which illustrates the plane crystallographic group p31m, the mirrors bisect the fish to form equilateral triangles enclosing a half-fish of each color.

Escher designed this pattern before he met Coxeter. Later, Coxeter sent him other mathematical ideas which Escher converted to art, a process he called "coxetering."[10]

Look closely: there's more than mirrors here. The red fish (and the black and the gray) are arranged in hexagonal rings. Except for their colors, the three sets of rings are congruent. The fish of each color correspond to subgroups of the tessellation's symmetry group, which permutes them. In other words, this pattern has *color symmetry*. Crystallographers use color symmetry theory to describe the positions of the different kinds of atoms in a single crystal, like the checkerboard pattern of Na and Cl atoms in salt.

Coxeter was intrigued by color groups; we corresponded intensively about them for a few years. He was particularly interested in the problem of notation, and developed symbols for color groups of certain types.

---

[9] H. S. M Coxeter, "A Simple Introduction to Colored Symmetry," International Journal of Quantum Chemistry, 31, 1987, 455-461.

[10] See D. Schattschneider, "Coxeter and the Artists: two-way inspiration", The Coxeter Legacy, Fields Communications v. 46, Amer. Math. Soc., Providence, 2005.

Nonperiodic honeycombs

Dear Dr. Miyazaki, What I would be interested to know is whether rhombohedra fill space in a manner that is essentially non-periodic (in the sense that no honeycomb composed of these particular bricks can have a translation into itself). If the answer is yes, we would have here a very nice 3-dimensional analogue for the non-periodic tilings of Roger Penrose. [H.S.M. Coxeter to Kojo Miyazaki, April 22, 1977.]

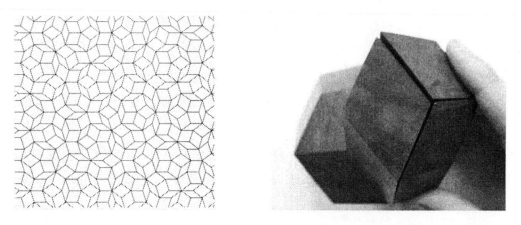

left: a portion of a Penrose tilings by rhombs; right: models of A6 and O6 made by A. G. Bomford

Like Haüy's arrays, kaleidoscope tilings are periodic: they repeat by translations, or shifts. Penrose tilings are nonperiodic: no tiling built with Penrose tiles repeats by translation in any direction. In the version shown above left, the Penrose tiles are rhombs with acute angles 72° and 36°, constrained by "matching rules" for putting them together. Though these rules forbid translation, configurations do repeat – but you can't predict just where. All seven "legal" arrangements of Penrose rhombs around a vertex occur again and again in the fragment above .

Like fractals, Penrose tilings repeat on every scale. Many of the tilings' remarkable features follow from this property, including their nonperiodicity. Coxeter was intrigued by the possibility of a three-dimensional analogue and proposed the two golden rhombohedra, A6 and O6, as tiles.[11] The dihedral angles of A6 are the polygonal angles of the thick Penrose rhomb, and those of O6 are those of the thin. He hoped to show, first, that these rhombohedra can build tilings that repeat on every scale, and second, that matching rules could be found to enforce it.

Earlier, in *Regular Polytopes*, Coxeter had shown that 10 A6s and 10 O6s make a Kepler triacontahedron, K30. Could that construction be repeated on larger scales *ad infinitum*?

A friend A.G. Bomford, an Australian engineer, made the wooden models of A6 and O6 shown above.[12] The blocks are handsome and smooth, but difficult to stick together. Thin tape worked well, up to a point, but even the thinnest tape creates cascading gaps eventually. Coxeter finally gave up, pleading with Bomford, *I don't have the time or patience to try it myself, so please don't embarrass me by sending the necessary pieces!*

---

[11] A polyhedron is golden if its faces are golden rhombs; a rhombus is golden if the lengths of its diagonals stand in the golden ratio.
[12] Richard Bomford has kindly photographed his father's models for this article.

pentagons meet at each vertex. Semi-regular tessellation refers to a tiling pattern, which are composed of two kinds of regular polygons so that two of each meet at each vertex alternately. There is a constant reduction is size of the polygons as they become distorted in their curved space nearing the circumference. The constant diminution is also represented by progressively smaller arcs, which cut the circle and are perpendicular to the diameter and the outer edge of the disc. The interior arcs mark an angle and parallel lines cross each other in ever-smaller distances. Its circumference represents infinity. The curvature of the arcs is constant as they decrease in size towards the bounding edge. It is a sequence towards the infinitesimal. The curvature of my 3D mosaic sculptures is hyperbolic and consists of a tiled pattern and surface division. The interior is a recessed pentagon within which other pentagons diminish in size. Some are formed through the psychology of visual perception.

(Fig.2),*HyperbolicDiminution–Blue*,(Fig.3),*HyperbolicDiminution-Red*,(Fig.4),*Hyperbolic-Diminution-Red-Five-fold Rotation*,(Fig.5),*HyperbolicDiminution–White*. The distortion that results in hyperbolic geometry led me to explore the use of geometric shapes and gradually alter them, (Fig.6) *Metamorphosis of a Hexagon,* in order to a achieve a transformation. The transformation takes place as the shape traverses the raised and lowered 3D planes. William Huff's work served as an inspiration [9]. This sculpture is a part of a series, which is in the process of being developed to achieve the concept of infinity in hyperbolic geometry.

5.3 Time and Energy
The concept of time and energy is metaphorically represented. One becomes aware of the time and energy expended in cutting and piecing the tiling pattern together from point to segment to shape. The subtractive and additive process is implicit in sculptures. The mosaic units combine to form a surface that resembles pixels on a computer screen. It is a part to whole relationship. The pattern consists of hand cut *tesserae* . The individual pieces are cubic or rectangular in shape. They are made from marble and glass. The *tesserae* cut from the initial large block of marble or glass and involve successive steps of rotating the polygon to achieve the desired small size. These tiny gems of glass or stone are then pieced together with tweezers using the direct method to form a tiling pattern. The process is similar to a jeweler cutting a diamond. Four hyperbolic sculptures as well as the sculpture (Fig.6), *Metamorphosis of a Hexagon* depicts the concept through the process. Time is implied in is the story of the transformation of a hexagon as it traverses different 3D planes. The hexagon bumps against a new plane and becomes distorted and assumes another configuration as it bumps against different planes and ultimately returns as a hexagon. The central axis in all sculptures is a recessed interior pentagon. (Fig.1), *Cutting " tesserae"*

5.4 Symmetry
It is a transformation that preserves the distance. The surface is composed of tiling patterns that have symmetry of design. The four kinds are translation, rotation, reflection and glide-reflection [10. My sculptures illustrate the use of mirror or bilateral symmetry and visually maps the shapes onto each other if cut in half through the center pentagon. There are multiple rhythms and patterns.

The sculpture *Hyperbolic Diminution-Red-Five Fold Rotation-* is composed of tiling patterns with an emphasis on the red square unit that forms a five-fold rotation. Some are constructed using only pentagons such as *Hyperbolic Diminution-Blue* with subdivisions of triangles with a light and dark pattern. *Hyperbolic Diminution-Red* is also composed of pentagons but the pattern looks very different due to the pigmented grout. *Hyperbolic Diminution-White* is a combination of pentagons and quadrilaterals. In these hyperbolic sculptures, the shapes are stretched as they decrease in size towards the bounding edge. The interior of all my sculptures has a recessed pentagon. Additional pentagons undergo rotation towards infinity within the interior of some of the sculptures. Because these sculptures are handmade, mechanically perfect symmetries are not possible.

6. Conclusion

Mosaic art provides a document of the great civilizations of the past. Because few sources on daily life exist from this time period, these mosaics are invaluable documents of the ancient times, which would otherwise not be known. The durability of material and permanence of color has survived throughout the centuries. For this reason, archeologists and art historians have been able to use them to provide us with an insight into the history of mankind. It is a fascinating excursion of the cultures that have since disappeared leaving behind their mosaic traces. Turning to the present, labor saving technology and innovations in diverse fields have had far reaching effects. Mosaic as a discipline has gained autonomy. We are witnessing a Renaissance of mosaic art. For now, its own independence seems assured. Fine artists must overcome performance anxiety and embrace the potential of working in mosaic as a medium and autonomous discipline. Bridging the gap will be the key.

7. Illustrations

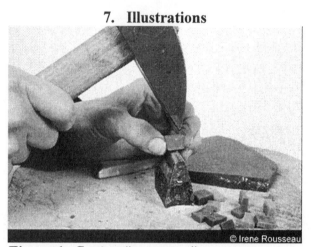

Figure 1: *Cutting " tesserae "*

Figure 2: *Hyperbolic Diminution-Blue*

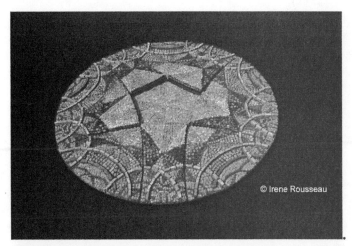

Figure 3: *Hyperbolic Diminution-Red*

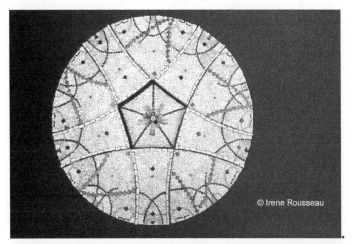

Figure 4: *Hyperbolic Diminution-Red-Five-fold Rotation*

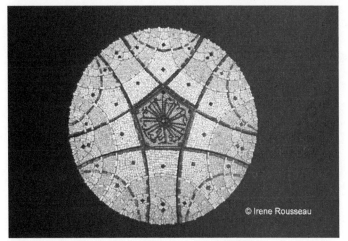

Figure 5: *Hyperbolic Diminution-White*

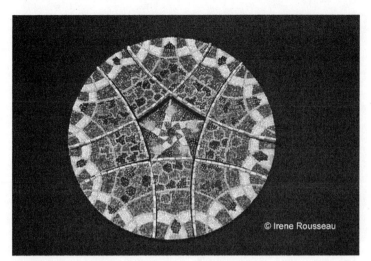

Figure 6: *Metamorphosis of a Hexagon*

References

[1] Cimok, Fatih. *Antioch Mosaic,* A Turizm Yayinlan Li.Sti., 1995.

[2] Irene Rousseau, primary research on location in Ravenna, Italy.

[3] Gleick, James. *Chaos: Making a New Science.* Penguin, New York, 1987.

[4] Rousseau, Irene. Colloque De L'AIEMA (archeology and ancient Greco-Roman mosaics) Paris, France (at press, in process of being published)

[5] Irene Rousseau, primary research at mosaic workshops, Italy.

[6] Fiori, Cesar. Quaderni IRTEC, nr.3 *Mosaico E Restauro Musivo*, Edit Faenza, 1992.

[7] Irene Rousseau, primary research at the Vatican School of Mosaics, Rome, Italy.

[8] Rousseau, Irene. *Geometric Mosaic Tiling on Hyperbolic Sculptures*, Proceedings, Bridges: Mathematical Connections in Art, Music and Science, 2003.

[9] Hofstadter, Douglas. *Metamagical Themas*, Basic Books Inc., New York, 1985.

[10] B. Grünbaum, G.C.Shephard. *Tilings and Patterns*, W.H.Freeman and Co, 1987.

Serial Polar Transformation Motifs Revisited

Gary R. Greenfield
Department of Mathematics & Computer Science
University of Richmond
Richmond, VA 23173, U.S.A.
ggreenfi@richmond.edu

Abstract

Elliot and Bleicher considered using compositions of polar transformations — functions from the plane to the plane viewed as transformations from polar to cartesian coordinates — as a method for generating computer images. In this paper we revisit this technique for creating what we call *motifs* in order to more carefully consider: (1) how these transformations are defined, (2) implementation and resolution issues, (3) motif coloring, and (4) the automated evolution of motifs.

1. Introduction

In [1], Bleicher presents an interesting gallery of images that were computer generated using a technique he calls "serial transformations of squares." The formal model for this technique requires a finite set of functions $\{f_1, \ldots, f_u\}$ where each function f maps the unit square $\{(\theta, r) : 0 \leq r, \theta \leq 1\}$ to the plane. This means that each f can be written in the form $(\theta, r) \longrightarrow (f_x(\theta, r), f_y(\theta, r))$. Suppose that the point (θ, r) is colored $c_{(\theta,r)}$. If we have a composition sequence g of the form $g = f_{i_1} \circ f_{i_2} \circ \cdots \circ f_{i_v}$, then we obtain an image, or *motif*, from g by coloring the point $g(\theta, r)$ using the color $c_{(\theta,r)}$. Because Bleicher uses his model to search for aesthetic motifs in the *space* of serial transformations, his image generation method is distantly related to the evolving expressions method of Sims [6]. And although the image generation method is completely different, it should be noted that many of the images in Bleicher's gallery bear a striking resemblance to the spirolaterals of Krawcyzk [4]. With respect to Bleicher's formal model, we note that compositions of transformations of the type Bleicher considers formed an integral part of a functional programming *design* language developed by Elliot [2] for image processing. Elliot's principal interests were *pattern* design and comparing his language to earlier design languages introduced by Maeda [5], Hudak [3], and others. In this paper we revisit the work of Bleicher and make further contributions by considering additional pattern, color, and genetic algorithm techniques.

2. The Polar Transformations

Following [1], the points (θ, r) of the unit square are viewed as parameterizing lines and circles in the plane by sending horizontal lines (fixed r) to circles, and vertical lines (fixed θ), to lines through the origin. In order to obtain such a map from the unit square to the unit square we must use translation of axes, so we define the polar transformation P by

$$P : (\theta, r) \longrightarrow ((1 + r\sin(2\pi\theta))/2, (1 + r\cos(2\pi\theta)/2)).$$

Note that the image of the vertical line segment in the domain from $(0,0)$ to $(0,1)$ is the vertical line segment in the range from $(1/2, 1/2)$ to $(1/2, 1)$. To invert this transformation, we use the polar (sic) transformation I determined from the equations

$$\theta = \arctan((2x-1)/(2y-1))/2\pi,$$
$$r = \sqrt{(2x-1)^2 + (2y-1)^2}.$$

We also consider the inversion though a circle transformation

$$C : (\theta, r) \longrightarrow (k^2\theta'/R' + 1/2, k^2r'/R' + 1/2),$$

where $\theta' = \theta - 1/2$, $r' = r - 1/2$, $R' = \sqrt{(\theta')^2 + (r')^2}$, and k is constant, together with the "displacement" transformation (the one suggested in [1] has a misprint) given by

$$D : (\theta, r) \longrightarrow (\theta' + a\sin(r'/b) + 1/2, r' + a\sin(\theta'/b) + 1/2),$$

where θ' and r' are as above, and a and b are constants chosen for their aesthetic effect. Finally, for future reference, we consider the polar arc transformation

$$A : (\theta, r) \longrightarrow ((1 + r\sin(2\pi((1-2\omega)\theta + \omega)))/2, (1 + r\cos(2\pi((1-2\omega)\theta + \omega)/2)),$$

where the constant ω is chosen to lie between zero and one-half.

3. The Resolution Problem

Even though our polar transformations are continuous almost everywhere, in order to visualize the effect of a polar transformation on an $n \times n$ pixel output display device, one must either consider inverse mappings to ensure that each pixel in the range is the image of some pixel in the domain, or forward mappings using the technique of over-sampling in the domain so that the transformation is treated as a mapping from an $m \times m$ array to an $n \times n$ array where $m \gg n$. We chose the latter. Moreover, the choices for the constants necessary to define some of our transformations, or the use of rotations (see below), may send some points of the unit square under the polar transformation mapping to points that lie outside the unit square, in which case clipping must be invoked. To emphasize these complications we show in Figure 1 the effect of applying the transformations P, I, D, C, and $P \circ P$ to a unit square that was colored using a black and white checkerboard pattern. The over-sampled resolution mapping is 800×800 to 200×200, and the "missed" pixels are shown in grey. This figure should be compared with Figure 1 of [1]. To generate what we are referring to here as motifs using serial transformations of the square, Bleicher interleaves the *polar arc* transformation with a sequence of transformations chosen from the set consisting of $R_1, \ldots, R_{11}$, where R_i is a counterclockwise rotation of $\pi i/6$ radians, together with the horizontal reflection H which, for our purposes, needs to be defined by setting $H(\theta, r) = (\theta, 1 - r)$. Adopting the abusive notation $R_{12} = H$, any finite numerical sequence of indices can be used to represent a serial polar transformation. For example, the sequence 2-7-12-5 specifies the serial transformation

$$A \circ R_5 \circ A \circ R_{12} \circ A \circ R_7 \circ A \circ R_2 \circ A.$$

In our implementation we chose the constant ω in A, which governs how pixels are distributed along the arc determined by θ as θ ranges from zero to one, to be 0.05. To see why this method successfully generates motifs, refer to Figure 2 which shows the iterates A^0, A^1, A^2, A^3, A^6, and A^9 applied to a solid patterned square where, once more, missing pixels are shown in grey. This figure should be compared to Figure 2 of [1]. Presumably, discrepancies between our first two figures and those in [1] arise from the use of forward mappings and/or the fact that transformations are not given *explicitly* in [1].

Figure 1: *From left to right, the polar transformations denoted J (identity), P (polar), I (polar inverse), C (inversion through the circle using $k = 0.2$), D (displacement using $a = 0.04$ and $b = 0.06$), and $P \circ P$ (double polar) applied to a unit square with a checkerboard pattern.*

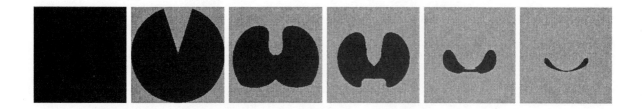

Figure 2: *From left to right, the motifs from the polar transformations $A^0 = J$, $A^1 = A$, A^2, A^3, A^6, A^9, where A is the polar arc transformation with constant ω set to 0.05 and J is the identity transformation, applied to a solid colored unit square.*

4. Randomly Generated Motifs

Since there are only $12 \times 12 \times 12 = 1728$ motifs that can be formed using interleaved sequences derived from *sequence identifiers* of the form i_1-i_2-i_3, it is conceivable that one could exhaustively generate and inspect them all. We chose to use a sampling approach instead by randomly generating 300 of these length three motifs in groups of twenty-five at a time. Like Bleicher, we observed wispy motifs such as those shown in Figure 3. We also obtained a cache of more compact motifs that we found equally intriguing such as those shown in Figure 4. Surprisingly, we found an extraordinary number of *mutant* motifs such as those shown in Figure 5. Mutant motifs were characterized as having hair-like appendages or cascades of isolated pixels. In fact, more than half of our randomly generated motifs were mutant!

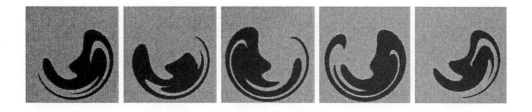

Figure 3: *Randomly generated wispy interleaved length three motifs with sequence identifiers 9-10-3, 3-1-8, 2-4-5, 3-3-12, 9-10-8.*

Figure 4: *Randomly generated compact interleaved length three motifs with sequence identifiers 10-2-3, 10-10-10, 12-3-9, 3-1-3, 2-1-6.*

Figure 5: *Randomly generated mutant interleaved length three motifs with sequence identifiers 11-7-1 and 3-6-3.*

5. Motif Colorings and a Simple Variation

In order to better understand how motifs are formed, we replaced the solid background pattern with a vertical gradient pattern consisting of nine vertical stripes in nine different shades of the same hue. To maintain the visual integrity of the motifs, when working with a fixed hue in HSV color space, we chose very narrow spreads in value and saturation. Figure 6 shows examples of such "shaded" motifs.

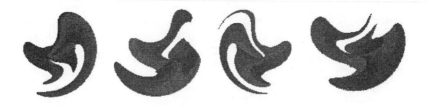

Figure 6: *Shaded, randomly generated interleaved length three motifs with sequence identifiers 3-9-9, 8-11-9, 2-3-3, 9-11-10.*

As an experiment, we also considered altering the *initial* polar transformation before reverting to interleaving the (length three) sequence with the polar arc transformation. Figure 7 shows two images obtained when the initial transformation was the displacement transformation D, while Figure 8 shows five examples obtained when the initial transformation was the polar inversion transformation I.

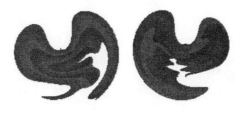

Figure 7: *Interleaved length three motifs where the displacement transformation replaces the initial polar arc transformation. Sequence identifiers are 3-9-11 and 6-6-1.*

Figure 8: *Interleaved length three motifs where the polar inversion transformation replaces the initial polar arc transformation. Sequence identifiers are 3-3-3, 8-1-1, 8-10-1, 12-11-10, 3-10-11.*

6. The Genetic Algorithm

To consider longer lengths for interleaved sequences, we kept the polar arc transformation as the initial transformation, and made use of the Genetic Algorithm. This method had been suggested by Bleicher but his results were inconclusive (private communication). The sequence identifier now represents the *genome* of an individual motif in the *population* of motifs. We used a population of size twelve, and at the conclusion of each fitness evaluation cycle, we used the four most fit genomes to repopulate by preserving their genomes into the next generation and applying a "point mutation" operator to copies of their genomes to obtain the rest of the individuals needed to fill out the population. To ensure diversity, we mutated the clones sufficiently until all members of the population were distinct. For our fitness function we chose to tally the number of *missed* pixels in the output image whose 3 × 3 pixel neighborhood did *not* consist entirely of missed pixels. The rationale behind this calculation was to measure the "boundary" of the motif. During most our runs we minimized this fitness function. For such runs the expectation was that we would evolve compact motifs and avoid mutants. The Genetic Algorithm was allowed to run for either five or ten generations. Figure 9 shows three images from our test run using length three genomes. There were no mutant images in the population but, surprisingly, wispy images did appear. Figure 10 shows motifs that were evolved in a run using length four genomes.

Due to space considerations, for our final example, we consider length five genomes, but now during each run we determine fitness by *maximizing* the tally of boundary pixels of the motif. Our objective, of course, is to evolve wispy motifs. The top row of Figure 11 shows the wispy motifs that were evolved in a run lasting five generations. The bottom row of Figure 11 shows wispy motifs from a different run that lasted ten generations. Mutants within such populations were present, but this was easily explained by the high mutation rates we used because, when mutants appeared, they rarely survived for more than one generation.

Figure 9: *The Genetic Algorithm applied to a small population of length three genomes. The fitness goal was to minimize the number of boundary pixels. Left to right the most fit, the average fit, and the least fit motifs present after five generations. Their sequence identifiers are 11-9-1, 2-1-1, 10-8-9.*

Figure 10: *The Genetic Algorithm applied to length four genomes. Sequence identifiers are 7-2-3-1, 4-1-3-1, 2-4-10-10, 6-10-8-10, 2-10-10-3.*

Figure 11: *The Genetic Algorithm applied to a small population of length five genomes. The fitness goal was to maximize the number of boundary pixels. The three on the left with sequence identifiers 10-8-7-8-5, 2-10-12-8-5, 2-12-10-5-5 were from a run lasting five generations and the three at the right with sequence identifiers 10-9-6-8-4, 10-9-6-8-6, 9-10-6-8-12 are from a run lasting ten generations.*

References

[1] Bleicher, L., Serial polar transformations of simple geometries, *ISAMA—CTI 2004 Proceedings* (ed. S. Luecking), 2004, 65–68.

[2] Elliot, C., Functional image synthesis, *2001 Bridges Conference Proceedings* (ed. R. Sarhangi and S. Jablan), 2001, 139–158.

[3] Hudak, P., *The Haskell School of Expression — Learning Functional Programming through Multimedia*, Cambridge University Press, New York, 2000.

[4] Krawczyk, R., The art of spirolaterals, *The Millennial Open Symposium on the Arts and Interdisciplinary Computing* (eds. D. Salesin and C. Sequin), 2000, 127–136.

[5] Maeda, J., *Design by Numbers*, MIT Press, Cambridge, MA, 1999.

[6] Sims, K., Artificial evolution for computer graphics, *Computer Graphics*, **25** (1991) 319–328.

Orderly Tangles Revisited

George W. Hart
Computer Science Department
Stony Brook University
Stony Brook, NY 11794 USA
E-mail: george@georgehart.com

Abstract

In the 1970s and 1980s Alan Holden described symmetric arrangements of linked polygons which he called *regular polylinks* and constructed many cardboard and stick models. The fundamental geometric idea of symmetrically rotating and translating the faces of a Platonic solid is applicable to both sculpture and puzzles. The insight has been independently discovered or adapted by others, but the concept has not been widely used because no closed-form method is known for calculating the dimensions of snugly fitting parts. This paper describes a software tool for the design and visualization of these forms that allows the dimensions to be determined. The software also outputs geometry description files for solid freeform fabrication, and image files for printing and cutting out paper templates. The paper templates make it easy to teach the concepts in a hands-on manner. Examples and variations are presented in the form of computer images, paper, wood, and solid freeform fabrication models.

1. Introduction

Figures 1 and 2 illustrate the key ideas of Holden's *regular polylinks* [5] [6] [7]. The six hollow faces of the inner cube are separated, translated radially outwards from the center, and each rotated the same angle clockwise about their center. In Figure 2, the original cube is removed, the faces are moved inward until they interweave, the rotation angle is adjusted slightly, the thickness of each plane is reduced to paper-thinness, and the size of each square hole is shrunk slightly to make a snug fit. Each square links with four others. From the underlying cube's symmetry, the rotational axes are preserved but not the mirror planes.

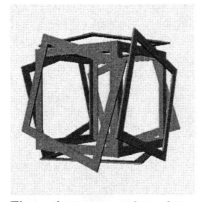
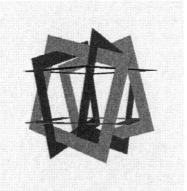

Figure 1. *Rotation and translation of cube faces.*

Figure 2. *Regular polylink with six squares.*

Figure 3. *Paper model of six linked squares.*

It is instructive to create a paper model of Figure 2 by cutting out six hollow squares and interweaving them. Four of the squares can be cut open, linked through the other two, and then taped together. Figure 3 is a photo of a model made using three colors of card stock, iso-coloring parallel faces. It is chiral so one must choose between two enantiomorphs. The only critical parameter is the ratio of the edge length of the outer square to the inner square hole. By means of the software described below, a ratio of approximately 15/11 is determined to be suitable. So the outer square can be 3.7 inches on edge with a 2.7-inch square hole, leaving 0.5 inch of solidity on four sides, and four fit within an 8.5 by 11 inch sheet. This is easily drafted and cut out from paper. Or simply make six enlarged photocopies of Figure 4. For even larger models, use cardboard. Figure 5 has the same weaving as Figure 3, but the strut cross section is made into squares, to give it enough internal substance to hold together when fabricated as a solid freeform fabrication model. This fused deposition model (FDM) is 2.5 inches in diameter.

Figure 4. *Hollow square template for making model in Figure 3.*

Figure 5. *FDM model with square strut cross sections.*

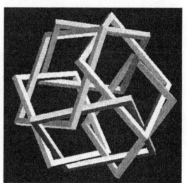

Figure 6. *A different weaving of six squares, also based on cube.*

Holden's regular polylinks are the topologically distinct polygon linkages that result from varying the rotation and radial translation starting with the faces of any of the five Platonic solids. There can be several distinct ways of linking the rotated faces from any underlying polyhedron. Figure 6 shows a second way of linking six squares, but they still lie in the face planes of an imagined cube. Starting from a dodecahedron, one regular polylink of twelve pentagons is shown in Figure 7.

The struts which form the polygon edges in Figures 1-3 have rectangular cross-sections, and in Figures 5-7 they have square cross sections. Holden made his models using ¼-inch diameter wooden dowels of circular cross section. The critical dimension for a snug fit is the ratio of the strut length to diameter. He experimented until he found the shortest lengths that could be assembled, and gave a table of his results for others who replicate the constructions with round dowels [7]. But different dimension ratios are needed if one prefers square, rectangular, or other cross sections.

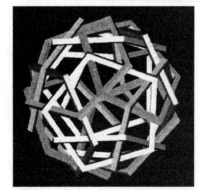

Figure 7. *Regular polylink with twelve pentagons.*

Figure 8. *Regular polylink with six pentagons.*

Figure 9. *Paper model of Fig. 8.*

Figure 8 illustrates a special case to consider. The faces of a dodecahedron are translated in to a distance of zero from the center. Then by proper choice of rotation angle, it is possible to cause opposite faces of the polyhedron to coincide. So the twelve faces of the dodecahedron fuse into six concentric interwoven pentagons of figure 8. A paper model of this, Figure 9, is made from pentagons of 3-inch edge, having pentagonal holes of 2.5-inch edge. Analogously, the six faces of a cube can be translated to the origin where they fuse into three orthogonal concentric squares. But because squares have an even number of sides, they intersect other squares (in either of two rotations) rather than forming a weave. With pentagons or triangles a non-self-intersecting polylink can be formed.

Figure 10. *Regular polylink composed of four triangles.*

Figure 11. *Paper 5-inch triangles, 2.5-inch holes, seen on 3-fold axis.*

Figure 12. *Three nested regular polylinks, each like Figure 8.*

The symmetric intricacy attainable with simple components makes polylinks very appealing aesthetically. Holden illustrates only small cardboard models and dowel models, but he suggests their use in "constructivist sculpture". I have run into a dozen or so examples of sculptures based on his suggestion or a rediscovery of the essential ideas, and there are many ways to adapt, combine, or extend them. For example, Robert Lang, George Odom, Rinus Roelofs, and Carlo Sequin have explored the minimalist construction of four triangles shown in Figure 10 [1, 8, 9, 10, 11]. It can be derived from either the tetrahedron or the octahedron by translating the triangles in to the origin. Deriving Figure 10 from a tetrahedron shows that a degree of rotational freedom remains. Starting from the octahedron explains its axis of 4-fold symmetry; a particular rotation angle causes faces to merge in pairs. Coxeter analyzed this construction and showed: (1) if made of zero-thickness material, the hole in each triangle has exactly half the edge length of the whole triangle, and (2) the twelve outer vertices lie at the midpoints of a cube's edges, i.e., the vertices of an Archimedean cuboctahedron [2]. I recommend the reader make a paper model, as in Figure 11.

A very large polylink sculpture is Charles Perry's 1976, twelve ton "Da Vinci", based on the six-pentagon polylink of Figure 9. See [3], plate D for a figure. Perry made flat steel pentagons 20-feet on a side, and nested two copies of the construction together. Figure 12 illustrates this idea but takes it further to have three concentric copies. The series can be extended inward to any depth because the components are progressively reduced in size geometrically towards the center.

Holden does not define *orderly tangle* precisely, but uses it loosely to subsume a variety of interesting forms such as highway interchanges, woven cloth, and polylinks. A form such as Figure 12 is not a regular polylink (because it is three regular polylinks) but it fits under the broader heading of orderly tangle.

2. Puzzles

A wooden puzzle based on the twelve pentagons of Figure 7 is shown in Figure 13. In Figure 14 is a wooden puzzle made of 30 identical sticks, which form ten triangles. It is based on an icosahedron, with the 20 faces translated to the center and rotated to coincide into ten pairs. In both puzzles, the square wooden sticks are cut longer than the polygon edges, and are notched to lock together gluelessly with half lap joints. I received these beautiful works as presents during a trip to Taiwan in July 2004. They were cleverly designed by Teacher Lin and expertly constructed by Sculptor Wu, both members of the Kaohsiung Puzzle Club. I received them disassembled for easy transport in my luggage and had to assemble them on arriving home.

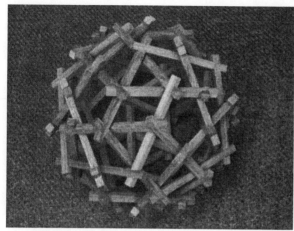

Figure 13. *Wooden puzzle by Lin and Wu.*

Figure 14. *Wooden puzzle by Lin and Wu.*

This puzzle idea of Lin and Wu can be applied to many other polylinks if one can determine the proper length to cut the wooden sticks. As a simple example, the polylink shown in Figure 5 can be built from square stock if the ratio of the outer edge to the cross-section edge is 9.8 to 1. This value comes from the software described in the next section, but as wood is flexible and compressible, some experimenting was still required. So from 1-unit square stock, one can cut 24 pieces, each 11.8 units long. Near each end, but from opposite sides, notch halfway through to leave a 1-unit overhang beyond the notch. Figure 15 shows the assembled result. Figure 16 is the analogous puzzle of thirty sticks assembled into six pentagons woven as in Figure 8. I built both of 0.5-inch square wood bars.

Figure 15. *Puzzle based on Figures 3 and 5.*

Figure 16. *Puzzle based on Figure 8.*

In these two experiments, I found that cutting the lengths a few percent shorter than the software suggests seems to compensate for the flexibility of the struts and the fact that the corners of wood struts may be compressed. So although the software provides a good initial value, the woodworker is advised to plan on some experimentation with scrap wood before investing in quality wood.

3. Software

To design and build regular polylinks and tangles of concentric polylinks, I wrote a program with sliders that can be adjusted to see a wide range of structures on-screen. The computer-generated images in this paper are from screen-shots of its operation. The user can specify any number of polylinks to be assembled concentrically, and for each set, the user selects the underlying polyhedron used as its basis. Then sliders allow the size, translation, and rotation of the components to be adjusted. At present, the edge cross sections are adjustable rectangles, allowing flat (paper) versions as the special case of width zero. As the sliders are adjusted, the dimensions of length, width, thickness, etc. are displayed, which can be used for making models of wood or other materials. When the user is happy with the form shown rotating on the screen, a click of a button generates an STL file for making solid freeform fabrication models, e.g., Figure 5. Clicking another button generates an image file that can be printed for making paper or cardboard models, e.g., Figure 4.

Three 4-cm examples made by selective laser sintering (SLS) from the program's STL output are shown below. Figures 17 is ten triangles, arranged as in Figure 14, but with a "tall" cross-section. Figure 18 is twenty icosahedrally arranged triangles, with the minimum possible linkage (analogous to the cubic form in Figure 6). Figure 19 is a weave based on the octahedron but with the triangles replaced by hexagons.

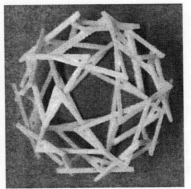

Figure 17. *10 triangle SLS model, based on icosahedron.*   **Figure 18.** *20 triangle SLS model, based on icosahedron.*   **Figure 19.** *8 hexagon SLS model, based on octahedron.*

The software is freely available online at my website [4]. It has only been tested on PCs, but it is written in java so should be transportable to other computing environments. For rendering 3D images on the screen, it uses Sun's freely available *java3D* extension, which must be installed on the user's computer. The coding is quite straightforward, with no clever algorithms or data structures needed. I believe it can be straightforwardly replicated by any software engineer with expertise in graphics programming.

Users may verify their understanding of its capabilities by replicating the figures of this paper, or one can simply start playing to create new objects. The software generates all regular polylinks including several icosahedral examples that Holden did not describe. Lang enumerated the regular polylinks with a computer search and showed there are 2 tetrahedral, 2 cubic, 3 octahedral, 5 dodecahedral, and 23 icosahedral varieties (excluding the extreme cases where polygons either are not linked or are merged into pairs) [8]. I can replicate these numbers with an independent geometric technique of counting subsets of symmetry axes that pierce the interior of a polygon centrally placed in the stellation diagram.

Many extensions of the program are possible. It could be straightforwardly modified to produce circular, triangular, or other shapes of cross sections for the polygon edges. Another possible addition to the software is a numerical search for slider settings that result in a snug fit. I planned for this feature when originally designing the software, but then discovered that it is simple to see on the screen if there are gaps or overlaps in the components, so manual adjustment seems sufficient.

4. Variations

There are an unlimited number of variations on the above ideas. For example, Holden made several models of linked polygonal stars instead of convex polygons. Similarly, one might try rectangles or rhombs instead of regular polygons; I have not implemented any of these with software. (For related rectangle linkages, see [11].) Another idea is to start with polyhedra other than the Platonic solids. Holden constructed examples based on Archimedean solids, e.g., the rhombicuboctahedron and the snub cube. One can symmetrically combine multiple polylinks based on different polyhedra; sets with the same symmetry combine to form a tangle with the same symmetry. Figure 20 shows the combination of a cubical and a tetrahedral form. It combines the tangles of Figure 2 and Figure 10 so each triangle links three squares while each square links two triangles. Figure 21 shows the union of a dodecahedral and an icosahedral form in which both puzzles of Figures 13 and 14 are intertwined.

Figure 20. *6 squares plus 4 triangles.*

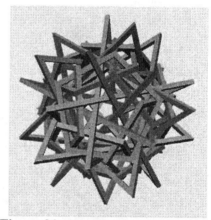

Figure 21. *12 pentagons plus 10 triangles.*

Another variation Holden tried was to put squares around the twelve 2-fold axes of a cube, i.e., in the planes of a rhombic dodecahedron. Here the squares only exhibit 2-fold symmetry, so their edges and vertices are not all equivalent, and the polylink is not regular. I find the results less attractive—fun to generate with the software but less interesting to look at. An example is shown in Figure 22. Here the twelve squares are grouped together as the sides of four triangular prisms. Extending his idea, it is natural to try putting thirty squares around the 2-fold axes of an icosahedron, i.e., in the planes of a rhombic triacontahedron. These can be grouped in many interesting ways, including five cubes or six pentagonal prisms. In Figure 23, the thirty squares are grouped together as the sides of ten triangular prisms. (When brought to the origin and fused into fifteen squares, they form five octahedra.)

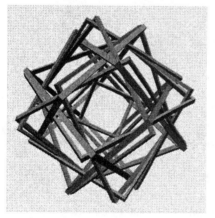

Figure 22. *12 squares, in four triangular prisms.*

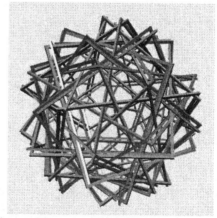

Figure 23. *30 squares in ten triangular prisms.*

Spiraling the faces in a series of concentric arrangements is another idea that can be explored with the software. Fig 24 shows a simple example based on an inner cube that is surrounded by nine layers, each slightly larger and rotated five degrees more than the previous. At the end of nine steps, the 45 degree rotation of the squares leads them to be arranged as in a cuboctahedron. This is not technically a "tangle" as no polygons are linked, but it is easy to generate other examples that are. Figure 25 shows an assemblage of triangles that smoothly rotate between an outer stella octangula and an inner form of four triangles, positioned as in Figure 4. Figure 26 shows a linked set of ten triangular helixes that each join a pair of opposite faces of the outer icosahedron. Charles Perry has explored this "face screwing" concept to great effect in a number of monumental sculptures, e.g. his 1973, 35-foot tall, "Eclipse", which starts with an inner dodecahedron. See [3], plate D for a figure.

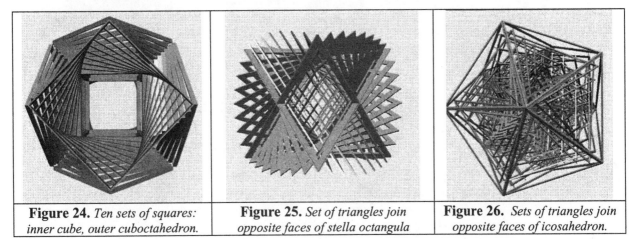

| **Figure 24.** *Ten sets of squares: inner cube, outer cuboctahedron.* | **Figure 25.** *Set of triangles join opposite faces of stella octangula* | **Figure 26.** *Sets of triangles join opposite faces of icosahedron.* |

Weaving is another way to generate variations on a polylink. The oldest example that I know of a form closely related to a regular polylink is the sepaktakraw ball, seen in Figure 27. Traditionally woven from rattan, it exhibits the dodecahedral pattern of figure 8. The design goes back centuries for use in traditional Asian "football" games. Figure 28 shows a "spherical basket" I wove of paper strips. The six dark central bands follow the same weave pattern of six pentagons shown in Figure 8. Neighboring bands, which get progressively lighter in color, simply alternate over and under in the natural weave pattern. Note the difference between this weave and the sepaktakraw ball. In Figure 28 the individual strands weave, while in Figure 27 the group of strands weaves as a whole.

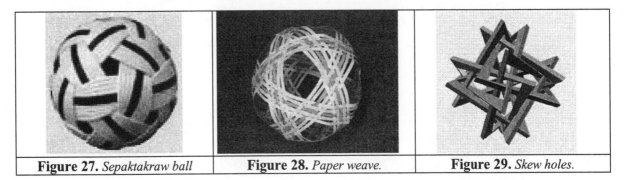

| **Figure 27.** *Sepaktakraw ball* | **Figure 28.** *Paper weave.* | **Figure 29.** *Skew holes.* |

Another variation, illustrated in Figure 29, is to allow a parameter for a relative rotation between the polygon and its hole. This adds a dynamic visual quality to the forms.

A different type of variation is to replace the straight edges of the polygons with curved paths. There are infinitely many ways to choose curves, but a particularly natural one is to perform an inversion about the center of symmetry. Central inversion replaces each point at distance r from the origin with a point in the same direction but at distance $1/r$. This transformation is well studied mathematically but little used in sculpture [12]. In this context, the chain of *n* rectangular struts that form the edges of an n-gon is replaced by a chain of *n* curved volumes bounded by four portions of spheres. Figure 30 shows an example in which a square-cross-section version of the four-triangle construction in Figure 10 is inverted into a structure that resembles four interlocked three-leaf clovers. The twelve corners are now on the inside, but remain 60-degree angles because central inversion is an angle-preserving transformation.

Figure 30. *Inversion of four triangles.*   **Figure 31.** *Five tetrahedra, an icosahedral polylink.*   **Figure 32.** *Inversion of five tetrahedra.*

Figure 31 is the well-known compound of five regular tetrahedra, which is easily generated as an icosahedral polylink. It is formed here with struts of rectangular cross section that overlap to make ribbed edges. These invert into the labial forms of Figure 32. The interior regions of Figures 30 and 32 are very interesting spaces, difficult to capture in a still image.

5. Conclusion

Regular polylinks are a rich source of fundamental forms that may be used as the basis for a gamut of 3D design ideas. Alan Holden's 1983 book abounds with creative inspirations displaying their symmetric elegance. But the spectrum of examples presented there and expanded upon here only scratch the surface. To introduce polylinks in a concrete manner, paper constructions such as Figures 3, 9, and 11 make a good hands-on activity. After that, I hope that the polylink-generation software described here will enable readers to explore new possibilities.

References

[1] H. Burgiel, D.S. Franzblau, and K.R. Gutschera, "The Mystery of the Linked Triangles," *Mathematics Magazine*, v. 69 (1996) 94-102.
[2] H.S.M. Coxeter, "Symmetric Combinations of Three or Four Hollow Triangles," *Math. Intel.* 16 (1994) 25-30.
[3] Michele Emmer (editor), *The Visual Mind*, MIT, 1993.
[4] George W. Hart, http://www.georgehart.com
[5] Alan Holden, *Shapes, Spaces and Symmetry*, Columbia Univ. Pr, 1971, (Dover reprint, 1991).
[6] Alan Holden, "Regular Polylinks," *Structural Topology*, No. 4, 1980, pp. 41-45.
[7] Alan Holden, *Orderly Tangles: Cloverleafs, Gordian Knots, and Regular Polylinks*, Columbia U., 1983.
[8] Robert J. Lang, "Polypolyhedra in Origami" in Thomas Hull (ed.) *Origami 3*, A.K. Peters, 2002.
[9] Rinus Roelofs, http://www.rinusroelofs.nl
[10] Doris Schattschneider, "Coxeter and the Artists: two-way inspiration", in The *Coxeter Legacy—Reflections and Projections*, (ed. C. Davis and E.W. Ellers), Fields Inst. Comm. v.46, Amer. Math. Soc., 2005. (to appear)
[11] Carlo Sequin, "Analogies from 2D to 3D, Exercises in Disciplined Creativity," Proc. of *Bridges: Mathematical Connections in Art, Music, and Science*, Winfield KS, Aug, 1999, and in *Visual Math.*, v. 3, no. 1.
[12] John Sharp, "Two Perspectives on Inversion", *Meeting Alhambra*, Barrallo et al. (ed), 2003.

Acknowledgments: Thank you *RJT Educational Training* (www.rjtedu.com) for making the model of Figure 5, and thank you Jim Quinn for making the models of Figures 17-19.

Factor Group Transformations on Escher Patterns

Joshua Jacobs
Department of Mathematics and Statistics
University of Minnesota Duluth
1117 University Drive
Duluth, MN 55812, USA

Abstract

The artist M.C. Escher intuitively expressed many mathematical concepts in his graphic designs. One of these concepts was that of transformations between different factor groups over the complex plane. We describe a method whereby any tiling that can be expressed as a rectangle system can be mapped to a multiplicative factor group over the complex plane.

1 Introduction

Ever since its creation in 1956, the blank spot in M.C. Escher's *Prentententoonstelling,* or *Print Gallery,* has fascinated enthusiasts of his work. Why is the sense of limit, so present in his other works, absent here? In 2003 Hendrick Lenstra and B. de Smit described how to express a version of the *Print Gallery* as a factor group over the complex plane [1]. This version of the picture repeats itself as its twists and shrinks down endlessly toward the center. The repeated picture is rotated clockwise by 157.62 degrees and scaled down by a factor of 22.58.

Though Escher's process was guided by his intuition and artistic skill, his result was much the same as Lenstra's: Images that utilize an isomorphism from one factor group of the complex plane to another. Escher started with a series of sketches that expressed a Droste effect scaled down by a factor of 256. A Droste effect occurs when an image contains a copy of itself. The term is named after the Dutch chocolate maker Droste for the visual effect on its boxes of cocoa. Any good Dutch dictionary will contain a reference to this effect [2]. Escher's sketches manifest the multiplicative factor group over the complex plane represented by $\mathbb{C}^*/\langle 256 \rangle$. He then used a spiraled grid to transform the picture into one that is very closely modeled by the multiplicative factor group $\mathbb{C}^*/\langle \omega \rangle$, where $\omega = (2\pi i + \ln 256)/(2\pi i)$.

Though *Print Gallery* was the first print of its kind, it was neither the first nor the last print that Escher did that can be replicated as factor group transformations (see *Development II* and *Smaller and Smaller*). Utilizing an exponential function on Escher prints over the complex plane similar to Lenstra's, complex factor group transformations can be realized in Escher's other works. The most notable of these is the *Path of Life* series of prints.

2 Path of Life Isomorphisms

Let us begin by looking at Escher's Regular Division Drawing 102 (Figure 1), done in 1958. This drawing was used as a basis for both Escher's *Path of Life I* and *Path of Life II*. To create a transformation of this drawing over the complex plane, we first need to explain how it will be placed on the complex plane. We proceed by laying this regular division upon the complex plane in such a way that eight tiles fit perfectly in a distance of 2π along the imaginary axis. This will give us the additive factor group $\mathbb{R}/\langle a \rangle \oplus \mathbb{R}i/\langle \pi/4 \rangle$, with **a** being the period in the real direction (in this case **a**=0.523598...).

By applying the exponential map $f(z) = e^z$ to Figure 1, we carry out an isomorphism from the additive factor group $\mathbb{R}/\langle a \rangle \oplus \mathbb{R}i/\langle \pi/4 \rangle$ to the multiplicative factor group $\mathbb{C}^*/\langle e^a \rangle$. If we were working with purely rectangular tiles, e^a would be the scaling factor between concentric circles in the resulting picture. In this case we will have each circle being e^a=1.68809 times larger than the circle inside of it.

Figure 1: Escher's Regular Division 102, 1958.

In looking at the resulting picture (Figure 2), we can see a striking resemblance to Escher's print *Path of Life I* (Figure 3). The noticable difference is where Escher chose to have his outermost fish curving back into the center. Otherwise, the differences are negligible.

Figure 2: Exponential mapping of Figure 1 with 8 tiles fitting in 2π distance along the imaginary axis.

Figure 3: *Path of Life I,* 1958.

The print *Path of Life II* can also be seen to possess a similar transformation. The difference is, when we place the tiling upon the complex plane we use four tiles to fit into the distance of 2π along the imaginary axis instead of eight. In comparing the result (Figure 4) to Escher's original (Figure 5) we can again see the similarity. This transformation would be an exponential mapping from $\mathbb{R}/<\mathbf{a}>\oplus\mathbb{R}i/<\pi/2>$ to $\mathbb{C}^*/<e^a>$, where $\mathbf{a}$ is the period in the real direction (in this case $\mathbf{a}=1.04719...$).

Figure 4: Exponential mapping of Figure 1 with 4 tiles fitting in a 2π distance along the imaginary axis.

Figure 5: *Path of Life II,* 1958.

Path of Life III, the last drawing in the series, can also be seen as a factor group transformation over the complex plane. The basis for this print is Escher's Regular Division Drawing 125 (Figure 6), done in 1966. We lay this division on $\mathbb{C}$ in such a way that we have six tiles fitting in the distance of 2π along the imaginary axis. We then use the exponential mapping to transform the image to $\mathbb{C}^*$. The result (Figure 7) can be compared to Escher's original (Figure 8). This transformation would be an exponential mapping from $\mathbb{R}/<\mathbf{a}>\oplus\mathbb{R}i/<\pi/3>$ to $\mathbb{C}^*/<e^a>$ (in this case $\mathbf{a}=1.03199...$).

Figure 6: Escher's Regular Division 125, 1966.

such a vertex a *split vertex*. If such a vertex has *a* right angles, *b* β angles, and *c* γ angles, then (2*a*,2*b*,2*c*) is a vertex vector. We call a vertex vector with all components even a *split vector*.

Except for a few exceptional cases, we can show that **more than one angle** must be involved in split vectors. One exceptional case is the (90°,108°,54°) triangle (figure 3), which does not tile the sphere edge-to-edge but does tile (in three ways) using no split vertex except for two right angles meeting at an edge [4]. It is also notable for the asymmetry of its tilings; two have symmetry groups of order 2, the third is asymmetric.

(4) The irrationality hypothesis. A little exposure to high school trigonometry should be sufficient to make it plausible that the numbers get messy quickly. To be more precise, angles with rational degree measures usually don't have rational trigonometric ratios. On the sphere, this leads to the following deliberately vague hypothesis:

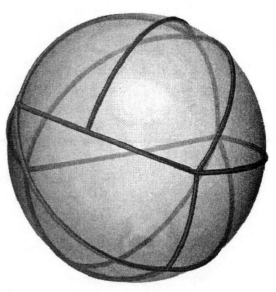

Figure 3: *A tiling with the (90°,108°,54°) triangle*

"With a few important exceptions, spherical triangles with rational angles don't have rational relations between their edge lengths."

This is left vague because there doesn't seem to be a hope of proving it without a major advance in transcendence theory. In the same way, we cannot prove that π^π is irrational (though most mathematicians would offer excellent odds that it is!) However, as our purpose is to show that certain sums of edge lengths cannot be obtained in more than one way, we just need to know that the edges (A,B,C) of certain specific spherical triangles do not satisfy $p\mathrm{A} + q\mathrm{B} + r\mathrm{C} = 0$ where p,q,r are integers with absolute value less than, say, 3; and this can be checked very easily (for instance, using a calculator).

For any tiling with N congruent triangles for which this holds, a maximal arc contained in the union of the edges that has p hypotenuses, q long legs, and r short legs on one side of it must have the same number and types of edges on the other side. Summing this over all arcs, we see that the total number $3N$ of triangle edges, and thus N, must be even. Moreover, if the tiles along such an arc don't meet edge-to-edge, the most common alternative arrangements have a rotational symmetry (whereas edge-to-edge arrangements often have reflectional symmetry). This explains why (as may be observed) chiral symmetries are the rule among non-edge-to-edge tilings and the exception among edge-to-edge tilings.

Figure 4: *Configuration along a great circle arc*

(5) Vertex equity. In any tiling by isosceles triangles, there are exactly twice as many base angles as apices; and in any tiling by scalene triangles, there are exactly equal numbers of each kind of angle. However, for some triangles, the possible vertex vectors do not reflect this balance. In particular, there are some triangles for which a certain angle appears more than another in every possible vertex configuration. Such a triangle clearly cannot tile!

We can also make more subtle uses of this principle. If there is only one configuration in which a certain angle appears in at least the target proportion, then that configuration must appear in any tiling. Moreover, if it can be shown – as is often the case – that such a configuration is always accompanied by nearby split vertices with a strong surplus of a different angle, it may still be impossible to create a tiling with vertices in the ratios in which the triangle provides them. In practice, if you try to create such a tiling, you end up with more and more of the hard-to-use species of angle on the boundary, until eventually you get stuck.

Known tiles. In the remainder of this paper we exhibit various tilings. We believe that these complete the list of isosceles and right-angled triangles that tile the sphere, though the proof of this is rather lengthy. (Some tiles are known to tile in huge numbers of ways; an actual enumeration of tilings, as oposed to tiles, is not expected soon.) Preliminary work suggests that the oblique triangles in the final section complete the list of *all* triangles that tile the sphere , but at this point this has not been definitely verified.

(1) New tilings with old tiles. Most of the tiles that tile the sphere in an edge-to-edge fashion also tile in other ways. The most common (and least interesting) variation is obtained from an edge-to-edge tiling by way of a "Rubik's Cube" twist along a great circle. (Fig. 5, left) This is a special continuous case of a usually-discrete process for changing tilings, which often yields non-edge-to-edge results. In general, if the union of some subset of the tiles has a symmetry group G larger than the symmetry group H of the subset, then any element of the quotient group G/H acts nontrivially on the tiling. An example is provided by any of the sets of four tiles filling an octant on the right of Fig. 5.

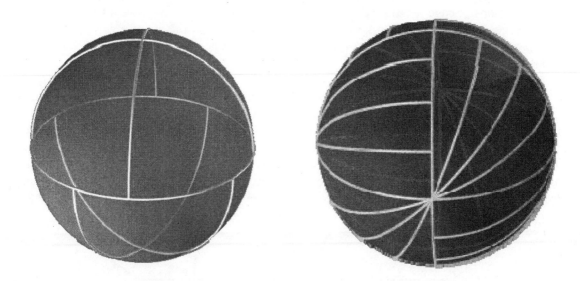

Figure 5: *Two tilings obtained by group actions*

If a tile will tile a lune with polar angle ϕ, and also some convex polygon P with angles $(\alpha_1, \alpha_2, ..., \alpha_n)$ such that ϕ divides $(180° - \alpha_i)$ for each i, then there exists a *swirl tiling* in which P and its mirror image occupy the "polar regions", while the space in between is filled with a swirl of lunes. Many variations on this these are possible! In Figure 6, the lunes, tiled with four tiles each, have polar angle 36°; two of the tiles make up one triangle of a spherical icosahedron; and the polar polygon is a pentagon with angles of 144°

Figure 6: *A swirl tiling with quarterlunes*

(2) Isosceles triangles. In a 2001 paper [3], I classified all the isosceles triangles that tile the sphere. These consist of the known edge-to-edge isosceles tiles found by Sommerville and Davies; three special cases; and an infinite family of *semilunes*, obtained by dividing the region between two great circles into two isosceles triangles as in Figure 7. This can be done whenever the polar angle ϕ is less than 120°; when ϕ also divides 360° the triangle tiles. If 360°/ϕ is odd, however, the triangle does not tile edge-to-edge. A tiling of this type is shown in Figure 2.

The three special cases are shown in Figure 8. They are the (80°, 60°, 60°), (100°, 60°, 60°), and (150°, 60°, 60°) triangles, which tile with 36, 18, and 8 copies respectively. The first of these tiles in exactly three distinct ways [2], the second and third uniquely. Note that the (100°, 60°, 60°) tiling is two-colorable.

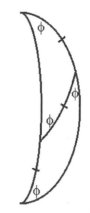

Figure 7: *Two isosceles semilunes*

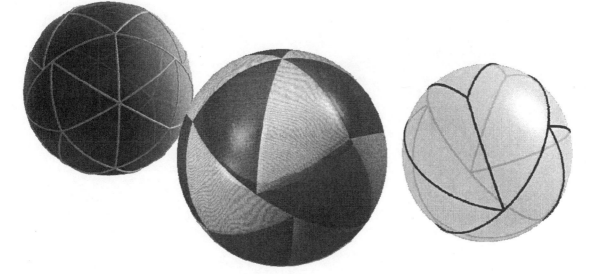

Figure 8: *Tilings with the* (80°, 60°, 60°), (100°, 60°, 60°), *and* (150°, 60°, 60°) *triangles*

(2) Right triangles. Over the course of two summers, I worked with an undergraduate student, Blair Doyle, on a complete classification of the right triangles that tile the sphere. We believe the classification to be complete but are still checking our work on a couple cases.

Every isosceles triangle that tiles the sphere, of course, gives rise by bisection to a right triangle tile. The (90°, 60°, 40°) tile obtained by bisecting the (80°, 60°, 60°) triangle tiles the sphere in many ways, none of them edge-to-edge, and might make a nice spherical puzzle!

Figure 9: *A design for a puzzle based on the (90°,60°,40°) triangle, which tiles in several ways*

There are also a number of other right triangles that tile the sphere. These include the (90°, 60°, 54°) triangle, three of which make up one of the (90°, 108°, 54°) tiles mentioned above. (The smaller tile was discovered first; my wife, Bridget Thomas, was looking at my sketch and noticed that they fitted together into larger tiles.) It also tiles in several other ways.

Another right-angled tile is the (90°, 72°, 30°) triangle, 60 copies of which tile the sphere. While both (72°, 72°, 60°) and (144°, 30°, 30°) triangles appear in this tiling, neither of them tiles the sphere on its own. The (90°, 105°, 45°) triangle (on the right of Figure 10), like the tile in Figure 3, is "right-obtuse". The twelve tiles have a delightfully twisty configuration.

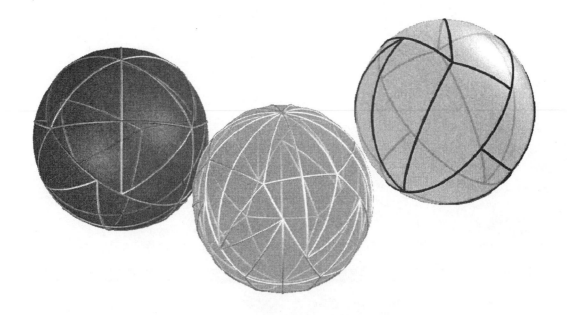

Figure 10: *Tilings with the (90°,60°,54°), (90°,72°,30°), and (90°,105°,45°) triangles*

The (90°, 75°, 45°) triangle tiles a 120° lune, three of which tile the sphere (Fig. 11, left). Moreover, by picking the orientations of these lunes properly, two of the three joins may be made edge-to-edge. The only non-edge-to-edge boundaries in this tiling are along the single meridian seen through the transparent front section of this sphere. While in one sense this tile comes extremely close to tiling the entire sphere edge-to-edge, it was easily ruled out by Davies because the (0,3,3) vertex, needed at the poles, could not be realized.

The final right-angled triangle tile, with angles of (90°, 78.75°, 33.75°), was discovered by Mr Doyle, in the last week of our search. It has only one tiling, a structure of great complexity (Fig. 11, right). In particular, the tiling is notable for having a very small symmetry group (order 4) for a tiling with so many (32) tiles. It has 8 different orbits under its symmetry group, a record for the "least symmetric most symmetric" tiling.

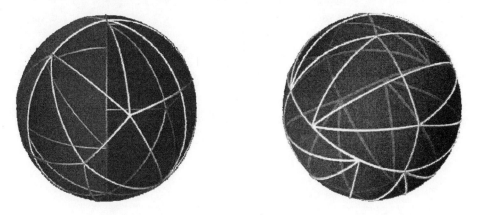

Figure 11: *Tilings with the* (90°, 75°, 45°) *and* (90°, 78.75°, 33.75°) *triangles*

(3). Other triangles. There are several other triangles that tile the sphere. The two in Figure 12 are members of infinite families. Both have polar stars joined by a helical equatorial belt of quadrilaterals, but the quadrilaterals divide into triangles differently. The diagonals dividing the quadrilaterals on the left run between obtuse vertices; on the right, they join acute vertices.

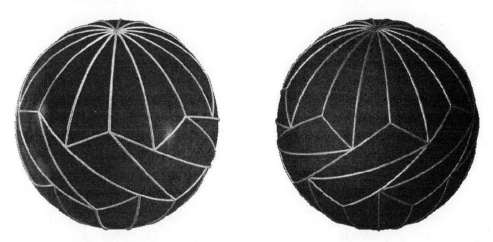

Figure 12: *Representative tilings from two infinite families*

The tiling in Figure 13 uses 48 (120°, 45°, 30°). triangles. It has polar stars like the tilings in Figure 12, but it has a double belt of quadrilaterals around its equator. The complex but symmetric pattern is remniscent of a Fabergé egg. There are not any other closely related tilings with more or less than 12 triangles meeting at the poles. To see this, note that with four different vertex figures, the set of linear equations determining the angles is overdetermined. Thus, in particular, the (3, 0, 0) vertex and the (1, 0, 2) and (0, 4, 0) splits force the (0, 0, 12) polar configuration.

This tiling is also unusual in that all of its triangles are paired into kites. Thus, we also have a non-edge-to-edge tiling of the sphere with 24 congruent (90°, 120°, 60°, 120°) kites.

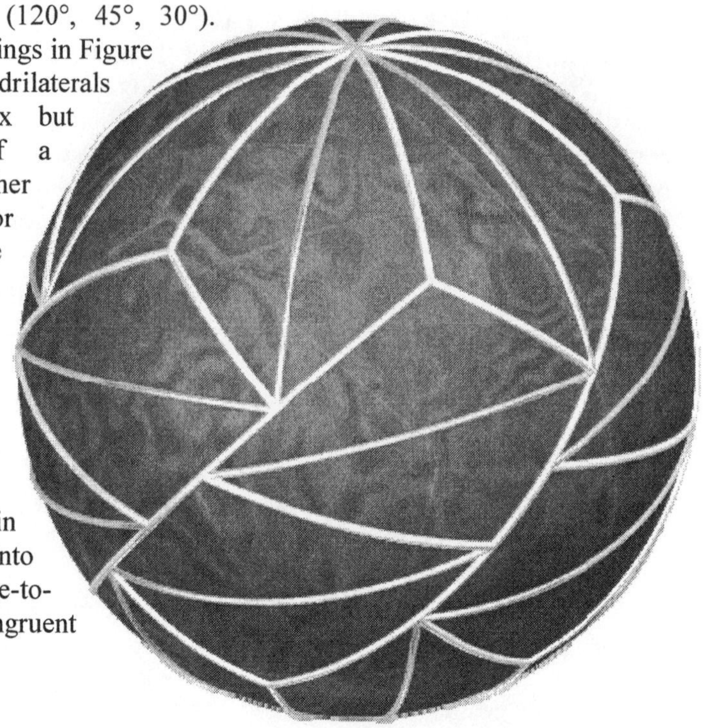

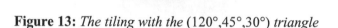

Figure 13: *The tiling with the* (120°,45°,30°) *triangle*

Acknowledgements. This research was funded by NSERC Canada. The illustrations were mostly done using the excellent and free raytracing package POV-Ray, available from www.povray.org.

References

[1] Davies, HL. , Packings of spherical triangles and tetrahedra, *Proc. Colloquium on Convexity*, Copenhagen 1965, 42-51

[2] Dawson, R., An isosceles triangle that tiles the sphere in exactly three ways, *Discrete and Computational Geometry* **30** [2003] 459-466

[3] Dawson, R., Tilings of the sphere with isosceles triangles, *Discrete and Computational Geometry* **30** [2003] 467-487

[4] Dawson, R., Single-split tilings of the sphere with right triangles; in *Discrete geometry: In Honor of W. Kuperberg's 60th Birthday* (A. Bezdek, ed.), Dekker 2003

[5] Sommerville, D.M.Y, Division of space by congruent triangles and tetrahedra, *Proc. Roy. Soc. Edinburgh* **43** (1923) 85-116

[6] Ueno, Y, and Agaoka, Y., Classification of the Tilings of the 2-Dimensional Sphere by Congruent Triangles, Technical Report 85, Division of Mathematics and Information Sciences, Hiroshima University, 2001

[7] Grünbaum, B., and Shepherd, G.S., "Spherical Tilings with Transitivity Properties", *The Geometric Vein,* eds. C. Davis, B. Grünbaum, and F. A. Scherk, The Coxeter Festschrift, Springer-Verlag, 1981, 65-98

H.S.M. Coxeter and Tony Bomford's Colored Hyperbolic Rugs

Douglas Dunham
Department of Computer Science
University of Minnesota, Duluth
Duluth, MN 55812-2496, USA
E-mail: ddunham@d.umn.edu
Web Site: http://www.d.umn.edu/~ddunham/

Abstract

Tony Bomford made six hooked rugs based on hyperbolic geometry, having received inspiration from the Canadian mathematician H.S.M. Coxeter. All rugs except one exhibit color symmetry to some degree. We will analyze the colorings of the other five rugs and suggest a new related rug pattern.

1. Introduction

A.G. (Tony) Bomford (1927–2003) was an Australian surveyor with wide-ranging interests. One of those interests was making mathematically based hooked rugs, of which Figures 1 and 2 are examples. My paper

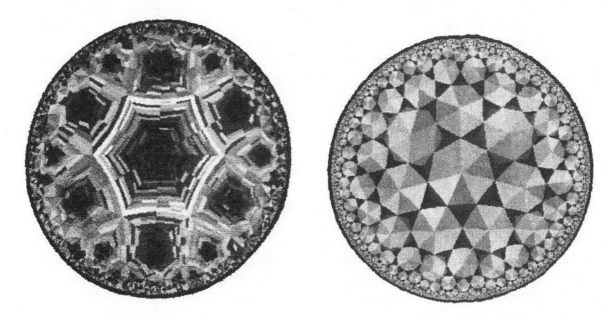

Figure 1: Tony Bomford's Rug #13: *Hyperbolic Lagoon.*

Figure 2: Tony Bomford's Rug #16: *Triangles and Heptagons.*

in Bridges 2004 contains a brief biographical sketch of Tony and some of the mathematics upon which his hyperbolic rugs were based [Dunham1].

The Canadian mathematician H.S.M. (Donald) Coxeter provided Bomford with two key inspirations. The first, in 1981, was a reproduction of M. C. Escher's hyperbolic pattern *Circle Limit IV,* which Tony saw in Coxeter's chapter "Angels and Devils" in *The Mathematical Gardner* [Coxeter3]. This inspired Tony to make his first hyperbolic rug, Rug #12 which he called *Hyperbolic Spiderweb*, (Figure 3). Tony went on to create five more hyperbolic hooked rugs between 1982 and 1989. He did not quite complete his last hyperbolic rug, Rug #18.

A second inspiration followed when Coxeter sent Tony a reprint of his article "Regular compound tessellations of the hyperbolic plane," [Coxeter2]; Figure 10 of that article provided Tony with information on how to color Rug #16 (Figure 2 above) and Rug #17. More details of the extensive Coxeter-Bomford interaction can be found in Doris Schattschneider's article in this volume [Schattschneider2], and in [Schattschneider1]. Tony Bomford's "Rug Book" contains a few sentences about each of his rugs and has a lengthy analysis of various tessellations embedded in Rugs #16 and #17 [Bomford1].

We start with a short review of essential geometrical concepts needed to analyze Tony's rugs. Tony created 18 rugs altogether; Rugs #12 through #18 are hyperbolic, except for Rug #14 which is a Euclidean design. We first analyze Rug #12 for color symmetries, then skip over Rug #13 (Figure 1 above), which, while quite colorful has no apparent color symmetry. Next, we discuss Rugs #15 and #18 which are related and have more color symmetry than Rug #12. Then, we analyze Rugs #16 and #17, which are also related and have even more color symmetry. Finally we show an original Coxeter-inspired design for a possible Bomford-like rug.

2. Hyperbolic Geometry, Tessellations, and Color Symmetry

Coxeter, Escher, and Bomford all used the *Poincaré disk model* of hyperbolic geometry whose points are the interior points of a bounding circle, and whose (hyperbolic) lines are circular arcs orthogonal to the bounding circle (including diameters). These circular arcs are apparent to various degrees in Tony's rugs and are made explicit in Figure 4 below. The hyperbolic measure of an angle is the same as its Euclidean measure in the disk model (we say such a model is *conformal*), but equal hyperbolic distances correspond to ever-smaller Euclidean distances as figures approach the edge of the disk. For example, all the heptagons in Figure 2 are hyperbolically congruent, as are all the hexagons in Figure 4.

There is a *regular tessellation,* $\{p, q\}$, of the hyperbolic plane by regular p-sided polygons meeting q at a vertex provided $(p - 2)(q - 2) > 4$. Figure 4 shows the regular tessellation $\{6, 4\}$, upon which Tony's Rugs #12 and #13 are based. Each regular tessellation $\{p, q\}$ gives rise to a semi-regular (or uniform) tiling $(p.q.p.q)$ in which two regular p-sided polygons and two regular q-sided polygons are placed alternately around each vertex. One can construct $(p.q.p.q)$ from $\{p, q\}$ by connecting midpoints of successive sides of each of the regular p-sided polygons. It can be seen in Figure 2 that Tony's Rug #16 is based on the tiling $(7.3.7.3)$, as is #17. Tony's Rugs #15 and #18 are based on the tiling $(5.4.5.4)$ (see Figures 5 and 6).

A *symmetry* of a pattern is transformation that maps the pattern onto itself. For example, disregarding color, reflection in the vertical diameter of the rug in Figure 2 preserves that pattern, as does rotation by $\frac{360}{7}$ degrees about the center. The only symmetries we will need to consider in our analysis are (hyperbolic) reflections and rotations. A reflection across a hyperbolic line in the disk model can be obtained by inversion in the orthogonal circular arc representing that line (of course reflection across a diameter is just a Euclidean reflection). As in Euclidean geometry, successive reflections across two intersecting lines results in a rotation about the intersection point by twice the angle between the lines.

A *color symmetry* of a pattern is a symmetry of the uncolored pattern that maps all parts of the pattern having the same color onto parts of a single color (possibly the same color) — that is, the symmetry permutes the colors. For example, in Figure 2 the reflection in the vertical diameter swaps pairs of tan colors of opposite triangles in the central heptagon and fixes the dark tan of the bottom triangle. The rotation by $\frac{360}{7}^{\circ}$ about the center of the rug permutes those seven shades of tan in a cycle. If every symmetry of a pattern is a color symmetry, that pattern is said to have *perfect color symmetry*. Tony's Rugs #16 and #17 exhibit perfect color symmetry (although, as we shall see, some interpretation needs to be made). For more information on color symmetry, see [Grünbaum & Shephard1], [Schwarzenberger1], and [Senechal1].

3. The Color Symmetries of Rug #12

Figure 3 shows Rug #12, *Hyperbolic Spiderweb*, Tony Bomford's first hyperbolic rug, inspired by M. C. Escher's hyperbolic pattern *Circle Limit IV*, which in turn was inspired by Figure 7, a hyperbolic tessellation of triangles in Coxeter's article "Crystal Symmetry and Its Generalizations" [Coxeter1]. (See [Schattschneider2] for details on Escher's inspiration.) Rug #12, *Circle Limit IV*, and Coxeter's figure are all based on the regular tessellation $\{6, 4\}$, in which four hexagons meet at every vertex (see Figure 4).

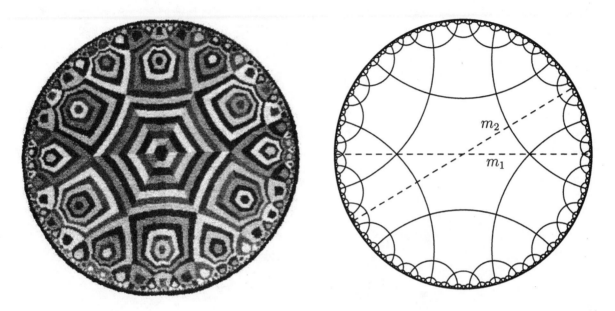

Figure 3: Tony Bomford's Rug #12: *Hyperbolic Spiderweb*

Figure 4: The regular tessellation $\{6, 4\}$ (solid lines), together with a diameter m_1 and side perpendicular bisector m_2 (dashed lines).

Tony used two sets of colors for Rug #12: three shades of tan (the lightest one almost white) and four shades of "reds" (the lightest almost orange and the darkest almost brown). There are eight hexagonal rings of color that make up the central hexagon, alternating between reds and tans, starting with reds at the center. The six edges of a tan ring contain all three shades of tans, progressing from lightest to darkest in clockwise order. The six edges in a red ring have two shades of red that alternate: the central ring (actually a small hexagon), and fifth ring (third red ring) use the two mid-level reds; the third and seventh rings use the orangish and brownish reds. The reds in two red rings of the same color are offset by 60 degrees, so that each of the 60-45-45 triangles comprising the central hexagon contains an edge of each of the four reds. For convenience, we number reds and tans from lightest to darkest: red1, red2, red3, red4, and tan1, tan2, tan3.

There are two kinds of reflections of the central hexagon onto itself: three reflections across the diameters of the hexagon (such as m_1 in Figure 4; these diameters connect opposite vertices), and three reflections across perpendicular bisectors of the sides (such as m_2 in Figure 4). The first kind of reflection interchanges red1 and red4, and red2 and red3, that is, each one produces the permutation (red1 red4)(red2 red3) of reds. But these reflections are not color symmetries of the whole pattern since they 'mix up' the tans. For example the horizontal reflection interchanges tan1 and tan3 in the eighth (outer) ring, but interchanges tan2 and tan3 in the sixth ring. Reflections across perpendicular bisectors also mix up the tans, so they are not color symmetries either.

On the other hand, a 60° counterclockwise rotation about the center of the circle *is* a color symmetry since it induces the following color permutation: (red1 red4)(red2 red3)(tan1 tan3 tan2). This rotation is produced by successive reflections across the horizontal diameter m_1 and the perpendicular side bisector m_2. So even though neither reflection alone is a color symmetry, the composition of the two reflections is a color symmetry. Also, this rotation is a color symmetry of the entire rug, not just the central hexagon.

There is one other kind of limited color symmetry that applies only to the six hexagons that share an edge with the central hexagon. These hexagons are made up of seven colored rings: four red rings alternating with three tan rings. When limited to such a hexagon, reflection across a diameter or rotation by 60° interchanges the two lightest and two darkest reds and fixes the tans: it produces the permutation (red1 red2)(red3 red4)(tan1)(tan2)(tan3) (a 1-cycle indicates a fixed color). Reflections across perpendicular side bisectors of those hexagons do not change any colors. All the other smaller (to our Euclidean eyes) hexagons are composed of rings of constant color, and so only have trivial color symmetry.

4. The Color Symmetry of Rugs #15 and #18

Bomford's next hyperbolic rug to display color symmetry is Rug #15, shown in Figure 5. Figure 6 shows the underlying tiling (5.4.5.4) upon which it is based. Tony used five shades of green to color the triangular regions that make up the pentagons and five shades of tan to color the regions that make up the squares. For discussion purposes, we number the greens and the tans from 1 to 5, from lightest to darkest.

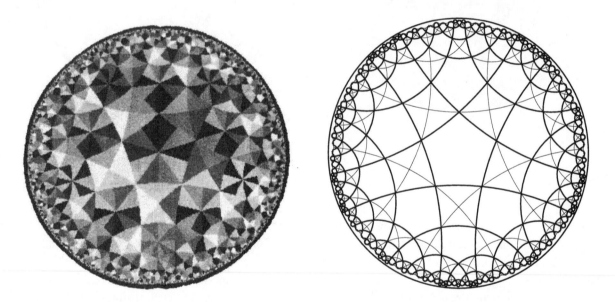

Figure 5: Bomford's rug #15 *Squares and Pentagons.*

Figure 6: The tiling (5.4.5.4) (bold lines) superimposed on the tessellation $\{5, 4\}$ (thin lines).

Reflection across the vertical diameter of the circle produces the color permutations (green1)(green2 green3)(green4 green5) and (tan1 tan5)(tan2)(tan3 tan4), where we emphasize that green1 and tan2 are sent to themselves by listing them as 1-cycles. The reflection about the diameter that makes an angle of 36° with the vertical diameter induces the color permutations (green1 green2)(green3 green5)(green4) and (tan1 tan4)(tan2 tan5)(tan3). If we perform these reflections in succession, we obtain a 72° counterclockwise rotation, which gives the color permutations (green1 green2 green5 green4 green3) and (tan1 tan2 tan5 tan4 tan3); the cyclic permutations for shades of greens and tans are the same. We note that the color permutation structure is the same for each of the five reflections across a diameter of the bounding circle that goes through a vertex of the central pentagon.

Playing Mathematics and Doing Music

John Belcher
CrossPulse Consultants
580 Harrison Avenue, 4th Floor
Boston, MA 02118
Email: jbelcher@crosspulseconsultants.com

Abstract

Generally, the art and science of pattern making and pattern discernment are at the core of mathematics and music. The forms and shapes of music, the ways in which music is used to structure time "space" can be viewed as rich mathematics structures. For example, the musical features of pulse, subpulse, cycle, and harmonic rhythm can serve as aural representations of key mathematical ideas, potentially providing a context for a deepened understanding of and "feel" for these ideas. Conversely, the act of translating mathematics structures into music forms can lead to powerful music insights. Exploring these domains in concert leads to possibilities for exciting synergies that address both conceptual and affective considerations about what it means to do-make music and mathematics.

Provocations

Symmetrical Music. Generally, it is much easier to recognize visual symmetry than aural symmetry, particularly "reflective symmetry". "Translational symmetry" is somewhat taken for granted in music; repeating patterns can be thought of as being copied and translated across a temporal background, sort of like aural wallpaper. Reflective symmetry turns up in surprising places. One source comes from "harmonic rhythm", which can be created by layering music cycles of different lengths.

Harmonic rhythm refers to a phenomenon, sometimes called "polyrhythm", which exists in many African and African Diasporic music traditions. The term "harmonic rhythm", in contrast to "polyrhythm", is meant to capture a set of aural and functional qualities in a rhythmic context, analogous to features that distinguish polyphony from harmony in a tonal context.

For example, combining a 2-beat cycle, in which the first pulse beat is sounded, with a 3-beat cycle, in which the first pulse beat is sounded, results in:

X		X		X		X
X				X		X

This can also be represented as a number sequence, in which numbers represent the lengths of intervals that begin with a sounded pulse beat and end with the next sounded pulse beat. The above pattern, with the two cycles merged together, which happens when the two rhythmic patterns are heard "harmonically", is represented by the sequence: 2, 1, 1, 2. The number sequence for a 3-beat cycle merged with a 4-beat cycle is 312213.

Interesting rhythmic structures can be created by playing with layering cycles of different lengths. When all pairs of cycle lengths are *relatively prime*, congruence arithmetic can be used to compute the places where cycles align. The sound/feeling of cycles coming in and out of alignment can be powerful. The Chinese Remainder Theorem provides one mathematical means for determining places of alignment, particularly when you are interested in finding alignments that aren't limited to lining up "ones".

For example, one might choose to align the fifth beat of a 7-cycle, the third beat of 3-cycle, the first beat of a 5-cycle, and the second beat of a 4-cycle. This is equivalent to solving:

$$x \equiv 5 \pmod 7 \ldots x \equiv 0 \pmod 3 \ldots x \equiv 1 \pmod 5 \ldots x \equiv 2 \pmod 4$$

In general, the Chinese Remainder Theorem guarantees a unique solution to a system of congruences, $x \equiv a_i \pmod{m_i}$, for pairwise relatively prime m_i, $1 \le i \le n$. The unique solution, modulo M (M, the product of all of the m_is), is given by:

$$x \equiv [a_1 e_1 + a_2 e_2 + \ldots + a_n e_n] \pmod M, \text{ where } e_i = M/m_i \times (M/m_i)^{-1} \pmod{m_i}.$$

The solution to the above system is $x \equiv 306 \pmod{420}$. Musically, this means if the 7, 3, 5, and 4 beat cycles are begun simultaneously, the desired alignment occurs on beat 306, with subsequent alignments occurring every 420 beats.

Investigating symmetry and asking mathematics questions to be answered in aural-temporal contexts leads to numerous and open-ended creative possibilities.

Aural Mapping and Transformational Music. Thinking of aural and/or rhythmic vocabulary as set elements and defining functions that map elements from one set to another leads to additional insights for playing with music structures. Thinking analogically is a critical aspect of exploring these possibilities, recognizing that there is rarely, if ever, one right way to translate musical ideas into mathematical ideas and vice-versa.

One possibility is to use set theory to map from one genre/tradition to another. For example, in the Ewe drum tradition of the Upper Volta region of West Africa, the master drum is called Atsimewu. The sonic vocabulary of Atsimewu consists of:

Dza (hand playing the center/bass tone, stick playing the side)
Dzi (hand playing the edge in a muted fashion, stick playing the side)
Ge (hand or stick playing the high tone)
T□ (hand pressing the edge, while stick strikes the center)
Re ("roll")

One might define a function that maps from 7 notes in a Western octave to the "notes" of Atsimewu in the following way:

C → Dza, D → Ge, E → Ge, F → Dzi, G → T□, A → Dza, B → Re

Such a mapping provides a means for translating a Western melody into a West African "drum song."

The use of linear transformations is an additional tool for "extending the mileage" of music structural ideas. For example, a function, such as:

$$f: R^2 \to R^3 \text{ defined by } f\begin{bmatrix} x \\ y \end{bmatrix} = \begin{bmatrix} x \\ 3x+2y \\ 2x-3y \end{bmatrix}$$

can be used to inform, motivate and stretch some music choices and possibilities. It can be interesting to consider what it means to map from 2 dimensions to 3 dimensions in the context of a music composition. One way of making this function musically meaningful is having the x-axis represent time, the y-axis represent pitch, and the z-axis represent volume (loudness). Clearly, there are other possibilities. Exploring these ideas opens up avenues for creating aural models, enabling other means for multi-dimensional representations beyond the means of visual graphs.

Conclusion

Perhaps and hopefully, the above explorations and provocations, which admittedly have skimmed the surface of possibilities, have, nonetheless, provided some insights into ways of traversing back and forth between mathematics and music.

Dynamic Geometry/Art in Mathematics Classroom

Mara Alagic, mara.alagic@wichita.edu
Diana Palenz, palenz@math.twsu.edu

Wichita State University
Wichita, KS 67260 – 0028

Abstract

This paper is our follow-up on the article Fostering Understanding of Mathematical Visualization [1]. It is focusing on mathematical visualization of two-dimensional geometric objects within the dynamic geometry environment. Furthermore, it attempts to bridge the gap (if one exists) between the geometry and art, suggesting dynamic geometry/art activities as central for students' understanding of geometric transformations.

1. Introduction

Arcavi suggests that "*visualization* is the ability, the process and the product of creation, interpretation, use of and reflection upon pictures, images, diagrams, in our minds, on paper or with technological tools, with the purpose of depicting and communicating information, thinking about and developing previously unknown ideas and advancing understanding" [3, p. 56]. How is Arcavi's definition of visualization related to artistic expression? *Visualizing* encompasses both the process and the product of creating, producing and constructing pictures, applets, images, icons, even symbols, in order to represent what we perceive to be relevant for an understanding and representing that understanding. Both mathematics and art have their own language, form, structure and mode of expression; mathematics, as well as art, requires creative problem-solving skills, facilitation of both informal and formal skills in order to develop and support creativity and intuition. Developing expertise in selecting appropriate tools, media and approaches are common, in their own contexts, to both mathematics and art apprenticeship [16].

Cox and Brna [5] have shown that when people are learning complex new ideas it helps to interrelate/manipulate various visual representations like diagrams, graphs and animations. If the learner can integrate information from representations with different formats then they often acquire a deeper understanding of the concept. On the other hand, if the learner fails to make the connection between the different kinds of information, then many of the benefits that multiple representations provide may not occur (e.g. [18]). Furthermore, *multiple representations* for certain concepts have been linked with greater flexibility in student thinking (Ohlsson [11] as cited in [9]) and visualizations have a particular place in acquiring adequate representations.

This paper provides a couple of randomly selected practical illustrations for fostering understanding of geometric visualization, as a means for both understanding certain mathematical processes and developing one's artistic expression. A full range of activities and illustrations will be prepared for the conference and available on a digital medium.

2. The van Hiele Levels of Geometric Thought

While Piaget and Inhelder [12] suggest that the development of perception as described by the types of geometry are sequential (i.e. Topological, Projective, Euclidean), other researchers believe that all types of geometric thinking continue to develop over time and become increasingly integrated. The stages of development suggested by Piaget & Inhelder are similar in that they demonstrate the child's naturally increasing ability to perceive and represent the geometric complexity of our three-dimensional world. Both sets of stages emphasize the importance of comprehending spatial relationships between objects and finding ways to show these relationships through 'perspective' drawing techniques.

Originally there were five van Hiele levels, which have been adapted and renamed by various researchers, but now van Hiele concentrates on the three levels that cover the regular schooling time. The *visualization* begins with 'nonverbal thinking'. Shapes are judged by their appearance and generally viewed as 'a whole', rather than by distinguishing parts. At the *analysis* level, students can identify and describe the component parts and properties of shapes. For example, an equilateral triangle can be distinguished from other triangles because of its three equal sides, equal angles and symmetries. Students need to develop appropriate language to go with the new specific concepts. However, at this stage the properties are not 'logically ordered', which means that the students do not perceive the essential relationships between the properties. At the *informal deduction level* properties of shapes are logically ordered. Students are able to see that one property precedes or follows from another, and can therefore deduce one property from another. They are able to apply what they already know to explain the relationships between shapes, and to formulate definitions. For example, they could explain why all squares are rectangles. Although informal deduction such as this forms the basis of formal deduction, the role of axioms, definitions, theorems and their converses, is not understood. Students can see (establish) interrelationships between figures and derive relationships among figures. Simple proofs can be followed but not understood completely. Students at the *deduction* level understand the significance of deduction and the role of postulates, theorems, and proofs. They can write proofs with understanding. Students understand how to work in an axiomatic system. They are able to make abstract deductions. Non-Euclidean geometry can be understood at this highest, *rigor* level ([17], [18]).

These stages of learning are significant in providing a framework for instruction aimed to develop understanding of the material or skills to be learned [4]. The main idea is that a learner cannot achieve one level of reasoning without *having passed* through the previous levels. What "having passed through" means in this case is achieving deeper understanding of concepts and relationships attached to that level of reasoning.

> You can say somebody has attained higher level of thinking when a new order of thinking enables him, with regard to certain operations, to apply these operations on new objects. The attainment of the new level cannot be effected by teaching, but still, by a suitable choice of exercises the teacher can create a situation for the pupil favorable to the attainment of the higher level of thinking [37, p. 39].

3. Visualizing with Dynamic Geometry.

Students' exploration with a variety of representations when building their conceptual understanding of mathematical ideas is very important and has been studied by many authors ([8], [6]). Demana and Waits emphasize "the ability of students to operate within and between different representations of the same concept or problem setting is fundamental in effectively applying technology to enhance mathematics learning" [6, p. 218]. Schultz & Waters [14] suggest careful consideration for selecting representations that will facilitate students learning. Visual representations in technology-augmented activities support mathematical connections in at least three ways: (a) linking multiple representations of the same mathematical idea, enhancing the context for reflective abstraction, (b) interconnecting mathematical topics and (c) connecting mathematics to real-world phenomena. Appropriate use of technology supports learners, both teachers and students, in bringing together multiple representations via intermediate representations and explicating connections among different representations of mathematical phenomena.

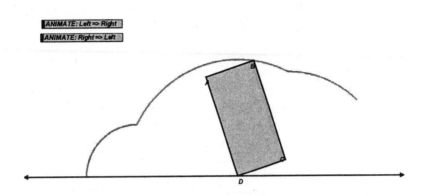

Figure 1: *Rolling rectangle tracer*

A visual solution to a problem can engage students with "meanings which can be easily bypassed by the symbolic solution of the problem" and can bring geometry-based representations to the aid of what seem to be purely symbolic processes [3, p. 62]. For example, one can symbolically study systems of equations with two variables without making a connection with geometry-based representation of the situation; relationships of two lines in a plane ([1]).

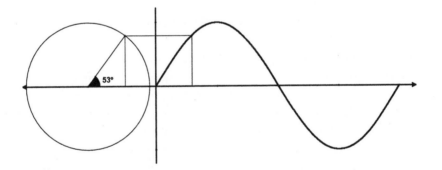

Figure 2: *A caption of an animated visualization of the sine function*

Dragging/animating a geometric figure across a computer screen illustrates dynamic behavior of geometry programs such as Geometer's Sketchpad, Cabri and Cinderella. That capability has significantly changed the quality and impact of geometry experiences. Furthermore, it has provided broad opportunities for learners to experiment with, explore and visualize objects in qualitatively new ways. One construction in one of these media, unlike on a piece of paper or a chalkboard, provides a source of experimentation with a range of examples, making available a collection of representations for further study. This learning to visualize differently requires learners to think differently. Change in the instructional strategies is an imperative, especially if teachers' education was traditional and opportunities have not been provided to bring teachers to the "speed" in a dynamic geometry classroom.

Unlike the static images constructed by hand using straightedge and compass, dynamic geometry figures can be manipulated, having the variant properties changed by dragging. One can consequently observe invariants, producing large amounts of data to analyze [13]. Dynamic geometry tools are engaging students in active learning in geometry. Solving problems, posing questions, creating conjectures, searching for connections, considering counter-examples or formal deductive proofs are enriched with our ability to visualize and reason using diagrams. In each of these formats, dynamic geometry is instigating a significant change. We are able to make more visible our internal representations of geometric figures and geometric transformations, and to refine them further when necessary.

A kaleidoscope can be visualized as two mirrors at an angle of $\pi/3$ or $\pi/4$ to each other. When an object is placed between the mirrors, it is reflected 6 or 8 times (depending on the angle). A dynamic geometric representation of this in Geometer's Sketchpad can produce interesting designs along with a better understanding of how the kaleidoscope's fascinating pictures come about.

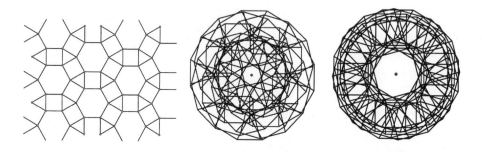

Figure 3: *Geometric transformations: Tiling and kaleidoscope(s)*

Pedagogical Implications

Technological tools available for visualization broaden both curricular and pedagogical opportunities. Geometry explored through geometric art is both motivating and real-life connected. Dynamic geometry provides for students' development of both internal and external representations in both geometry and artistic expression. It has already been noted that as technology develops, its uses in the classroom provide both opportunities and major challenges. There are many new pitfalls and misconceptions, along with new ways of motivating students and providing a broader range of experiences in a shorter timeframe ([10], [13], [1]). Not only do teachers need to be continually aware of what their students are really seeing in the dynamic geometry representation, which may be quite different from what the teacher expected, but also the pedagogical instructions and questions themselves need to change [3]. For example, after constructing the three medians of a triangle, a paper-and-pencil student might be asked to describe what he/she observed and to repeat the exercise with a different triangle, while a dynamic-geometry student could be asked to manipulate the original triangle to see what will happen to his/her construction as the shape of the triangle changes. And the construction may or may not "hold together" to verify the teacher's expected result, depending on the steps the student took in the construction. Also, new possibilities arise for investigation, such as the "split points" command, with which a more advanced student might experiment, to explore how many different ways a single point in the construction has been used.

References

[1] Alagic, M. (2004). Fostering understanding of mathematics visualization. In M. Alagic & R. Sarhangi (Eds.), *Bridges for teachers, teachers for bridges: 2004 workshop book* (pp. 1-17). Bel Air, MD: Academx Publishing Services.

[2] Alagic, M. (2003). Technology in the mathematics classroom: Conceptual orientation. *Journal of Computers in Mathematics and Science Teaching (JCMST), 22*(4), 381-399.

[3] Arcavi, A. (1999). *The role of visual representations in the learning of mathematics*. In Proceedings of the Annual Meeting of the North American Chapter of the International Group for the Psychology of Mathematics Education, Morelos, Mexico. (ERIC Document Reproduction Service No. ED 466382).

[4] Bruner, J. (1973). *Going beyond the information given*. New York: Norton.

[5] Cox, R., & Brna, P. (1995). Supporting the use of external representations in problem solving: The need for flexible learning environments. *International Journal of Artificial Intelligence in Education, 6*(2), 239-302.

[6] Demana, F., & Waits, B. K. (1990). Enhancing mathematics teaching and learning through technology. In T. J. Cooney & C. R. Hirsch (Eds.), *Teaching and learning mathematics in the 1990s, 1990 yearbook of the national council of teachers of mathematics* (pp. 212-222). Reston, VA: National council of Teachers of Mathematics.

[7] Dreyfus, T. (2002). Computer-rich learning environments and the construction of abstract algebraic concepts. In Borovcnik, M., & Kautschitsch, H. (Eds.) *Technology in Mathematics Teaching, Proceedings of ICTMT5 in Klagenfurt 2001*. Schriftenreiche Didaktik Der Mathematik, Band 25 (pp.17-32). Vienna: öbv&hpt.

[8] Greeno, J. G., & Hall, R. P. (1997). Practicing representation: Learning with and about representational forms. *Phi Delta Kappan, 78*(5), 361-367.

[9] Leinhardt, G., Zaslavsky, O., & Stein, M. K. (1990). Functions, graphs, and graphing: Tasks, learning and teaching. *Review of Educational Research, 60*(1), 1-64.

[10] National Research Council (2000). *How people learn: Brain, kind, experience, and school.* Washington, DC: National Academy Press.

[11] Ohlsson, S. (1987). Sense and reference in the design of interactive illustrations for rational numbers. In R. W. Lawler & Masoud Yazdani (Eds.), *Artificial intelligence and education* (pp. 307-344). Norwood, NJ: Ablex.

[12] Piaget, J., & Inhelder, B. (1967). *The Child's Conception of Space*. New York: Norton.

[13] Schattschneider, D., & King, J. (1997). Preface of geometry turned on: Dynamic software in learning, teaching, and research. Washington, DC: Mathematical Association of America. Retrieved March 26, 2004 from http://mathforum.org/dynamic/geometry_turned_on/about/Preface.html

[14] Schultz, J.E., & Waters, M.S. (2000). Why Representations? *Mathematics Teacher, 93*(6), 448-454.

[15] Smith, D.A. (2002). *How people learn mathematics*. In Proceedings of International Conference on the Teaching of Mathematics (at the Undergraduate Level), Hersonissos, Greece. (ERIC Document Reproduction Service no. ED 472 053).

[16] Shaffer, D. W. (1995). Symmetric Intuitions: Dynamic Geometry/Dynamic Art. *Symmetry: Culture and Science,, 6*(3), 476-479.

[17] Van Hiele, P. (1986). *Structure and Insight: A theory of mathematics education*. Orlando, FL: Academic Press, Inc.

[18] Van Hiele, P. (1999). Developing geometric thinking through activities that begin with play: Teaching children mathematics. In L. J. Sheffield (Ed.), *Developing Mathematically Promising Students* (pp. 310-316). Reston, VA: National Council of Teachers of Mathematics.

Index